The
BUTTERFLIES
of Wiltshire

Dedicated to the Memory of a Dear Sister

Sally Patricia Fuller

1946–1969

The BUTTERFLIES *of Wiltshire*

Their History, Status and Distribution
1982–1994

Michael Fuller

Edited by Beatrice Gillam

PISCES
PUBLICATIONS

Pisces Publications is the imprint of the Nature Conservation Bureau Limited

First published by Pisces Publications 1995. Pisces Publications is the imprint of the Nature Conservation Bureau Limited.

British Library-in-Publication Data.
A catalogue record for this book is available from the British Library.

ISBN 1 874357 06 4

Designed and produced by the Nature Conservation Bureau Limited, 36 Kingfisher Court, Hambridge Road, Newbury, Berkshire, RG14 5SJ.

Printed by Information Press, Oxford.

Cover photograph: Adonis blues at Bratton Castle Earthworks by Ian Grier.

CONTENTS

FOREWORD

Wiltshire is an extraordinary and evocative county, with wide open skies and rolling downs. It has a landscape steeped in human history and it is easy to think that time has stood still in this ancient place. However, sadly Wiltshire has not escaped the agricultural intensification of the twentieth century which has caused unprecedented losses of traditional habitats and their associated wildlife right across lowland Britain.

Butterflies are particularly sensitive indicators of environmental changes and this book provides some vital information on the impact of modern agricultural and forestry practices. Its production owes much to the dedication and enthusiasm of its author Michael Fuller who, virtually single-handedly, has coordinated and encouraged butterfly recorders over many years to produce such a comprehensive account. It was my great privilege to live in Wiltshire in the late 1980s, during which time I came to know some of its exceptional wildlife habitats and witnessed first-hand the enormous effort that Mike has put into mapping its butterflies. For over ten years he has produced annual summaries of the season's records and sent updates to his army of recorders. He has now brought together these painstaking observations in a book that represents a landmark for the county and its butterflies and will serve them well for years to come.

Wiltshire is an extremely rich and varied county with extensive tracts of chalk downland, numerous large blocks of woodland, clay vales in the north and a little piece of New Forest heathland in the south. Its butterfly fauna is also one of the richest anywhere in Britain with 47 species known to have bred in recent years. The county also includes major national strongholds for scarce species including the Adonis blue, chalk hill blue, Duke of Burgundy and marsh fritillary.

Recording butterfly distributions has a number of vital uses. It helps our understanding of the habitat requirements of different species, it identifies their main strongholds and it helps to identify natural cycles, declines and expansions. Above all, it provides a vital platform on which we can build an effective conservation strategy. Whilst it is sad that this book shows that many butterflies are declining in Wiltshire, it is also greatly encouraging to know that so many people are interested in observing and recording them. This excellent publication will hopefully raise awareness of the plight of Wiltshire's rich butterfly inheritance and should prove a turning point in their conservation. All those involved in the Wiltshire countryside are being given a firm foundation from which to save their butterflies for future generations to enjoy.

Dr Martin Warren
Head of Conservation, Butterfly Conservation
Dorset
July 1995

AUTHOR'S PREFACE

Prior to moving to Wiltshire in 1978 I had never lived in good butterfly country. Essex, central London, mid-Scotland, the East Midlands and, briefly, Tyneside could offer very little apart from the commoner species. It is true that some of these areas did have their own interesting specialities such as the black hairstreak and large copper near Peterborough, but it was not until I settled in Wiltshire that my early boyhood interest in butterflies was reawakened. I soon realised how very fortunate I was to have an occupation which, from 1978 until 1990 was based in Westbury with superb woodland and downland sites only a few minutes drive away. Picket Wood, which I chanced upon one warm July evening, looked good and subsequently proved to be among the best butterfly woods in Britain in the early 1980s. Forty species have been recorded since I started monitoring there in 1978. The Bratton Castle Earthworks chalk grassland site was shown to me by the late Bowmont Weddell, the eminent Trowbridge entomologist. I have recorded 32 species there

since I began monitoring in 1980, the site's speciality being the famous Adonis blue colony which has been known to lepidopterists for many years. There must be those who would envy me being able to spend my lunch hours at these two beautiful locations which, in 1986, together supported 41 of the county's 47 breeding species, one of the highest totals for any 10 km square in Wiltshire and possibly in Great Britain.

The contents of much of this book are the result of many happy hours spent mainly at Picket Wood, Bratton Castle and Upton Cow Down. From my own observations and those of other recorders from their own favoured locations, I have tried to produce, as far as is possible, a non-technical text presented in a form for the non-scientist to understand and to illustrate what can be achieved by amateurs using simple methods and observations. I trust this will be found to be the case and, if at times I appear to get carried away, then I hope the reader will come with me into the beautiful and fascinating world of the butterfly.

ACKNOWLEDGEMENTS

It has been a privilege to have had Beatrice Gillam, one of Wiltshire's premier all-round naturalists, as my editor following the completion of her editorship of *The Wiltshire Flora* in 1993. Her editorial and organisational skills, patience and enthusiasm have been the driving force throughout the preparation of this publication. Her many helpful suggestions, her eye for detail and her written contribution of 'Habitats for Wiltshire Butterflies' have greatly enhanced the book.

John Rayner, with his business experience and as treasurer of the Wiltshire Natural History Forum, has assisted in many ways. I am indebted to him for handling the financial and promotional aspects of the publication in such an efficient manner and for dealing with contractual matters with the Nature Conservation Bureau. I am also very grateful to him, Dorothy and Eric Cooper and Patricia and Syd Froud for undertaking the final proof-reading.

The distribution maps were produced from data checked and processed by the Wiltshire Biological Records Centre at the Wiltshire Archaeological and Natural History Society's museum at Devizes. I am most grateful to the Biological Recorder, Sally Scott-White, her staff, in particular Kathryn Harrold and Avis Lloyd, for the many hours spent entering and checking the thousands of records. I would like to express my gratitude to the many recorders without whose efforts there would have been no distribution maps.

The exacting and time-consuming task of processing the text onto computer disc was carried out by Michael Balfe and Bill Griffiths to whom I am greatly indebted. To the staff of the Nature Conservation Bureau I owe many thanks, especially to Peter Creed, Martin Harvey and Michael Dunbar who assisted in many ways with the presentation of the material. I believe the result is an outstanding publication. I wish to thank Paul Harding at the

National Biological Records Centre for making historical Wiltshire records freely available and to Ernie Pollard, Marney Hall, Tina Yates and Nick Greatorex-Davies, the staff responsible for the national Butterfly Monitoring Scheme, for providing data from monitored sites.

The contributions and support of the staff of English Nature and the Wiltshire Wildlife Trust, who also kindly furnished records and monitoring data, have been much appreciated.

I offer my thanks to all those dedicated volunteers who weekly walk the transects on the monitored sites for obtaining and supplying the data and allowing me to use it. Without their endeavours our knowledge of butterfly habits would be very much the poorer, and the comprehensive graphs of indices of abundance could not have been produced.

A butterfly book without colour is quite unthinkable and I would like to express my thanks to the many people who loaned colour transparencies for selection by the publishers. I trust there will not be too many disappointed photographers. I am most grateful to those who allowed me to quote from the results of their research, published, unpublished and in personal communications, in particular Barry Fox, Ted Gange, Beatrice Gillam, Avis Lloyd, Matthew Oates, Stephen Palmer, Dick Ryan, Ian Small, Godfrey Smith, Paul Waring, Martin Warren and Ken Willmott.

Finally, I acknowledge the support and patience of my family during the Wiltshire Butterfly Mapping Scheme which has taken up a large part of my life. To Jennifer, my wife, and my sons, Christopher and Paul, I offer my sincere thanks.

Michael Fuller
Bradford-on-Avon
August 1995

FINANCIAL ASSISTANCE

This publication has been grant-aided by **English Nature.**
The **Wiltshire Wildlife Trust** contributed towards the cost of colour printing.
The **Wiltshire Archaeological and Natural History Society, Butterfly Conservation (West Country Branch)** and the **Great Western Community Forest** made donations.
Interest-free loans were provided by the **Bentley Wood Charitable Trust** and the **Salisbury and District Natural History Society.**
The **Wiltshire Natural History Forum** provided financial assistance.

The author gratefully acknowledges the support of the above organisations and the individuals named below who assisted with donations or loans. Without their generous support this publication would not have been possible.

Ray Anscombe
Kate Ashford-Brown
Jean Baker
Lesley Balfe
Monica Blake
Maj Gen Robin Brockbank
Audrey Brown
Sqn Ldr Jim Buchanan
Tom Burnard
Dr Susan Clarke
Jack Coates
Dr Hamish Cole
Stan Constable
Paul Darby
Peter Darch
John d'Arcy
Patricia Dashwood
Prof Wilfred Dowdeswell
Ann and Stan Durnell
Henry Edmunds
Dr Doreen Ellis

Diana Forbes
Katherine Forbes
Barry Fox
Patricia Froud
Roy Fussell
Beatrice Gillam
John Grearson
Alan Greenfield
Ann Hutchison
Prof Humphrey Kay
John Kerr
Roger Kiddle
Barbara Last
Dick Last
Ken and Avis Lloyd
Capt Francis Lowe
Malcolm Lyell
Dr George Osmond
Stephen Palmer
David and Jackie Peart
Jack and Sylvia Pile

Brig John Platt
Ken and Sue Rawles
John Rayner
Eileen Rollo
Joyce Smith
Phillida Sneyd
Audrey Summers
Ruby Thomas
Richard Thompson
Ruth Timbrell
Christine Tracey
Anthony and Heather Tyers
Graham Wall
Christine White
Lt Cdr Peter Whitehead
Bill Wilder
Gwyneth Yerrington
George Yorke
Ian Young
Prof Ian R Young

RECORDERS

An asterisk denotes that the recorder was also a transect walker and/or the organiser of a transect walk.

Keith Alexander
Keith Andrews
*Dominic Ash
Dr Jim Asher
Kate Ashford-Brown
Maurice Avent
Susan Bailey
Helen Baker
Jean Baker
Dr Norman Baldock
Lesley Balfe
Ellen Barber
Simon Barker
Ken Barton
*Roger Beckett
Maj Anthony Bedford-Russell
Harold Bennett
Judith Biss
David Blackford
Monica Blake
Rosemary and
    Graham Borthwick-Clarke
Joyce Bowker
*Jill Bowler
Roger Bristow
Maj Gen Robin Brockbank
Hans Bromley
David Brotheridge
*Audrey Brown
Keith Brown
Marion Browne
Ted Browning
Sqn Ldr Jim Buchanan
Martin Buckland
Tina Bull
Tom Burnard
Steve Button
John Buxton

Geoff Carefoot
Ches Carpenter
Noel Chadwick
Steve Chamberlain
Jo Chapple
Barry Checksfield
Ron Churchill
*Arthur Cleverly
Philip Cleverly
Jack Coates
Winifred Compton
Stan Constable
Aileen Cotton
Caroline Coulthard
Steve Covey
Jonathan Cox
Richard Creighton
Susan Cross
Harold Crossley
Jeff Curd
Eileen Curtis
Paul Darby
Peter Darch
John d'Arcy
Steve Day
Dr Colin Dodd
Jane Donald
Geoff Doré
John Douglas
Prof Wilfred Dowdeswell
Ann and Stan Durnell
Henry Edmunds
Stephen Edwards
Edward Elliott
Dr Doreen Ellis
Capt Hugh Ennion
Elaine and Brian Entwistle
Simon Evans

Peter Eyles
Wayne Fennell
Victor Fielding
Charles Flower
Andrew Forbes
Diana Forbes
Kathrine Forbes
*Barry Fox
Marjorie and Gerald Foxwell
*Jeremy Fraser
Patricia Froud
*Michael Fuller
Roy Fussell
Ted Gange
W Gardner
Tim Garroway-Jones
Kathleen Gifford
*Beatrice Gillam
Nick Goddard
Tony Goddard
Dick Godfrey
Daphne Graiff
Peter Grainger
Ian Gray
*John Grearson
David Green
Beryl and Alan Greenfield
Daphne Greville-Heygate
Dr Ian Grier
Robin Griffiths
Frank Halsey
Nick Hamlin
Jane Hammond
Michael Hamzij
Alec Harmer
Steve Harvey
Denise Herrod-Taylor
Linda Hill

Claire Holloway
Valerie Hopkinson
Linda Howe
Len Ingram
Brian Jones
Cynthia Jones
Mary Jones
Prof Humphrey Kay
John Kerr
Roger Kiddle
*Albert Knott
Mary and Phil Lambert
Stewart Lane
Barbara Last
Nick Lear
Dorothy Lewis
Hazel Lewis
Lorna Llewellyn
Avis Lloyd
Audrey Lovett
Capt Francis Lowe
Michael Lyell
Gordon Mackie
Adam Manolson
Paul Mapplebeck
Jean Matthews
Bruce Maxfield
Colin Maxfield
Carol and Roy McInerney
*Piers Mobsby
Rob Murdoch
Joy Newton
*Gerald Nicholls
Kay Nicol
Liz and Steve Oakes
Matthew Oates
Ken Orpe
Dr George Osmond
Shirley Packham
*Stephen Palmer
Tom Parker
Charlie Patrick
Patricia and Bunny Pattrick
*Keith Payne
Graham Pearce
David Peart
Roger Perkins

Christopher Perraton
Sylvia and Jack Pile
Bryan Colin and Trevor Pinchen
Alan Pitcher
Brig John Platt
B Playle
Richard Pooley
Melvyn Potter
Phil Potton
Revd Michael Powell
James Power
Dennis Powney
Frances and Stan Price
Ivan Randall
John Rayner
Dominic Rey
David Robertson
Major John Robinson
Prudence Robinson
Eileen Rollo
John Rowe
Mike Russell
*Dick Ryan
Nick Salmon
Lt Col Edward Sawyer
Dr Nicolette Scourse
Peter Shallcross
Dr David Shirt
David Simcox
*David Simpson
Michael Skelton
Ann Skinner
Lorna Slade
Andrew Sloan
Dr Ian Small
Ed Smith
Godfrey Smith
Graham Smith
Joyce Smith
Michael Smith
Philip Smith
Simon Smith
Louise and Michael Sneyd
Caroline Stainthorpe
*Dee Stephens
Michael Stevenson
Geoff Strange

Martin Styles
Audrey Summers
C E Summers
*Richard Tambling
Celia Tanner
Ruby Thomas
Peter Thompson
Ruth Timbrell
Phil Tolerton
Prof Charles Tottle
*Christine Tracey
Gordon Trebilcock
Guy Troughton
John Tubb
Rob Turner
Heather and Anthony Tyers
John Tyler
Mervyn Tyte
Kurt Vickery
Penny Wakefield
*Dr Sue Walker
Graham Wall
Jean and David Wall
Joan Ward
*Dr Paul Waring
Dr Martin Warren
Geoffrey Webber
Richard Wells
Peter Wheeler
*Lt Cdr Peter Whitehead
Ralph Whitlock
Steve Whitworth
Rob Wild
Mike Wilkinson
Mike Williams
Tom Williams
Christopher Wiltshire
*Dr Pat Woodruffe
Frank Woodward
Lucy Wreford
Andrew Wycherley
Nick Wynn
Nigel Wynn
Jennifer Yeadon
Gwyneth Yerrington
Ian Young
Sylvia Young

ABBREVIATIONS

AONB	Area of Outstanding Natural Beauty
BC	Butterfly Conservation
BMS	Butterfly Monitoring Scheme
BRC	Biological Records Centre
BSR	Butterfly Site Register
EN	English Nature (formerly NCC, Nature Conservancy Council)
ESA	Environmentally Sensitive Area
FC	Forestry Commission
IoA	Index of Abundance
ISR	Invertebrate Site Register
MCNHS	Marlborough College Natural History Society
MOD	Ministry of Defence
NT	National Trust
NNR	National Nature Reserve
SDNHS	Salisbury and District Natural History Society
SPTA(W)(C)(E)	Salisbury Plain Training Area (West) (Central) (East)
SSSI	Site of Special Scientific Interest
WAM	Wiltshire Archaeological Magazine
WANHS	Wiltshire Archaeological and Natural History Society
WBMS	Wiltshire Butterfly Mapping Scheme
WBRC	Wiltshire Biological Records Centre
WFMP	Wiltshire Flora Mapping Project
WNHF	Wiltshire Natural History Forum
WWT	Wiltshire Wildlife Trust (formerly WTNC, Wiltshire Trust for Nature Conservation)

HABITATS FOR
WILTSHIRE BUTTERFLIES

Wiltshire is a large and mainly rural inland county in the south of England. The largest centres of population are in the Swindon area in the north and the Salisbury area in the south. In the west there are a number of smaller towns, Malmesbury, Chippenham, Corsham, Melksham, Bradford-on-Avon, Trowbridge, Westbury and Warminster. Devizes and Calne in the centre, Wootton Bassett in the north and Marlborough in the east are the other main towns. Many of the villages lie in the river valleys, particularly in the south. In the north they are scattered in localities above the wettest low-lying land.

The construction of the M3 and M4 motorways and the upgrading of most of the A303 to dual carriageway have so reduced the travelling time from London and the heavily-populated south-east that extensive urban expansion has taken place. This has been at a phenomenal rate in the Swindon area and at Wootton Bassett and Chippenham, towns in the M4 corridor. Considerable expansion continues around Salisbury, Trowbridge and Westbury. In addition to the area of land actually developed, the increase in population has made further demands on the countryside for roads, shopping areas with their associated car-parks, waste disposal sites and recreational facilities. In an effort to diversify from farming, some landowners have constructed golf courses which, fortunately, are not always completely disadvantageous to butterflies, their foodplants and nectar sources.

Land-use in the countryside is largely dictated by the soil types. On the dry, gently rolling chalk hills in the south and north-east arable crops are grown. Formerly, most would have been of cereals but now, oilseed rape, linseed, lucerne and maize are common, interspersed with uncultivated set-aside land. Steep downland slopes, particularly in the south, remain as grassland, some unimproved

and some having had fertiliser applied by aerial spraying in the 1960s and 1970s. Too steep to plough, these downs are now grazed by sheep and/or beef cattle.

To the west of Chippenham a small area of the Limestone, which forms the Cotswolds, lies within the county. Here too there are steep slopes along the valley sides which have unimproved grassland used for grazing. All these grassland sites are good for butterflies and include many privately-owned areas of downland designated as Sites of Special Scientific Interest (SSSI), eight National Nature Reserves (NNR), four reserves owned by the Wiltshire Wildlife Trust (WWT) and an extensive National Trust (NT) holding.

Salisbury Plain, similar in size and shape to the Isle of Wight, includes nearly 20,000 hectares (49,420 acres) of relatively undisturbed chalk grassland owned by the Ministry of Defence (MOD) for military training and was designated an SSSI in 1993. Porton Down, north-east of Salisbury is also owned by the MOD and covers 2,833 hectares (7,000 acres). It is the largest tract of unimproved chalk grassland in Great Britain and, with a total of 44 species of butterfly having been recorded there, it is probably the most species-rich site in the country. Boscombe Down airfield has eleven conservation areas within its boundary and 35 species have been recorded there in recent years.

Oxford and Kimmeridge clays are the most extensive soil types in the north and north-east of the county. The wettest parts of this land are more suitable for growing grass than cereals and have a long history of dairy farming, the grass being cut for hay to feed the stock in winter. Today, farming systems require the production of several cuts of silage per year, instead of two cuts for hay. This change has resulted in the removal of hedges to enlarge some of the small fields which have then

Map 1. Topographical map of Wiltshire showing locations most frequently referred to in the text; NNR = National Nature Reserve, SPTA = Salisbury Plain Training Area

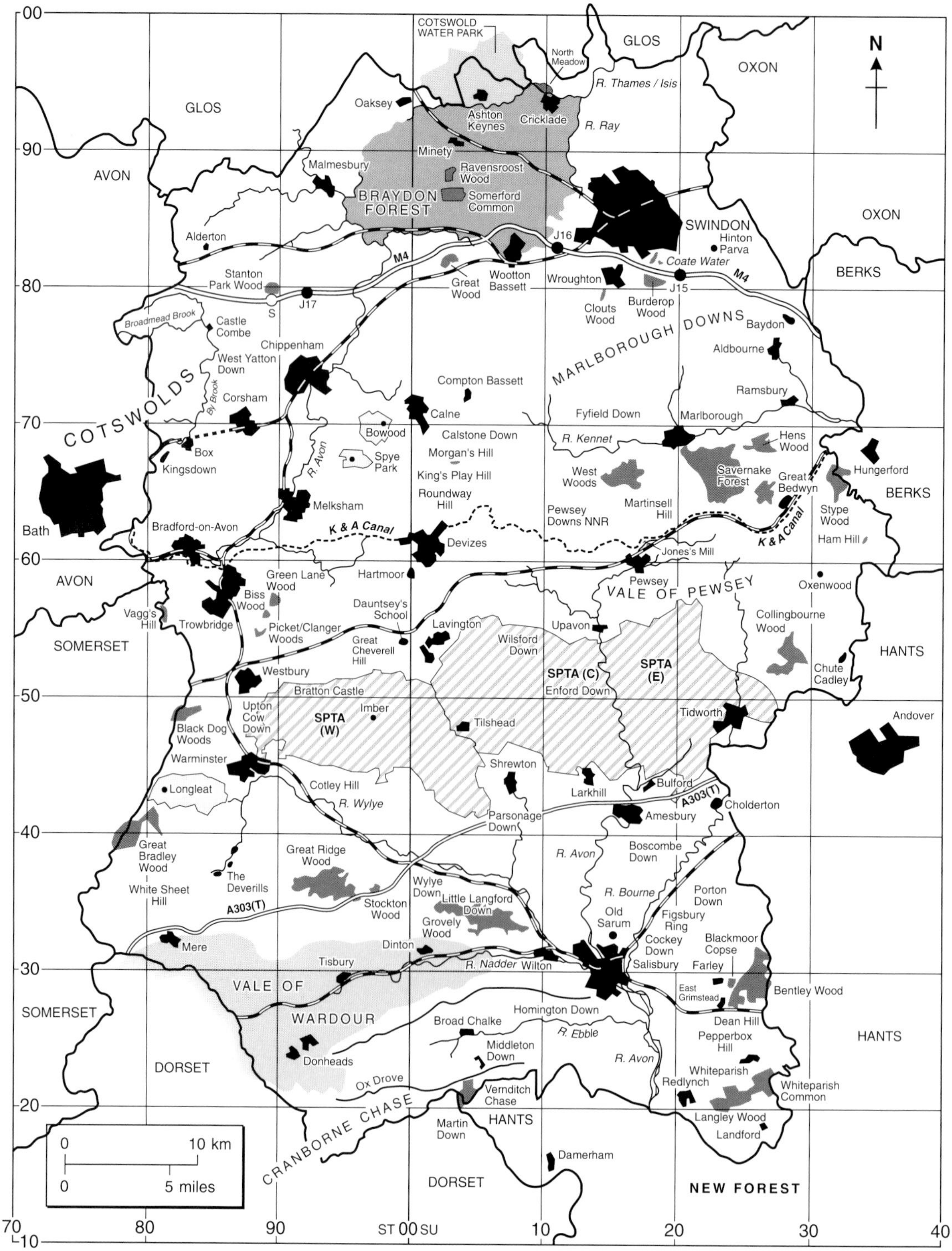

COTSWOLD WATER PARK
GLOS
OXON
N
North Meadow
GLOS
R. Thames / Isis
Oaksey
Ashton Keynes
Cricklade
R. Ray
AVON
Malmesbury
Minety
Ravensroost Wood
Somerford Common
SWINDON
Hinton Parva
OXON
Alderton
BRAYDON FOREST
J16
Coate Water
BERKS
Stanton Park Wood
M4
Great Wood
Wootton Bassett
Wroughton
J15
M4
Broadmead Brook
Castle Combe
S
J17
Clouts Wood
Burderop Wood
Baydon
West Yatton Down
Chippenham
Aldbourne
MARLBOROUGH DOWNS
Corsham
By Brook
Compton Bassett
Ramsbury
COTSWOLDS
Calne
Fyfield Down
Marlborough
Hens Wood
Bowood
Calstone Down
R. Kennet
Box
Morgan's Hill
Savernake Forest
Great Bedwyn
Hungerford
Kingsdown
R. Avon
Spye Park
King's Play Hill
West Woods
Melksham
Roundway Hill
Martinsell Hill
Stype Wood
BERKS
Bath
Bradford-on-Avon
K & A Canal
Devizes
Pewsey Downs NNR
Jones's Mill
K & A Canal
Ham Hill
AVON
Green Lane Wood
Hartmoor
Pewsey
VALE OF PEWSEY
Oxenwood
Biss Wood
Vagg's Hill
Trowbridge
Dauntsey's School
Lavington
Upavon
Collingbourne Wood
SOMERSET
Picket/Clanger Woods
Great Cheverell Hill
Wilsford Down
SPTA (C)
SPTA (E)
Chute Cadley
HANTS
Westbury
Bratton Castle
Enford Down
Andover
Upton Cow Down
Imber
SPTA (W)
Tilshead
Tidworth
Black Dog Woods
Warminster
Shrewton
Longleat
Cotley Hill
R. Wylye
Larkhill
Bulford
A303(T)
Cholderton
Parsonage Down
Amesbury
Great Bradley Wood
Great Ridge Wood
Wylye Down
R. Avon
Boscombe Down
The Deverills
Little Langford Down
R. Bourne
Porton Down
White Sheet Hill
A303(T)
Stockton Wood
Grovely Wood
Old Sarum
Figsbury Ring
Blackmoor Copse
Mere
Dinton
Cockey Down
Farley
Tisbury
R. Nadder
Wilton
Salisbury
VALE OF
East Grimstead
Bentley Wood
WARDOUR
Broad Chalke
Homington Down
R. Ebble
Dean Hill
Pepperbox Hill
HANTS
SOMERSET
Middleton Down
R. Avon
DORSET
Donheads
Ox Drove
Verditch Chase
Whiteparish
Redlynch
Whiteparish Common
Martin Down
HANTS
Langley Wood
Landford
Damerham
CRANBORNE CHASE
DORSET
NEW FOREST

0 — 10 km
0 — 5 miles

Based on the 1984 & 1988 Ordnance Survey 1:250 000 maps, sheets 8 & 9, with the permission of the Controller of Her Majesty's Stationery Office. © Crown Copyright.

Map 2. Geological map of Wiltshire (modified from British Geological Survey 1:250,000 Series for Solid rocks and 1:50,000 and 1:63,360 Series for Drift deposits)

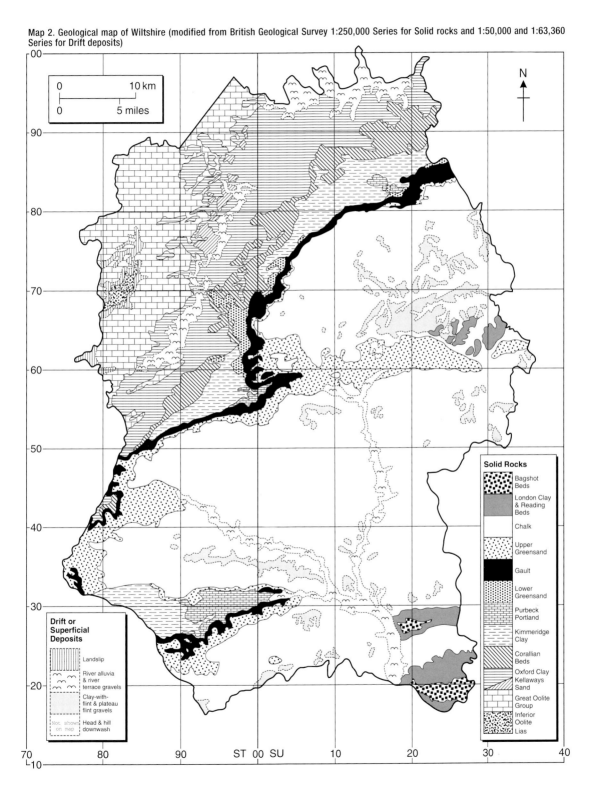

N

Scale:
0 — 10 km
0 — 5 miles

Drift or Superficial Deposits

- Landslip
- River alluvia & river terrace gravels
- Clay-with-flint & plateau flint gravels
- Head & hill downwash (Not shown on map)

Solid Rocks

- Bagshot Beds
- London Clay & Reading Beds
- Chalk
- Upper Greensand
- Gault
- Lower Greensand
- Purbeck Portland
- Kimmeridge Clay
- Corallian Beds
- Oxford Clay Kellaways Sand
- Great Oolite Group
- Inferior Oolite
- Lias

ST 00 SU

been drained and sown with quick-growing grasses. Efforts are being made by conservation organisations to find ways, through purchase or various enhancement schemes and grants, to ensure that the remaining hay meadows, with their rich flora and invertebrate fauna, are preserved.

Large woodlands are absent from the Chalk but do occur on the Clay-with-flint which overlies it in Savernake Forest, West Woods and Collingbourne Forest in the east and Great Ridge and Grovely Woods in the south. There are large oak woods on the clay both in the north in the Braydon Forest area and in the south at Bentley Wood and woods near Whiteparish. Smaller woods survive from the old Selwood Forest in West Wiltshire. Several of these large and small woods were leased or purchased by the Forestry Commission (FC) in the 1940s and 1950s. Sections were felled and planted with conifers creating unsuitable habitats for much of the native wildlife dependent on deciduous trees. Fortunately, most of these woods have retained at least some areas of ancient woodland and, where wide open rides and clearings have been maintained for timber extraction, woodland butterflies have survived although in fewer numbers than before the planting of the conifers.

Several woods that had become dense and shaded by the 1950s and 1960s have been bought by conservation organisations or, in the case of Biss Wood near Trowbridge, by a private individual, and are now being managed with consideration for their wildlife. Clanger Wood and the adjoining Picket Wood, now owned by the Woodland Trust (WT) and designated an SSSI, were oak with hazel coppice until the 1960s when blocks of conifers were planted leaving 25–30 metre wide strips of oaks between each block. The conifers are now being felled and in these opened areas the woodland ground flora is returning and with it, perhaps, an increase in the butterfly populations. The WT also owns Colerne Park Wood which lies on a steep valley slope in the Cotswolds. It was formerly dominated by wych elm which is regenerating following Dutch elm disease. Oak and ash are now the principal

standard trees and management has begun to open up this long-neglected wood to which butterflies may return.

Butterfly monitoring has been carried out by volunteers for several years in most of the non-commercially owned woodlands referred to. Data from these censuses will enable the effect of the management to be assessed and adjusted if necessary.

Unimproved grassland on the chalk and limestone downland, hay meadows on the Clay and rides in the old deciduous woodlands are the habitats where the greatest variety of wild grasses and herbs are still to be found. These are the strongholds of many of the county's butterflies, a fact illustrated by comparing the geology map (page 3) with some of the species distribution maps.

The mainly acidic soils in the extreme south-east corner, derived from Bagshot Beds, London Clay and Reading Beds, occur nowhere else in the county. This is part of the New Forest lowland heath, dominated by heather (*Calluna vulgaris*), heaths (*Erica* spp.) and gorse (*Ulex* spp.), which has a long history of grazing by commoners' stock but is a habitat that has been drastically depleted in the last 150 years. Continued grazing or burning that maintained the open areas in the past are essential for the survival of Wiltshire's only colonies of silver-studded blues.

Within the agriculturally and domestically managed countryside and built-up areas there are other habitats which can support some of the commoner species. For example, fields of lucerne (*Medicago sativa*) are irresistible as nectar sources to common blues, painted ladies, small tortoiseshells and peacocks and also to clouded yellows both for nectaring and breeding, while rape (*Brassica napus*) is much sought after by the whites. Old and new road and railway cuttings and embankments, especially those having a southerly aspect, may become colonised by plants that are the larval foodplants of one or more species. An excellent example is to be found on a cutting on the A303 near Wylye where a south-facing chalk slope was quickly colonised by horseshoe vetch (*Hippocrepis comosa*) which, in turn, has been colonised by a strong colony of Adonis blues. The ballast on which the sleepers rested on disused railway lines and, in some cases, the steep banks, take many years to become covered with tall vegetation. During this period, they are gradually colonised by low herbs and grasses and, because they are in warm and sheltered conditions, butterflies are attracted to them.

Well-established sunny hedgerows and scrub, especially if they contain flowering brambles (*Rubus fruticosus* agg.) and have nectar-producing herbs in adjacent grassland, are valuable to butterflies for feeding, basking and providing sheltered spots where males can lie in wait for passing females. They also act as corridors linking habitats and encouraging mobility in some species. Baines (1984) estimated that there were over one million acres of gardens in Great Britain. He provided a list of native and exotic tree, shrub and herb species that gardeners might plant which would support a range of dependent insects. The planting of native wildflower seeds, either collected legally from the wild or produced and sold commercially, is now popular with gardeners sympathetic to wildlife conservation. Although few exotic species are used as larval foodplants there are those that need to be cross-pollinated and therefore produce nectar to attract their insect pollinators. Butterflies are particularly attracted to butterfly bush (*Buddleja* spp.), lavender (*Lavandula spica*), michaelmas-daisy (*Aster* spp.) and ice plant (*Sedum spectabile*). Unfortunately, some herbaceous garden plants that do not need to be propagated by seed have had nectar bred out of them making their flowers useless as a source of food for butterflies. A few wild flowers in a garden such as dandelion (*Taraxacum* spp.), oxeye daisy (*Leucanthemum vulgare*), knapweeds (*Centaurea* spp.), field scabious (*Knautia arvensis*) and marjoram (*Origanum vulgare*) will attract far more insects than dozens of unscented exotics. However, gardens, allotments and urban waste places are where most people see butterflies and without them populations of the common species would be severely depleted and interest in these beautiful insects would be greatly diminished.

Butterflies and the Weather

Although weather conditions have a very considerable effect on whether butterflies are seen flying in search of mates and food, the small geographical variations that occur over an area the size of Wiltshire (84 km from north to south and 59 km from west to east) are probably of little significance. Variation in the altitude, aspect and topography of a locality are more likely to have an impact and, even within a habitat, there are micro-habitats where the temperature may be significantly higher than elsewhere.

To state, for example, that the county's average rainfall over a given period amounted to 750 mm (30 ins) or that the average temperature in July was 22°C is meaningless. Hidden within such figures will be springs and summers of both exceptionally high and low rainfall and temperatures. Sunshine averages would be equally misleading. However, the relation between weather and butterfly sightings is very real.

It must be remembered that the butterfly is only one of four very different stages in the life of a lepidopterous insect of which at least one must survive throughout the winter. Only four British species hibernate as adults, the remainder overwinter as eggs, caterpillars or chrysalises. For these the weather may be critical though much work is still needed to discover the precise requirements of each. In general terms, mild and damp conditions are probably more harmful than cold and dry.

THE HISTORY OF BUTTERFLY RECORDING IN WILTSHIRE

Before 1900

Very little information on the county's butterflies was recorded prior to 1900. Unlike that for many other counties, the *Victoria County History* for Wiltshire did not include a section on its natural history. The early butterfly publications of Lewin (1795), Rennie (1832), Duncan (1835), Morris (1853), Stainton (1857), Coleman (1860), Newman (1869), Lucas (1893), Barrett (1893) and Tutt (1896) incorporated county lists for some species which sometimes included those from Wiltshire but detailed information and locations were rarely given.

During the 19th century the publication of various entomological periodicals commenced, the earliest being *The Entomological Magazine* which ran for five volumes from 1833–1838. This was followed by three or four others including *The Entomologist* (Ent.) in 1840 which is still published monthly and was the prime publication of records and observations during much of that period. *The Entomologist's Record and Journal of Variation* (Ent. Rec.) was founded in 1890 and is still published bi-monthly. None of these pre-1900 publications have been searched for early Wiltshire records and, judging by the post 1900 issues that have been investigated, it would be surprising if there were many except possibly from the Marlborough College Natural History Society (MCNHS) whose entomological reports have been studied and from which records have been frequently quoted.

The publications of the MCNHS, which was founded in 1864, were the only sources of records in the north of the county. The first, in 1865, was a list of all the lepidoptera records from within a ten mile radius of Marlborough and from which the section referring to butterflies is reproduced in Figure 1. Subsequent detailed lists were frequently produced, the last appearing in 1956. Incidentally, its co-author was Stephen Sutton, a college pupil at

the time and now a lecturer at Leeds University and co-editor of *The Butterflies and Moths of Yorkshire* (1989). The Society became inactive in 1966, since when there has been very little systematic recording in the area.

1900–60

Dauntsey's School, at West Lavington in the centre of the county, produced informal and incomplete lists of lepidoptera occurring in the school grounds and surrounding area from 1931 to 1948 since when there has been no further recording.

Records for the south of the county came almost exclusively from the great all-round naturalist, the late Roy Pitman of Whaddon, near Salisbury. His first Lepidoptera Report for the county in 1936 was published in the Wiltshire Archaeological and Natural History Society's Magazine (WAM) Vol. 48, December 1937. From 1952 until his death in October 1986 he was the entomological recorder for the Salisbury Field Club which was founded in November 1952 and later became the Salisbury and District Natural History Society (SDNHS). He reported entomological observations in the Society's monthly bulletins and annual reports. After Roy's death at the age of 81, Ted Gange, who was his good friend and neighbour at Whaddon, has continued these monthly reports until the present time (1995).

Roy's only son Brian, who now lives at West Orchard near Shaftesbury in Dorset, has kindly allowed me to study his father's detailed diaries which provide much fascinating and valuable information on the butterflies in the Salisbury area. The first diary is for 1928 followed by a gap of ten years. Those for 1940 to 1944, if they existed, are missing but, except for five years, between 1945 and September 1986 the series is complete. It is believed that Roy's extensive collection of butterflies and moths was largely

Figure 1. The first Lepidoptera List of the Marlborough College Natural History Society published in the 1865 Report

THE object of publishing the following List is not so much to show how rich the neighbourhood of Marlborough is in Lepidoptera, but rather to show how much has yet to be done ere we can profess to have even a tolerably complete List. Absence from the College during July and August, two of the best months in the year for collecting, must be our excuse for its meagreness, especially in Noctuæ; but now that its defects are known it is to be hoped that in the course of the next two or three seasons they will be greatly remedied.

Names of those whose initials are given in the following List :—

A. C. A...... A. C. Almack
W. J. B.... Mr. W. J. Baverstock
F. B. .... F. Bonney
R. H. B.... R. H. Brown
J. F. B. .... J. F. Buckler
E. H. D. .... E. H. Davis
W. W. D. .... W. W. Dayman
H. A. E. .... H. A. Evans
C. R. W. H. .... C. R. W. Hardy
R. R. P. H. .... R. R. P. Hilton
F. C. L. .... F. C. Lightfoot
J. W. L........ J. W. Lukis, Esq., quoted in Rev. F. O.
Morris' "British Butterflies."
A. M. .... A. Marshall
W. W. M. .... W. W. Melville
J. W. M. .... J. W. Mills
G. K. M. .... G. K. Mills
W. G. N. .... W. G. North
H. R. P. .... H. R. Parrington
J. W. P......... J. W. Parrington
J. P. .... J. Pole
T. A. P.......... Rev. T. A. Preston
P. S. R. .... P. S. Robinson
F. T. S. .... F. T. Sharp
J. S. .... Rev. J. Sowerby
G. T. S. .... G. T. Spankie
R. H. T. .... R. H. Tyacke
J. W. W. .... J. W. Whitaker

iv

25. CYNTHIA CARDUI. *Painted Lady.*
Common in 1863, 1864, and 1865.
26. VANESSA ATALANTA. *Red Admiral.*
27. V. IO. *Peacock.*
28. V. ANTIOPA. *Camberwell Beauty.*
A specimen taken near the Eight Walks in Savernake Forest, in 1860, by W. J. B.
29. V. POLYCHLOROS. *Large Tortoise-shell.*
Great Bedwyn, *Rev. F. O. Morris*; occasionally met with; has been taken by F. B. and W. J. B.; seen by J. P.
30. V. URTICÆ. *Small Tortoise-shell.*
32. ARGYNNIS PAPHIA. *Silver-washed Fritillary.*
Savernake Forest, J. S.; near Great Bedwyn, rather uncommonly, J. W. L.
33. A. ADIPPE. *High-Brown Fritillary.*
Savernake Forest, J. S.; taken June 21st, 1865, near the Railway Station, by — Johnson.
34. A. AGLAIA. *Dark Green Fritillary.*
Savernake Forest, J. S.; near Great Bedwyn, Rev. F. O. Morris; near the Railway Station, June 19th, 1865, J. W. W.
36. A. SELENE. *Small Pearl-bordered Fritillary.*
Savernake Forest, abundant.
37. A. EUPHROSYNE. *Pearl-bordered Fritillary.*
Savernake Forest, abundant; Rabley Copse, West Woods, and Manton Copse, abundant.
38. MELITÆA CINXIA. *Glanville Fritillary.*
Near Great Bedwyn, "very rarely," J. W. L.
39. M. ATHALIA. *Heath Fritillary.*
Near Great Bedwyn, J. W. L.
40. M. ARTEMIS. *Greasy Fritillary.*
Abundant on a bank at Clatford Bottom; near Great Bedwyn, *Rev. F. O. Morris.*
41. NEMEOBIUS LUCINA. *Duke of Burgundy Fritillary.*
Manton Copse and Rabley Copse, common in May; West Woods, W. J. B.; rather uncommon near Great Bedwyn, Rev. F. O. Morris.
42. THECLA BETULÆ. *Brown Hairstreak.*
Near Great Bedwyn, Rev. F. O Morris; West Woods, W. J. B.; seen, but not captured, in the Wilderness in the College Grounds, by J. P.
45. T. QUERCUS. *Purple Hairstreak.*
"Not commonly," near Great Bedwyn, Rev. F. O. Morris.
46. T. RUBI. *Green Hairstreak.*
Clatford Park Farm, May 28, 1864, C. R. W. H.; near Great Bedwyn, Rev. F. O. Morris.
47. CHRYSOPHANUS PHLŒAS. *Small Copper.*

LEPIDOPTERA.

[The numbers prefixed to the species refer to "Stainton's Manual."]

RHOPALOCERA.

2. GONEPTERYX RHAMNI. *Brimstone.*
3. COLIAS EDUSA. *Clouded Yellow.*
Common in 1858. Taken June, 1865, near the turnpike on the Old Swindon road, J. W. W. Several seen and captured the same Autumn. Variety (Helice), taken on Ogbourne Downs, W. J. B.
6. PIERIS BRASSICÆ. *Large White.*
7. P. RAPÆ. *Small White.*
8. P. NAPI. *Green-veined White.*
10. ANTHOCHARIS CARDAMINES. *Orange-tip.*
11. LEUCOPHASIA SINAPIS. *Wood White.*
Sergeant Doel's, F. B.; Savernake Forest, E. H. D.; Rabley Copse, W. J. B.; Rarely near Great Bedwyn, J. W. L.
12. ARGE GALATHEA. *Marbled White.*
Great Bedwyn, G. T. S., J. W. L.; Savernake Forest, E. H. D.; seen near West Woods, A. M.
13. LASIOMMATA ÆGERIA. *Speckled Wood.*
Rabley, J. W. M., J. P.; Copse near Preshute, A. M. This insect appears to be rather uncommon in this neighbourhood.
14. L. MEGÆRA. *Wall.*
15. HIPPARCHIA SEMELE. *Grayling.*
Sparingly near Great Bedwyn, J. W. L.
16. H. JANIRA. *Meadow Brown.*
17. H. TITHONUS. *Gate-keeper.*
18. H. HYPERANTHUS. *Ringlet.*
Great Bedwyn, G. T. S. Plentiful on White Horse Down, W. J. B.
22. CŒNONYMPHA PAMPHILUS. *Small Heath.*
24. APATURA IRIS. *Purple Emperor.*
Has been taken in Savernake Forest, W. J. B.

v

51. POLYOMMATUS ALSUS. *Bedford Blue.*
Abundant in Clatford Bottom; near Great Bedwyn, J. W. L.
53. P. ARION. *Large Blue.*
Savernake Forest, not Marlborough Downs, as stated in "Young England," W. J. B.
54. P. CORYDON. *Chalk-hill Blue.*
Rainscombe Park, W. J. B.; near Great Bedwyn, J. W. L.
56. P. ALEXIS. *Common Blue.*
58. P. AGESTIS. *Brown Argus.*
Moderately common.
60. THYMELE ALVEOLUS. *Grizzled Skipper.*
61. THANAOS TAGES. *Dingy Skipper.*
Savernake Forest, H. A. E.; Great Bedwyn, T. A. P.; Martinsell, J. W. M.; Clatford, H. A. E.
63. PAMPHILA LINEA. *Small Skipper.*
West Woods, J. W. M.; Savernake Forest, G. K. M.; Martinsell, W. J. B.; not so common as the following, H. A. E.
65. P. SYLVANUS. *Large Skipper.*
Common in most Copses.
66. P. COMMA. *Pearl Skipper.*
Martinsell, W. J. B.; one specimen taken there by J. F. D.

unlabelled, but there is no doubt that most of the specimens were taken by him in the Salisbury area. The collection was disposed of in various lots and no attempt has been made to trace any part of it. Relevant comments from his diaries have been included within the species accounts when they were felt to be of interest or significance. His book, *A Naturalist at Home* (1984), contains some interesting entomological information particularly concerning an attempt to establish the large blue on the south Wiltshire downs.

The late Bowmont Weddell (Bow) moved to Trowbridge from his homeland in the Scottish Borders in 1931. His lepidoptera diaries for the county, which contain many details of his observations particularly in West Wiltshire, were started in the following year and continued until the time of his death in January 1990 at the great age of 96. In his later years he concentrated on moths and became the county's expert particularly on the micromoth species. His close association with Godfrey and Michael Smith of nearby Ashton Common has enabled his great knowledge and experience to be passed on to the next generation. Godfrey retains Bow's diaries to which he has kindly allowed me access.

Weddell's first annual entomological report for WAM appeared in 1947 and is reproduced in Figure 2. Except for Pitman's 1936 Report, this was the first comprehensive lepidoptera article published by the WANHS since it was founded in 1853. The plea from its first secretary, the Rev William Collings Lukis MA, FSA is interesting (WAM Vol. 1, 1854). This was basically a request for county specimens to be donated to the Society, with special emphasis on careful labelling and accurate data such as location, date etc. Whether members responded to this request is not known,

Figure 2. Bowmont Weddell's first Entomological Report for the Wiltshire Achaeological Magazine 1947

248

ENTOMOLOGICAL REPORT FOR 1947.

I write at the close of what must be the most remarkable season, entomologically, within living memory. Today, November 5th, a Clouded Yellow (*C. croceus*) was flying in my garden. A friend with over 50 years' experience recorded as his latest date for this beautiful butterfly October 3rd. They had propitious migrating conditions in May and June, and the subsequent fine spell allowed them to breed through August, September and into October. Every clover field in Wilts must have produced its quota of scores or hundreds. The pale lemon variety of the female, known as *Helice*, usually occurs at the rate of 1%, but this year it has been estimated nearer 10%. The Pale Clouded Yellow (*C. hyale*) is always much rarer, and I have only one report in Wilts, above Bratton.

Another interesting insect is the Humming-bird Hawk-moth (*M. stellatarum*). Like the Clouded Yellow it invaded the country in force in late May and June. I saw it first on May 24th. The food plant, Yellow Bedstraw, is abundant, and the weather has encouraged them to raise large families. They have been much in evidence in our gardens, flying in the sun and supping nectar on the wing.

A delicately beautiful little moth, the Vestal (*R. sacraria*) has appeared sparingly in Wilts. A friend near Salisbury took two, one the typical British, the other the Continental form. They were fairly plentiful near the coast, but few penetrated this far inland. Apparently they established themselves in the wheat fields, the larvæ feeding on Knotgrass. It is unlikely any could survive an English winter.

This applies also to the Clouded Yellows, and indeed to many of our well-known butterflies and moths, such as the Red Admiral, Painted Lady, Silver Y, etc. It is not usually realized that these and many other native species die out every winter, the stock being replenished by migrants each spring.

Wiltshire, considering it is a non-maritime county with next to no fenland, could produce a very good list of lepidoptera. It would be most interesting to have records, date and place, from all parts of the county, and I hope that members and non-members will send theirs in. Our knowledge of the distribution and frequency of our macrolepidoptera is very far from complete, but if sufficient reliable records are sent in, a complete authentic county list may be built up by degrees.

B. W. WEDDELL, 13, The Halve,
Trowbridge.

By B. W. Weddell. 249

LEPIDOPTERA LIST.

1947.			
17th Jan.	Large White	*P. brassicae*	Clarendon, Salisbury.
23rd March	Speckled Wood	*P. ægeria*	Devizes.
3rd April	Northern Drab !	*T. opima*	Trowbridge.
7th May	Orange Tip	*E. cardamines*	Marlborough.
8th ,,	Small White	*P. rapae*	,,
14th ,,	Limespeck Pug	*E. oblongata*	Semington.
,, ,,	White Ermine	*S. menthastri*	Marlborough.
17th ,,	Cinnabar	*H. jacobææ*	,,
20th ,,	Chocolate Tip	*P. curtula*	,,
24th ,,	Pearl-bordered Fritillary	*A. euphrosyne*	,,
,, ,,	Hummingbird Hawk	*M. stellatarum*	Trowbridge.
25th ,,	Latticed Heath	*S. clathrata*	,,
28th ,,	Clouded Yellow	*C. croceus*	Marlborough.
,, ,,	Common Blue	*L. icarus*	,,
1st June	Small Heath	*C. pamphilus*	,,
9th ,,	Meadow Brown	*E. ianira*	,,
10th ,,	Blomers Rivulet	*E. blomeri*	,,
,, ,,	Bordered Sallow !	*C. umbra*	,,
,, ,,	*Netted Pug	*E. venosata*	Conkwell.
11th ,,	Lobster	*S. fagi*	,,
,, ,,	Bordered Gothic !	*E. reticulata*	,,
15th ,,	*Netted Pug	*E. venosata*	Marlborough.
16th ,,	Marbled Brown	*D. trimacula*	Trowbridge.
18th ,,	Pale Shining Brown !	*M. advena*	Conkwell.
,, ,,	Figure of Eighty	*P. octogessima*	,,
,, ,,	Blotched Emerald	*E. pustulata*	,,
22nd ,,	White Admiral	*L. sibylla*	Trowbridge.
4th July	Elephant Hawk	*D. elpenor*	Pitton.
13th ,,	Comma Butterfly	*P. c-album*	Bradford.
,, ,,	Small Skipper	*A. thaumas*	Bratton.
14th ,,	Small Emerald	*E. vernaria*	Conkwell.
,, ,,	Bordered Beauty	*E. apiciaria*	Trowbridge.
,, ,,	Lackey	*C. neustria*	,,
16th ,,	Dot	*M. persicariae*	Erlestoke.
19th ,,	Essex Skipper !	*A. lineola*	Bradford.
26th ,,	Purple Emperor (seen) !	*A. iris*	Salisbury district.
29th ,,	Least Yellow Underwing	*T. interjecta*	Trowbridge.
,, ,,	Orange Swift	*H. sylvina*	,,
8th Aug.	Brighton Wainscot !	*C. musculosa*	Tilshead.
24th ,,	Red Underwing	*C. nupta*	Trowbridge.
28th ,,	The Vestal	*R. sacraria*	Salisbury District.
23rd Sept.	Convolvulous Hawk	*S. convolvuli*	Devizes.
8th Nov.	Clouded Yellow	*C. croceus*	Tinhead.
,, ,,	†Hummingbird Hawk	*M. stellatarum*	Trowbridge.

* First time for many years. † My latest observation of these.

The following unconfirmed reports are worthy of note.

August *Large Tortoiseshell* *V. polychloros* W. Lavington.

This insect may be overlooked owing to its habit of hibernation very soon after emergence. In this county of elm trees it is well worth looking out for.

Camberwell Beauty *V. antiopa* W. Lavington.

Persistent reports of this butterfly over the last 15 years in the Avon Valley, at Westbury and W. Lavington, etc., suggest that it should be considered a possible whenever its food plant, Crack Willow, is abundant.

but, if any specimens or records were donated to the Society, they no longer exist. I have inspected the collections in the Museum and found no material from this period.

From 1947 to 1986, annual species lists were published by WANHS, compiled by Weddell 1947–75, John d'Arcy 1976–83 and Michael Fuller 1984–86. These included records from such notable entomologists as Miss Vere Temple of Tollard Royal, Colonel Charles Floyd of Holt, Baron de Worms (mainly as a visitor to Wiltshire), Major General C G (Kit) Lipscomb of Crockerton, Captain Reginald Jackson of Codford St Mary and from Ian Heslop recording in the Salisbury area and Pitman in the Clarendon area. Unfortunately, location details were rarely included, a requirement for inclusion in the mapping schemes of today. In the 1930s and 1940s, when most species were much more abundant and widespread than they are now and the imminent destruction of much of our countryside could not have been foreseen, the need for such detail was not recognised. In an age when intensive collecting was still in vogue and rivalry and competition to have a superior collection to one's fellow lepidopterists was a factor, the need for a degree of secrecy was also a consideration for the scarcer species.

By the 1950s and early 1960s however, changes were under way and Weddell's comments sadly tell the story. In 1958 he said, 'One hears of locality after locality being ruined by intensive cultivation including the use of selective weedkillers and other sprays. The disappearance of the rabbit too ... is having the effect of radically altering the vegetation. The rank grasses ... now tend to overgrow and smother certain low growing foodplants with dire results. Add to the above handicaps the weather we had to suffer during 1958 and you get a picture that would make our forebears turn in their graves'. Again in 1959, 'There is a distressing change taking place in the ecology of the county. The absence of rabbits ... plus intensive cultivation has utterly ruined most of our noted downland localities. Much of our woodland too is being ruthlessly cleared and

either ploughed or replanted with quick yielding conifers' and in 1961 '... it is doubtful if insects can withstand the massive interference with the balance of nature which man is carrying out today'. In his diaries, Pitman echoes these sentiments concerning his favourite sites in the Salisbury area.

From 1900 onwards, the Ent. and the Ent.Rec. have been extensively, but not completely, searched for Wiltshire data and any significant findings have been quoted. Even so, considering its butterfly richness, references to Wiltshire are few except from the annual reports of de Worms, occasional reports from Heslop and, in more recent times, from Lipscomb and Jackson. The county's butterfly records have been very under-published in spite of frequent visits from collectors in the past for the rare variations of the blues.

Two other known sources of Wiltshire data, the collections and notebooks of Heslop held at Bristol Museum and those of Lipscomb held at The Natural History Museum in London, have not been examined and no doubt there is an opportunity here for further study. Both men spent much of their time collecting and observing butterflies in the county and, although Heslop was primarily concerned with the purple emperor in the south-east of the county, other interesting information could be awaiting discovery.

1961–76

Since the early 1960s much has happened both nationally and within the county regarding the study and protection of wildlife areas and, in several instances, butterflies have been a prime consideration in action that has been taken.

De Worms was the first to bring together all the available information concerning the county's lepidoptera. He was one of the country's great lepidoptera collectors who travelled extensively. He was a prolific writer of articles and annual reports which were published in the Ent. and the Ent.Rec. spanning 49 years from 1930 until his death in 1979. He lived in Salisbury while working as an Experimental Officer in charge of one of the chemical research laboratories at Porton Down from 1940 to 1944 and often visited friends in other parts of the county. Both Pitman and Weddell mention him frequently in their diaries and accompanied him on collecting trips in the county. In 1962, *The Macrolepidoptera of Wiltshire*, compiled by de Worms largely from data supplied by Pitman, Weddell and Jackson, was published by WANHS. It did not include county distribution maps but information from all the sources previously mentioned and records from other recorders from within and outside the county were incorporated. Their number was quite small and, from the section on butterflies, it is apparent that there were only about a dozen sources of records from which the status of each species was described. Nevertheless, this was the most comprehensive review of the county's lepidoptera since the days of Edward Meyrick's reports for the Marlborough area in the 1920s.

In the same year, the Wiltshire Trust for Nature Conservation (WTNC), now the Wiltshire Wildlife Trust (WWT), was founded by a group of dedicated naturalists including the lepidopterists Floyd, Lipscomb, Pitman and Weddell. One of its prime aims was to secure land for wildlife conservation. However, it has only been in the last few years that systematic and detailed recording of the lepidoptera on some of the Trust's reserves has been carried out. In 1994, 39 reserves were either owned or managed by the WWT of which 13 are important for their butterflies.

In 1964, *Notes and Views of the Purple Emperor* by Heslop, George Hyde and Roy Stockley was published. Much of the contents, which included references to several other species, were based on studies and observations in the woods to the east and south of Salisbury, notably at Blackmoor Copse, Bentley Wood and the woods around Whiteparish. In fact Heslop was the driving, almost fanatical, force in establishing Blackmoor Copse as a nature reserve in December 1956. It was managed by the Society for the Promotion of Nature Reserves (SPNR), now the Royal Society for Nature Conservation (RSNC), until 1963 specifically for lepidoptera and, in particular, for the requirements of the purple emperor. It is now leased by the WWT and

management for lepidoptera continues to be given high priority.

During this period a local natural history society was founded at Westbury in 1963, at Box in 1969, at Tisbury in 1981 and at Sedgehill in 1973, the latter being dissolved in 1994. These groups rarely produced any published records but they have raised the level of natural history awareness and interest in the county.

The Wiltshire Natural History Forum (WNHF) was set up in 1974 to bring together, for discussion and action, all the voluntary natural history organisations and the statutory bodies concerned with the planning and management of the countryside. These include the County Planning and Highways Department and the Library and Museums Service. The Forum initiated the Wiltshire Flora Mapping Project (WFMP) and launched an ambitious eight-year project in 1984 with the aim of updating Donald Grose's *Flora of Wiltshire* (1957) by mapping the county's flora. The recording was carried out to a tetrad base from which distribution dot maps were produced as part of *The Wiltshire Flora* (edited by Gillam) published in October 1993. Recorders for the project were encouraged to note and submit butterfly sightings as they travelled round the county. Many did so and their contributions have helped to ensure that the butterfly distribution maps are as comprehensive as possible.

1977–94

The Wiltshire Farming and Wildlife Advisory Group (FWAG) was inaugurated in 1977 and acts as an important link between farmers and naturalists in conservation matters.

Between 1977 and 1980 the establishment by the Ministry of Defence (MOD) of three conservation groups, West, Central and East, on the Salisbury Plain Training Area (SPTA) was a significant event. The formation of the Imber (1977), Larkhill/West Down (1980) and Bulford (1979) groups promoted detailed recording and cooperation between civilian and military personnel in the following years. Data obtained by members of these groups was a major factor in the decision by English Nature (EN) to designate SPTA a Site of Special Scientific Interest (SSSI) in 1993. This large area has proved to contain nationally important sites for butterflies including large populations of some of the country's scarce and declining species such as the small blue, Adonis blue, Duke of Burgundy, dark green fritillary and marsh fritillary. Unfortunately, public access is necessarily restricted even to members of the conservation groups. Site dossiers and maps of sensitive natural history and archaeological areas have been compiled and management plans are currently being drawn up under the expert guidance of Paul Toynton who has had many years of experience in such matters while English Nature's warden of Martin Down National Nature Reserve (NNR) on the Wiltshire/Hampshire/Dorset borders, a superb chalk grassland site rich in butterfly species.

Further MOD conservation groups were established in the mid-1980s at Porton Down and Boscombe Down in the south-east of the county, two nationally important sites for invertebrates.

In the summer of 1983, Paul Waring, now National Moth Conservation Officer for Butterfly Conservation (BC), carried out an intensive survey of the lepidoptera of Bentley Wood when it was owned by the Forestry Commission (FC). His voluminous and detailed report has been a valuable source of information for the present owners when deciding on the future management of the wood. This 688 hectare (1,700 acre) woodland, which lies east of Salisbury adjacent to the Hampshire border, was purchased in 1983 from the FC by a Charitable Trust. One of the aims of the management plan, drawn up by Bob Gibbons in 1987/88, is to maintain and enhance its important wildlife of which the butterflies are a major consideration. Since acquisition by the trust 41 species have been recorded in the wood. Barry Fox coordinates the monitoring of five butterfly transects established to assess the fluctuations in abundance of each species and to assist in implementing appropriate management for their survival.

The worrying decline in numbers of many invertebrate species prompted the commissioning of national Invertebrate Site Registers (ISR) by the Nature Conservancy Council (NCC) in 1982 in which butterflies were the main group listed. The edition for Wiltshire was produced by Caroline Peachey (now Steel) in 1983. The aim of compiling the ISRs was to locate and list the prime invertebrate sites in each county. Earlier literature was scrutinised and recorded information, including the current status of species, was sought from entomologists in the county. With a few exceptions, these sites were NNRs, SSSIs or WWT reserves.

In 1985, the NCC commissioned Martin Warren to update the ISR butterfly data for the south-west region. The Butterfly Site Register (BSR) for Wiltshire, published in 1987, included data obtained from the Wiltshire Butterfly Mapping Scheme (WBMS) which had been established in 1982/83. Martin lived in Marlborough in 1986 and 1987 while working on the project and contributed valuable data to the mapping scheme. In 1993 he became BC's first conservation officer and subsequently its Head of Conservation.

At a national level, EN has established eight NNRs in Wiltshire three of which, Pewsey Downs, Langley Wood and Prescombe Down, have important habitats for butterflies. There are about 120 SSSIs designated in order to protect their semi-natural vegetation from detrimental damage. Many of these support important butterfly populations.

The establishment of Areas of Outstanding Natural Beauty (AONB), Country Parks and Environmentally Sensitive Areas (ESA) aims to give protection to the countryside from indiscriminate development and/or management.

The National Trust (NT) now owns considerable areas of land within the county and five of its properties, Cley Hill, Pepperbox Hill, White Sheet Hill, Calstone and Cherhill Downs and Figsbury Ring are important for butterflies.

The Woodland Trust, founded in 1972, owns a few important sites, notably Picket, Clanger and Colerne Park Woods. From time to time, all these organisations have carried out natural history surveys on their land and butterflies, being a popular and distinctive group, have featured prominently.

The Wiltshire Butterfly Mapping Scheme 1982–94
The national Biological Records Centre (BRC) was established in 1962 at the Institute of Terrestrial Ecology at Monks Wood Experimental Station, Huntingdon. In 1970 it published the first provisional national atlas of butterfly distribution maps under the direction of the late John Heath. An updated atlas was produced in 1975 (Skelton and Heath) and the final atlas was published in book form in 1984, two years after recording had ceased (Heath, Pollard and Thomas). The British Butterfly Conservation Society, now Butterfly Conservation (BC), founded in 1968, has processed records in conjunction with the BRC since 1983.

The national recording scheme stimulated the establishment of BRCs in some counties and several produced their own butterfly atlases during the 1980s and early 1990s. The national scheme adopted the Ordnance Survey 10 km square as the base for its distribution maps. This was also used by Berkshire, Buckinghamshire and Oxfordshire (1985) but Dorset (1984) used a 1 km square base and Suffolk (1986) the tetrad (2 km square). The tetrad would appear to be the most suitable for county maps, the 10 km square being too imprecise and the 1 km base tending to indicate an exact location of a species which might be detrimental to the continued existence of some scarce or rare species. The tetrad base may make it more difficult to pinpoint a location but, no doubt, the unscrupulous and determined collector would find it whichever base was used! Nearly all published county butterfly books have used the tetrad as a base for the distribution maps and it has been used for the maps in this book although most of the records received were to a 1 km square grid reference.

A Wiltshire Biological Records Centre (WBRC) was established on a voluntary basis at Devizes Museum in 1975 but it was a further ten years before funding was made available by the County Council's Library and Museums Service for staffing and a further two years before computer equipment was purchased. Claire Appleby was the first biological recorder. Sally Scott-White succeeded her in 1989 and has developed systems for recording and mapping which offer great potential for county recording schemes in the future and for providing accurate, detailed information very quickly. The distribution maps in the *The Wiltshire Flora* (1993) were produced by the WBRC.

In the late 1970s many of the best butterfly sites in the county were already known to the conservation bodies but it appeared that there had been no coordinated collecting and processing of the records of the many amateur recorders since de Worms' book was published in 1962. It was also apparent that it was important to know the whereabouts of as many of the county's good sites as possible, in addition to the NNRs, WWT reserves and SSSIs. Many of these had not been properly surveyed for their butterflies for many years. Extinctions of colonies, particularly of the woodland fritillaries, appeared to be occurring in many parts of southern and eastern England and it seemed it could be only a matter of time before this situation began to occur in Wiltshire.

The time seemed right to try to establish a team of county recorders in order to produce a book describing the current status of Wiltshire butterflies and including distribution maps for the 48 species believed to be present in the county. In the spring of 1983, several butterfly enthusiasts, the secretaries of various Natural History societies and the 10 km square coordinators of the WFMP which had fortuitously recently been established, were contacted. All were asked to submit sightings of butterflies. Records, including many for 1982, began to arrive at the end of the 1983 season and were plotted manually to a 1 km square grid base on a master map for each species. The quantity of material was such that it was possible to produce the first provisional atlas of distribution maps at the end of the 1984 season. From further records received during 1985 an updated provisional atlas was issued to all recorders in March 1986. Even in the very poor butterfly year of 1986 many records were received and the third provisional atlas was

Table 1. Progress of the coverage of the county's tetrads during the WBMS and the number of active recorders in each year

Year	Active recorders	Accumulative number of tetrads from which records received
1983	c.50	274
1984	86	416
1985	74	577
1986	71	693
1987	86	764
1988	71	816
1989	83	879
1990	88	940
1991	80	949
1992	82	949
1993	62	951
1994	96	951

produced in February 1987. Coverage of the county progressed and the fifth and final provisional atlas was issued to recorders in February 1991.

All records received have been scrutinised and passed to the WBRC for entry in the database. A detailed and substantial baseline of information for comparison with any future recording and mapping scheme is now available. This book is the result of 13 years of informal, but thorough, recording and monitoring mainly by enthusiastic volunteers.

The annual progress of the coverage of tetrads during the WBMS is summarised in Table 1. Approximately 180 recorders were involved at various times but only about half of these were active in any one year. By 1987 at least one record had been received from 80% of the 952 tetrads covering the county and by 1990 the coverage was more or less complete. A tetrad which is partly in Gloucestershire and covers a small area of Kemble airfield was the only one not to have been visited. Records from other part-tetrads on the county border were only accepted if they were from within Wiltshire.

The Future of Recording

Now, in 1995, the efforts of all the mapping scheme's recorders have enabled the production of this book. However, this is not the end of butterfly recording because there are plans for a national atlas to be compiled at the end of the millennium from records collected from 1995 onwards. This will rely heavily on observers in the counties and area branches of Butterfly Conservation gathering and collating records on a standard computer format which will be fed into a central base. This, as far as Wiltshire is concerned, will be a natural extension and continuation of the existing recording structure with a rationalisation of some of the forms and procedures to fit in with the national criteria. The Wiltshire Biological Records Centre will probably play a major role in this project.

THE STATUS OF BUTTERFLY SPECIES IN WILTSHIRE

Each resident species that has occurred in Wiltshire since 1982 and the two commoner immigrants from overseas, the red admiral and painted lady, has been allocated to one of six status categories listed below. Rarer immigrants, which are very occasionally reported in the county, and species that have been recorded in the past but are no longer present, are referred to briefly on pages 192–195.

Table 2. Status of buuterflies in Wiltshire

Category	Number of species
1. Nationally rare	4
2. Rare	9
3. Scarce	2
4. Widespread but only locally common	10
5. Widespread, common but thinly distributed	4
6. Common	18
Total	47

Many species are probably much less common than they were in the past for a variety of reasons but the following are probably the major causes of present-day scarcity. The intensity of modern agriculture, the felling and/or replanting of woodlands with conifers, the ploughing of downland, the agricultural improvement of meadows and grassland, the spread of urbanisation and the general tidying up of the countryside. Many breeding areas have been destroyed during the last 50 years, particularly for those species that occur locally or colonially. Most of the species in categories 1–4 now occur only on protected land such as nature reserves, SSSIs and MOD land, having been all but exterminated from the remainder of the county.

The clouded yellow, scarcest of the three regular immigrants, has been omitted because it does not really fit into any of the categories. Although scarce in most years, which would place it in category 3, very occasionally large immigrations occur, as in 1983, 1992 and 1994, when it would have been considered a category 5 or 6 butterfly. In good butterfly years when most species fare exceptionally well, as in 1982 and 1984, the four category 5 species would possibly be considered as belonging to category 6.

CATEGORY 1. NATIONALLY RARE
Small blue, Adonis blue, Duke of Burgundy and marsh fritillary.

Arguably only four species fall into this category which defines them as being rare in most other counties but found to be widespread in Wiltshire where they occur locally and often in strong colonies. Between 25% and 50% of the known colonies that occur in England are in Wiltshire. All favour grassland/downland habitats in the county although the marsh fritillary and Duke of Burgundy also occur in selected rides and clearings in a few of the woodlands. Their main strongholds are on the MOD lands and the north and west escarpments of Salisbury Plain. Other strongholds in England for these species are in Dorset for the Adonis blue, in Gloucestershire for the Duke of Burgundy and in Devon for the marsh fritillary. The small blue and marsh fritillary are widespread but very local in other counties and absent from many. The small blue is even found, here and there, on the extreme north coast of Scotland and the marsh fritillary as far north as Argyllshire.

CATEGORY 2. RARE
Silver-spotted skipper, one large colony. **Wood white,** believed to be extinct, only one colony having been known until 1987 but not found since. **Brown hairstreak,** two populations. **Silver-studded blue,** two or three colonies. **Large tortoiseshell,** nationally rare, probably extinct in Wiltshire. **Small pearl-bordered fritillary and pearl-**

bordered fritillary, both now restricted to approximately four, mainly small, woodland colonies. **High brown fritillary**, now believed to be restricted to two woodlands. **Grayling**, four or five colonies.

These nine species are now (1995) considered to be rare in the county for a variety of reasons. It would appear from the literature that some of them have never been common except for the small pearl-bordered and pearl-bordered fritillaries and, perhaps, the high brown fritillary which has declined in the last 50 years in Wiltshire and nationally.

CATEGORY 3. SCARCE
White-letter hairstreak and purple emperor.

These two elusive territorial butterflies would require to be specifically searched for but, at the same time, cannot be considered rare or special in the county at present. Both are almost certainly more frequent in some other counties but are seldom common. The status of the purple emperor in the county is probably much as it was 40 years ago with six populations spread across large woodland areas. In spite of its large size and attractiveness, it is an elusive creature and often only seen high up on and/or over the tree canopy.

The white-letter hairstreak is even more elusive and restricted to small, often isolated colonies which can easily go un-noticed. Its status is the least known of all the county's species.

CATEGORY 4. WIDESPREAD BUT ONLY LOCALLY COMMON
Essex skipper, dingy skipper, grizzled skipper, green hairstreak, purple hairstreak, brown argus, chalkhill blue, white admiral, dark green fritillary and silver-washed fritillary.

Except for an occasional vagrant these species are unlikely to be seen in the agricultural countryside. They would usually be found without too much difficulty in their suitable, often fragmented habitats if searched for during the relevant flight period.

CATEGORY 5. WIDESPREAD, COMMON BUT THINLY DISTRIBUTED
Small copper, holly blue, comma and wall.

These species are generally widespread and are often encountered in small numbers in the general countryside as well as in some urban areas. The abundance of all four tends to fluctuate considerably from year to year, the holly blue and wall dramatically so.

CATEGORY 6. COMMON

'Common' does not mean that a species is distributed throughout every part of the county, but that it is common only within the habitats where the food required by the caterpillars and adults occurs. These occupy only a small fraction of the total land available.

Small skipper, large skipper, brimstone, large white, small white, green-veined white, orange-tip, common blue, red admiral, painted lady, small tortoiseshell, peacock, speckled wood, marbled white, gatekeeper, meadow brown, ringlet and small heath.

These 18 species are likely to be seen in quite large numbers and in a variety of localities by the casual observer. The caterpillars of the six members of the brown family and the two skippers are all grass feeders and these butterflies are therefore likely to be seen in many grassy habitats. The common blue often occurs where common bird's-foot-trefoil (*Lotus corniculatus*) grows. The other species are highly mobile and non-colonial. They roam the countryside and occur in towns and gardens in their search for nectar-producing flowers growing in sunny situations.

THE BUTTERFLY
MONITORING SCHEME

The Transect Count

A method which enables a person with relatively little experience to assess the changes in abundance of butterflies in their locality was developed by Dr Ernie Pollard at Monks Wood Experimental Station in 1975. Transect counts are now used in the Butterfly Monitoring Scheme (BMS), a national scheme organised by the Institute of Terrestrial Ecology (ITE) and supported jointly by ITE and English Nature. Since 1976, many sites have been registered and 107 were monitored in 1994. Of these, Picket Wood, Pewsey Downs NNR and Somerford Common are in Wiltshire.

The transect count is a method of sampling the butterflies that occur in a defined area. It does not necessarily provide a record of the total number of species or the size of their population. An 'Index of Abundance' (IoA) can be calculated from the figures obtained. Annual comparisons are dependent on continuity of monitoring from year to year and the IoA on weekly continuity during each year. A transect is a fixed route through the site along which a walk is made at least once a week for 26 weeks starting on 1 April each year. The site can be deliberately chosen to include a variety of habitats and the transect can be divided into sections, each being either a discrete habitat or a subdivision within it. There can be sections under different types of management, those rich in particular species and those requiring regular visits for other purposes. It is convenient to restrict the route to rides and paths, the boundaries of which are clearly defined. In open habitats, established paths should be used as far as possible but, in their absence, the butterflies within a convenient distance either side of the observer will be the area counted. The precise width is not important provided it remains constant. The transect is walked at an even pace and only those butterflies seen within an imaginary 5 × 5 metre box surrounding the observer are recorded.

Weather conditions will have a considerable effect on the number of butterflies seen. In order to ensure that recording is consistent the following rules should, ideally, be adhered to. The transect should be walked between 10.45 and 15.45 hours BST in sunshine and a minimum temperature of 13°C. At least 60% sunshine is required if the temperature is below 17°C but sunshine is not too critical if the temperature is higher. The wind speed should not exceed 5 on the Beaufort Scale.

Analysis of the Data

After completion of the recording at the end of September, the annual IoA for each species can be

Map 3. Monitored sites in Wiltshire

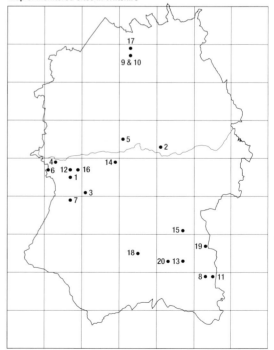

calculated by adding together the weekly counts. It is important to stress that the annual IoA is not an estimation of the population and can only be used to indicate the relative annual abundance of butterflies at a particular site.

After a few years of recording, changes in butterfly numbers from year to year become apparent and can be related to the management of the site and to the weather. Sometimes the reasons for these changes are very obvious. The flight

Table 3. Monitored sites in Wiltshire

Map Ref. No.	Site	Main habitat type and ownership	Monitor	Start date
1	Picket and Clanger Woods, near Westbury	Ancient woodland mainly replanted with conifers in 1960s. Removal of conifers and return to coppice management started in 1980s. Woodland Trust owned.	Michael Fuller	1978
2	Pewsey Downs NNR Walker's Hill	Downland. Mainly facing south and east.	David Painter, Keith Payne et al. (EN)	1979
3	Bratton Castle Earthworks east ditch	Steep, mainly south-facing chalk grassland slopes. English Heritage owned.	Michael Fuller	1980
4	Kennet and Avon Canal towpath, Bradford-on-Avon	Towpath and south and west-facing hedgebank, managed by British Waterways most years.	Michael Fuller	1980
5	Roundway Hill Covert near Devizes	Woodland, scrub and chalk grassland on west-facing slope.	Beatrice Gillam	1981
6	Vagg's Hill, Tellisford	East bank of River Frome and rough ground near Pomeroy Wood.	Audrey Brown	1982
7	Upton Cow Down, Upton Scudamore	Scrub and chalk grassland on fairly steep south and west-facing slopes. MOD owned.	Michael Fuller	1983
8	Blackmoor Copse, near Salisbury	Ancient woodland managed by WWT.	Peter Whitehead et al. Patricia Woodruffe et al. Sue Walker et al.	1983-91 1992 1993
9	Somerford Common, Braydon Forest	Ancient woodland mainly replanted with conifers by FC.	Jeremy Fraser et al. (EN) John Grearson	1984 1991
10	Somerford Common	Ancient woodland, WWT owned.	Jeremy Fraser et al. (EN)	1984-89
11	Bentley Wood, near Salisbury 4 transects	Ancient woodland mainly replanted with conifers by FC in 1950s. Removal of conifers, return to coppice management begun 1984. Owned by Charitable Trust.	Paul Waring Barry Fox et al.	1983 2 transects 1986 4 transects
12	Biss Wood, near Trowbridge	Privately-owned ancient woodland. Programme of felling and replanting begun 1986.	Audrey Brown	1987
13	Cockey Down, near Salisbury	Chalk grassland on fairly steep west-facing slope. WWT owned.	Piers Mobsby	1988 only
14	Hartmoor, Devizes	Bridleway and grazed pasture.	Arthur Cleverly	1988
15	Boscombe Down, near Amesbury	South-facing embankment of disused railway. MOD owned.	Gerald Nicholls	1989
16	Green Lane Wood, near Trowbridge	Ancient woodland and scrub/grassland under National Grid power lines. WWT owned.	Roger Beckett	1991
17	Ravensroost Wood, Braydon Forest	Ancient woodland, WWT owned.	Christine Tracey	1993
18	Little Langford Down, Grovely Wood	Chalk grassland, woodland edge. WWT leased from FC.	David Simpson Paul Stokes	1992
19	Porton Down	Chalk grassland, woodland edge. MOD owned.	Dick Ryan Clive Bealey	1994
20	Old Sarum, near Salisbury	Chalk grassland. Earthworks. English Heritage owned.	John Tubb	1994

period of the butterflies in the area and the annual changes are provided by the weekly counts. Table 3 lists the sites in Wiltshire that have been monitored using this method and their locations are shown on Map 3. Data from these sites has been referred to in the text and used to produce the flight period diagrams. The IoA graphs can be found on pages 182–191, following the species accounts.

The Essex skipper, silver-spotted skipper, wood white, brown hairstreak, white-letter hairstreak, silver-studded blue, purple emperor, large tortoiseshell, high brown fritillary and grayling were not monitored by transect counts. Two of these butterflies are extinct, three are too elusive to be counted by this method and four are rare and do not occur on any of the monitored sites. Essex skippers cannot be separated from small skippers during a transect walk due to the necessity for close inspection. If present, they will have been recorded as small skippers.

INTRODUCTION TO THE SPECIES ACCOUNTS

Naming the Species

The origin and meaning of the scientific names and the history of the vernacular names have been taken from the books by Emmett, and Emmett and Heath, listed in the Bibliography on page 196.

Thomas Mouffet, Moffet, Mouffett, Moufet or Muffet, as his name has been variously spelt, brought together the writings of the sixteenth century naturalists Conrad Gesner, Thomas Penny and Edward Wotton. His *Insectorum Theatrum* was published by Sir Theodore Mayerne in 1634, 30 years after Mouffet's death in 1604. This was the first publication to describe insects but not name them. It was written in Latin and illustrated with woodcuts. In 1597 Mouffet obtained a seat in Parliament as the member for Wilton, near Salisbury, and was buried in its parish church. His daughter may well have been the 'little Miss Muffet' of the familiar nursery rhyme.

Sources of Records

The first published Wiltshire record is quoted. For many species this was accredited to J W Lukis from Great Bedwyn by the Rev Francis Morris in 1853. Many records have been taken from the Marlborough College Natural History Society's Annual Reports and Lists (1865–1964), from the diaries of Roy Pitman (1928–86) for the Salisbury area, from the Dauntsey School Fauna List (1931–48) and from the diaries of Bowmont Weddell (1932–78) for the Trowbridge area. These are brought together and freely quoted along with references to a few other early Wiltshire records. The last major publication referred to is that of Baron de Worms (1962).

The Species

A brief description of the adult butterfly and its life history is given. The excellent colour photographs contributed by Wiltshire butterfly recorders are aids to identification. The reader can find further details, good colour photographs and illustrations of the butterflies in other publications listed in the Bibliography on page 196.

Larval foodplants mentioned are not to be taken as being comprehensive. This is especially true for the grass-feeders and those species having catholic tastes but, for the majority of species, the main foodplant only is given. Nectar sources listed are based on the author's personal observations of the butterflies at Picket Wood and Bratton Castle Earthworks and those of Beatrice Gillam, largely from sites on the Chalk. Observations of recorders from elsewhere in the county have also been incorporated. Plants visited are those which are in flower and producing nectar accessible to the butterfly during its flight period. The English nomenclature used for the wild plants follows that adopted by Dony, Jury and Perring in *English Names of Wild Flowers* (2nd Edition 1986). Latin nomenclature follows Kent's *A List of Vascular Plants of the British Isles* (1992).

The Flight Period

One of the major achievements of the national Butterfly Monitoring Scheme (BMS) is the accumulation of detailed information concerning butterfly flight periods. From the information collected annually during monitoring at Picket Wood, Bratton Castle Earthworks and several other sites in Wiltshire, diagrams have been compiled showing emergence times, flight period, peak flying time and the flight sequence for those species having multiple generations. Examples for many of these butterflies are included in the text. Each flight period refers to the whole adult population not to an individual butterfly, and figures are given for the total number of weeks in which the butterfly was seen, regardless of number of broods. Flight periods vary from year to year depending mainly on weather conditions. Males always emerge a few days before the females.

Measures of Abundance

Index of Abundance (IoA) values have been calculated for most species from information obtained from monitored sites. Those sites with sufficiently large populations to make interpretation of the data as meaningful as possible have been selected for inclusion in the text. Values for species with more than one generation or flight period have been totalled to give an annual value. For a few species, national values from the Butterfly Monitoring Scheme (BMS) have been referred to in order to compare local fluctuations with national trends. The majority of the values are accurate, resulting from complete annual transect coverage, but a few are estimates where the data was incomplete. Much of the analysis and interpretation refers to three sites, Picket Wood, Bratton Castle Earthworks and Upton Cow Down, which have been regularly monitored by the author and for which data is most comprehensive. It should be emphasised however, that results from these sites do not necessarily reflect the situation elsewhere.

The Maps

A detailed account is given of the recorded distribution of each species except for the clouded yellow and butterflies classed as 'common' on page 15. The distribution maps have been plotted to a tetrad base (2 × 2 km square), each dot representing at least one record from a tetrad since 1982. Dots are all the same size on the maps for the commoner species and give no indication of abundance. Each dot may represent a record of one individual or many. These species are those commonly seen and are currently considered not to warrant further comments on their distribution. For most of the other species three sizes of dots have been used to indicate abundance.

· a single record of one individual
• 2–9 individuals recorded
● 10+ individuals recorded
✳ record of a vagrant
○ pre-1982 record

This notation has been used mainly for colonial species in an attempt to highlight the strength of a colony. The two smaller dots indicate a single record or a colony of only a few individuals. The largest dot indicates that a strong, large colony was present. When considered to be of interest or significance, sightings of vagrants have been plotted as for the chalkhill blue and white admiral which normally remain within their breeding areas.

For some of the species which are now scarce or rare but which were relatively common until the early 1950s, an indication of their past recorded distribution is included on the map in order to highlight the decline of their range. However, there were fewer mobile recorders in the county 40 years ago and there was little coordination of individuals' records so that recorded distribution of many species was far from complete. This should be borne in mind when studying the maps.

A map showing the Wiltshire distribution of the larval foodplant is included for a few species where it helps to illustrate the close correlation between distribution of the plant and the butterfly. One example is the relationship between kidney vetch (*Anthyllis vulneraria*) and the small blue. Maps are also included for some species where there is complete lack of correlation as between sheep's-fescue (*Festuca ovina*) and the silver-spotted skipper.

Confidentiality of Records

Confidentiality was considered when deciding whether some localities referring to rarer species should be named and whether the tetrads involved should be represented on the distribution maps. Only two species, the wood white and the brown hairstreak, were considered to be in potential danger from collectors. Alas, the wood white became extinct in its only known locality during the WBMS. The brown hairstreak occurs in only two populations but these have been found to extend over very large areas of the countryside. The elusive adults are probably not threatened by collectors, but the eggs, which are surprisingly easy to locate in the winter months, are threatened by the practice of modern hedge-trimming when up to 80% may be destroyed (Thomas). With the consent of Matthew Oates, who provided details of the range of one of the populations, it was decided to plot all tetrads, most of which represent records from egg-searches.

Records of several other species including the woodland fritillaries, grayling and silver-studded blue, which are in danger of county extinction due to habitat deterioration or loss, have also been plotted using the tetrad notation.

Notes on Butterfly Families

The systematic arrangement and the nomenclature follow those used by Emmet and Heath (1989) beginning with the most primitive species and ending with the most specialised.

Hesperiidae – Skippers

First named 'Skipper' in 1766 by Moses Harris. Eight species in Great Britain, six in Wiltshire where Essex skipper is on the edge of its range. All except dingy and grizzled are grass-feeders. Overwintering takes place in egg, caterpillar or chrysalis according to the species. Small inconspicuous insects. Adults have three pairs of functional legs.

Pieridae – Whites and Yellows

Seven species. Wood white became extinct in Wiltshire in 1987. Three whites, brimstone and orange-tip are common. Clouded yellow an immigrant. Brimstones overwinter as adults, other species as chrysalises. Adults have three pairs of functional legs. Medium to large conspicuous butterflies.

Lycaenidae – Hairstreaks, Coppers, Blues and Metalmarks

Large, colourful family of small butterflies. Sixteen species in Great Britain, two now naturally extinct, large blue re-established since 1983. Adults, except metalmarks, have three pairs of functional legs.

Hairstreaks. Five British species, four in Wiltshire. All elusive. Green overwinters as chrysalis, adult flies in spring in grassland with scrub. Brown , purple and white-letter overwinter as eggs, adults fly from mid-June mainly in tree canopy.

Coppers. Small copper only survivor in Great Britain.

Blues. Seven naturally occurring species in Great Britain, all in Wiltshire. Holly blue's behaviour similar to that of hairstreaks. Others colonial and wing coloration different in the two sexes, males blue (except brown argus) females brown. Principal larval foodplants of five species require calcareous soil restricting their range. Some of these species rely on ants for survival.

Metalmarks. Duke of Burgundy only European member of the sub-family Riodininae. Strong colonies in suitable Wiltshire habitats.

Nymphalidae – Vanessids, Fritillaries and Browns

Family having both the largest and most colourful and the most drab species. Adults have two pairs of functional legs.

Vanessids. Eight British species, all in Wiltshire though large tortoiseshell no longer breeding. Red admiral and painted lady common immigrants. Small tortoiseshell, peacock and comma widespread, hibernating as adults. Purple emperor and white admiral restricted to woodland.

Fritillaries. Eight British species, six in Wiltshire, three large and three medium-sized. All have dark markings on an orange background. Silver spots on underside of wings distinguish the species. All caterpillars spiny. Overwintering takes place in egg or caterpillar stage according to species. Small pearl-bordered, pearl-bordered and high brown in rapid decline. Dark green, silver-washed and marsh have strong colonies in Wiltshire.

Browns. Eleven British species, eight in Wiltshire. All common except grayling. All have prominent forewing eyespot except marbled white. Caterpillars grass-feeders, feeding at night. Overwinter as caterpillar, speckled wood also as chrysalis.

SMALL SKIPPER
Thymelicus sylvestris (Poda)

The generic name *Thymelicus*, given to the small and Essex skippers by Hübner in 1819, is a reference to dancers in Greek drama and reflects the lively movement in the flight of these two butterflies. The specific name *sylvestris*, meaning pertaining to a wood, was given by Poda in 1761. This little butterfly was first described by James Petiver in 1704 from specimens taken on Hampstead Heath. He considered the male and female to be two distinct species and named the male 'The streaked Golden Hogg' and the female 'The spotless Hogg'. In 1766 Moses Harris named it the small skipper.

The wings are of a fairly uniform orange-brown colour, the forewings of the male having a distinctive curved black sex-brand line. A female is shown in Nick Wynn's photograph. The flight is fast and darting.

The main sources of nectar are the large purple flowers of the two knapweeds (*Centaurea nigra* and *C. scabiosa*), field scabious (*Knautia arvensis*) and thistles (*Cirsium* and *Carduus* spp.). It is not unusual for a single flower-head to host three or more butterflies at the same time.

The white eggs are laid in batches in the leaf sheaths of several grass species, Yorkshire-fog (*Holcus lanatus*) being used most frequently. Immediately after hatching, the caterpillar eats its eggshell, spins a cocoon and enters into hibernation. It begins feeding on young grass leaves in April and in mid-June pupates in a tent of leaves which it has spun together at the base of the plant.

The Flight Period
Small skippers are rarely on the wing until early July and, in favourable years, can be seen until early September. Numbers usually peak at the end of July.

In Picket Wood, the longest flight period between 1980 and 1994 was ten weeks in 1980, 1981 and 1985, and the shortest was five weeks in 1986, 1990 and 1994. The highest number counted on a weekly visit varied from 116 in July 1981 to six in August 1993. The earliest WBMS sighting

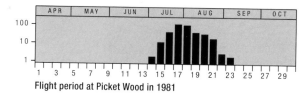

Flight period at Picket Wood in 1981

was 17 June 1982 at Picket Wood and the latest 17 September 1985 at Bratton Castle. The earliest county sighting on 12 June 1916 was recorded in the Marlborough College report for that year.

Measures of Abundance 1980–94 (Figure 4)
From a population explosion at Bratton Castle and Upton Cow Down in 1984 numbers slumped for the next four years and peaked in 1989 and 1990. At Picket Wood the decline occurred with the increasing shadiness of the habitat. The high counts of the early 1980s followed the felling of many broadleaf trees and their replacement with young conifers which created a grassy meadow habitat for a few years. Since the mid-1980s, when the peak weekly number was about 100, this skipper has been restricted to the ride edges and numbers have peaked at about a dozen.

Numbers increased at most of the monitored sites in 1994 but, except for Upton Cow Down, were well below the site averages for the 13 year period.

Status Before 1982
The earliest Wiltshire record appears to be that of the Rev Francis Morris in 1853. He stated 'It is rather uncommon in Great Bedwyn and Sarum, Wiltshire, as J W Lukis Esq informs me, but in most parts of England is very abundant'.

In the first Marlborough College List of 1865, there were reports of the small skipper from West Woods, Savernake Forest and Martinsell. It was stated to be 'not so common as the large skipper' but this may have been because the College term ended in early July before the butterflies had reached their peak emergence. It was included in the Rev T B Eddrupp's 1899 list from near Calne and in E Cook's 1902 list from near Devizes.

Roy Pitman recorded this skipper from Old Sarum in July 1928 and in his 1936 report made

the surprising comment that it was 'not as common as the dingy and grizzled skippers, but never rare and perhaps not so widely distributed'. Bowmont Weddell did not mention the species from the Trowbridge area in any of his diaries from 1932 to 1978. In 1962 Baron de Worms stated that it was common all over the county.

Status Since 1982
In most years the small skipper is common and widespread across the whole of southern England, East Anglia, the Midlands and Wales, more local in the north as far as Cleveland and absent from Scotland and Ireland. Its distribution is probably regulated by climatic factors since its range is not restricted by the larval foodplants.

The small skipper probably occurs in most of the tetrads covering the county. During the WBMS (1982–94) it was recorded from 584 tetrads (61%). Colonies were found in areas of tall grass in many situations, notably on SPTA, but less commonly on grazed areas.

Map 4. Distribution of small skipper

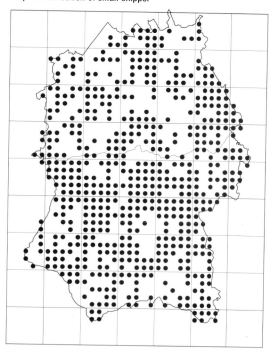

ESSEX SKIPPER
Thymelicus lineola (Ochsenheimer)

The Essex skipper was described in Germany in 1791 and named *Papilio lineola* by Ferdinand Ochsenheimer. It was not until 1889 that it was recognised as a British species. Three were identified in the collection of Mr F W Hawes who caught them at St Osyths in Essex in July 1888 and the fact was published in January 1890. Subsequent examination of 'small skippers' in British collections revealed that Essex skippers had, in fact, been captured in the early 1860s (Frohawk 1924).

This was the last of our resident British species to be discovered and was initially known only by its Latin name *lineola*, meaning a 'small line' referring to the male sex-brand which is much shorter and less distinct than that of the male small skipper. In 1906, Richard South named it the Essex skipper.

The main distinguishing feature between these very similar species is the black underside of the antennae tips of the Essex skipper, the limit of the black being very marked in contrast to the dull orange or brown of the small skipper. This can be seen in Jim Asher's photograph on page 25. The black sex-brand on the forewing of an Essex male is shown in Ian Grier's photograph (above).

Essex and small skippers can be found nectaring together on knapweeds (*Centaurea* spp.), field scabious (*Knautia arvensis*) and thistles (*Cirsium* and *Carduus* spp.) in tall vegetation and selfheal (*Prunella vulgaris*) in shorter swards.

Small batches of pale lemon-coloured eggs are laid in grass leaf sheaths, cock's-foot (*Dactylis glomerata*) being the preferred species. The caterpillar develops and then hibernates inside the eggshell until the following spring. It feeds on young grass leaves before pupating in a loosely-woven cocoon in the base of a grass tussock.

The Flight Period
The first Essex skippers are usually seen in mid-July, about a week after the first small skippers are on the wing, and are rarely seen after mid-August. Transect walks are not suitable for obtaining

An Essex skipper on black knapweed. The undersides of the antennae appear as if dipped in black ink. The undersides of those of the small skipper are brownish-orange.

flight period details or for assessing the abundance of this species due to the detailed inspection required to differentiate them from small skippers. Counts of these two butterflies seen at monitored sites were all recorded as being small skippers and the values used in Figure 4 for this species include sightings of both. At sites where Essex skippers are either absent or occur in very small numbers the values are probably a true reflection of the status of the small skipper. At Bratton Castle and Upton Cow Down, where the Essex is occasionally the dominant species, the values may be a reflection of its status rather than that of the small skipper. During the WBMS, the earliest date it was recorded was 21 June 1992 at Langley Wood (Graham Smith) and the latest 30 August 1985 at Botley Drove (Jack Coates).

Records Before 1982

Following the discovery of this skipper in 1889 on the Essex marshlands it has been found to be a widespread species in the south-east and central-southern parts of England and in the East Midlands. Wiltshire is at the western edge of its range except for one to two isolated populations in Devon and Cornwall. It has rarely been recorded in Dorset and, in 1984, there were no positive recent records (Thomas and Webb 1984). Its distribution in Wiltshire, as in most other counties, has always been uncertain due to the ease with which it can be overlooked and probably a general lack of interest in it by the average lepidopterist.

The first Wiltshire record appears to be that of Ian Heslop in 1928 from Dorset and south Wiltshire. The author has been unable to determine the exact location but it may have been in territory which is now in Dorset or Hampshire. Surprisingly, Roy Pitman did not mention the species in his 1936 report although it was probably common in the Salisbury area at that time. There was a record for 15 July 1945 from Erlestoke in the Dauntsey School List. In 1948, C Blathwayt found that Essex skippers were well established near Westbury and in 1947, 1948 and 1949 Bowmont Weddell received records of singletons from Bradford-on-Avon. He referred especially to this species in the WANHS entomological report for 1950: 'Another species that must be specially mentioned is the Essex skipper *A. lineola* which has been recorded in singletons the last few years. This year a good strong colony was located by Capt Reginald Jackson'. There are three Essex skippers labelled Yarnbury 28.7.50 in Weddell's handwriting in the lepidoptera collection in the WANHS Museum in Devizes. He also saw one at Bratton in 1954.

One was taken at Camp Down near Salisbury in 1954 by C M Ranger and in 1955 Pitman stated it was 'Much over-looked, very common in the district' and two years later he reported 'several colonies in the area'. In 1958 Heslop stated 'Probably quite common in the Blackmoor Copse area. Quite recently it was observed to be common on Pepperbox Hill'. No new records were added by Baron de Worms in 1962.

These reports indicate that in the south-eastern area of the county the Essex skipper had probably existed undetected, except for Heslop's 1928

record, until the 1950s. Significantly it was never reported, nor even commented upon, by the MCNHS in the 100 years from 1865 when the publication of College records began. The dedicated naturalists Meyrick, Manders, Sladen, Pierson and others did not find it during their many field trips and expeditions in the Marlborough district.

Status Since 1982

The Essex skipper was not recorded north of the Kennet and Avon Canal until 1982 at Roundway Hill Covert (Beatrice Gillam) and it remains very rare north of a line from Corsham to Marlborough where it was first recorded in 1987 (Steve Covey). Small populations were recorded near Membury in 1991 (Fuller), at Hinton Parva in 1994 (George Osmond), near Clouts Wood in 1994 (Mike Williams) and a colony on the A429 road verge near the M4 motorway in 1987 (Steve Covey) which was still present in 1994 (Fuller). Singletons were recorded from road verges near Dauntsey Green in 1989 (Fuller) and near Broad Town in

Map 5. Distribution of cock's-foot

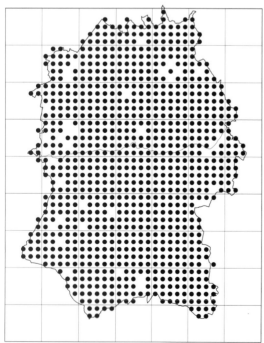

Map 6. Distribution of Essex skipper

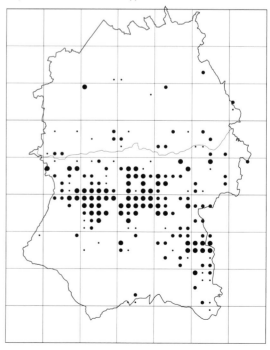

1992 (Simon Barker). It has not been recorded from the Limestone in the Castle Combe and Colerne areas in the north-west, from the frequently visited woods and meadows in Braydon Forest, from the Marlborough Downs or from the Swindon area.

There are small populations in Savernake Forest and to the south and east of the Forest, in West Woods and on Pewsey Downs NNR. In 1994, 77 were counted along a byway at Southcott near Pewsey (John Tubb) which was the largest population recorded from this area. Small populations occur on the downs north of Devizes and there are small numbers on grassland in much of West Wiltshire especially around Trowbridge.

The Essex skipper has its stronghold on Salisbury Plain where it is widely distributed. It is often common and sometimes seen in hundreds on SPTA and Porton Down. Its present frequency on these sites strongly suggests that the species had been well-established for many years but was undetected until the formation of the MOD conservation groups which allowed for greater accessibility. It is rare in the extreme south of the county but occurs sparsely in the woodlands east of Salisbury, in Langley Wood near Redlynch and in small numbers in Grovely and Great Ridge Woods. The only record from the south-west is of a worn singleton seen in Bradley Wood in 1987 (Martin Warren). There are isolated populations in the Vernditch Chase area where records, mainly of singletons, have been received over the years but, on the remainder of these southern grasslands, it has not been detected in spite of careful searching.

Since 1983, many records of the Essex skipper have been received, some probably being chance observations rather than the species having been deliberately searched for. Since 1985, the author has tried to establish its range within the county by visiting areas where the small skipper was known to occur in good numbers and where one would expect to locate Essex skippers if they were present. The distribution map is considered to reflect accurately the present distribution. During the WBMS (1982–94) this species was recorded from 187 tetrads (20%).

The rather curious distribution in the county is not easy to explain since the main larval foodplant, cock's-foot, is common and widespread as shown on the distribution map. Most of the other grasses that are known to be used are also widely distributed. However, because tall, uncut grass on which the female lays her eggs is required, management of the grasses probably limits distribution of the butterfly, grazed or regularly cut grass being unsuitable.

Future Prospects

If, as is thought by some lepidopterists, the Essex skipper is extending its range westwards from Oxfordshire and Berkshire, further populations should be discovered in the east and north-east of Wiltshire in the future. It may also extend its range into the north-west, south and south-west where there appear to be suitable habitats.

SILVER-SPOTTED SKIPPER
Hesperia comma (Linnaeus)

The generic name *Hesperia*, given to the silver-spotted skipper by Fabricius in 1793, was taken from the name of one of the nymphs who guarded the golden apples of Hera. The specific name *comma*, given by Linnaeus in 1758, refers to the male's sex-brands on the upper forewings.

Early authors considered that this species had been illustrated by Thomas Mouffet in 1634 and described by Christopher Merrett in 1666. It is now generally acknowledged that the details of the species given by them were too vague and that they were probably referring to the much commoner large skipper. In 1775, Moses Harris named *H. comma* the pearl skipper and it was first named the silver-spotted skipper by Adrian Haworth in 1803. However, many authors reverted to Harris's name which continued to be used for many years.

The silver-spotted skipper is larger than the small skipper but superficially resembles the large skipper which is the same size. It has the same fast, erratic flight and needs to be examined at close quarters to make a positive identification. Silver spots on the greenish underwings are the distinguishing feature which can only be observed by a careful approach. They are clearly shown in Graham Wall's photograph. Barbara Last's photograph on page 29 shows the typical habitat for this butterfly.

Dwarf thistle (*Cirsium acaule*), common knapweed (*Centaurea nigra*), rough hawkbit (*Leontodon hispidus*) and the late-flowering autumn gentian (*Gentianella amarella*) are the main sources of nectar.

The eggs are laid singly in August on un-nibbled blades of sheep's-fescue (*Festuca ovina*) especially where the grass is adjacent to, or growing in, patches of bare chalk. The eggs over-winter and the larvae hatch in the following March. The caterpillar spins a nest among the fine grass leaves from which it stretches out to feed. When full grown it wanders from the nest and spins a cocoon near the ground in which it pupates.

Porton Down, where Wiltshire's only silver-spotted skipper population occurs. Bare chalk, interspersed with a sward of varying heights, and areas of scrub, which provide shelter, meet this butterfly's exacting requirements.

The Flight Period

The butterfly is on the wing during late July and August. By this time, in most years, the very similar large skipper is no longer flying. No details of flight periods or indices of abundance are available for this species in Wiltshire.

Records Before 1982

The first published Wiltshire record was that of James Duncan in 1835 who simply stated 'in Wiltshire'. Other early records are those of the Rev Francis Morris in 1853 and William Coleman in 1860 who both listed 'Old Sarum, Wiltshire'. In 1869 Edward Newman stated 'one specimen near Martinsell, in 1865 – T A Preston'. In September 1876, Neville Manders, a pupil at the College, recorded it as 'abundant on Martinsell'. It was seen 'flying freely' on the lower slopes of Oare Hill on 11 August 1911 by Edward Meyrick and, in the 'memorable season' of 1917 was recorded on 15 August. The last record from this part of the county was that of A C H Bell on 13 August 1923.

It may also have occurred further west on Pewsey Downs NNR. Two 1950s records (WANHS) were possibly from there.

No doubt silver-spotted skippers were common on much of the downland in the south of the county early in the twentieth century. Steven Corbet found the species to be unusually abundant in July 1921 near Damerham, which was then in Wiltshire, but it was not until 1928 (apart from Coleman and Morris's references to Old Sarum) that it was positively recorded from the south by Roy Pitman. He saw it at Stonehenge but, strangely, it was not mentioned in his 1928 diary. In 1936 he stated that it was 'locally common in favourite spots; confined to the chalk downs, at times very common near Salisbury, Bulford and on Pepperbox Hill'. Subsequently it was often reported as common from several downland sites mainly in the area around Salisbury until the mid-1950s. Baron de Worms stated that it was abundant on Standlynch Down in 1942 and listed Pitman's records as common at Old Sarum in 1945 and at

Camp Hill, Homington Down and Pepperbox Hill in 1951. He also listed Stratford Down (Jackson), Tidworth (Addison) and the Redlynch area (Burras). The silver-spotted skipper was reported from Laverstock Down in 1950 and Pepperbox Hill in 1954 (Richard Thompson). He recollected that, at that time, it was restricted to the roadside verge and was probably exterminated a year or two later when the road was re-built and widened. Pitman's last records were of singletons at Camp Hill in July 1965 and Pepperbox Hill in August 1966, sites from where he described it in his diaries as being very common in 1938 and 1939.

Thompson saw silver-spotted skippers on Buxbury Hill near Swallowcliffe in the south-west of the county in 1953 and 1954. This was probably where a rare aberration was taken in August 1957 (Martin Pring). This species was also observed by Pitman on Knapp Down near Broad Chalke in August 1955, at nearby Church Bottom in August 1957. It probably occurred on many of the other downs in this area at that time but these are the only known records. Bowmont Weddell did not

refer to it in his diaries (1932–1978), the only record from the Trowbridge area coming from the BRC for 1950 which was presumably from the Salisbury Plain escarpment near Bratton.

Records Since 1982

The silver-spotted skipper has probably always been a very local downland species in southern England. In 1993 it was estimated that only 54 colonies survive south of the Chilterns, over half of these occurring on the escarpment of the North Downs in Surrey. It is absent from Gloucestershire and counties to the west of Wiltshire. Dorset has colonies at Fontmell Down and Martin Down NNR and Hampshire has six, one of which is on Porton Down straddling the Wiltshire-Hampshire border. This is one of the largest colonies in England.

This species does not appear to have been mentioned in the literature from Porton Down until 1978 (BRC) although it was known to be common there in the 1960s (Roy Stockley). In recent years its status and range have been

Map 7. Distribution of sheep's-fescue

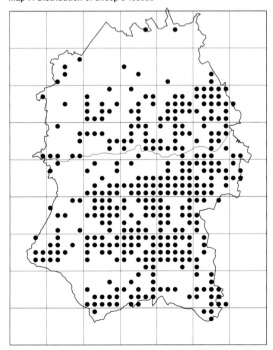

Map 8. Distribution of silver-spotted skipper

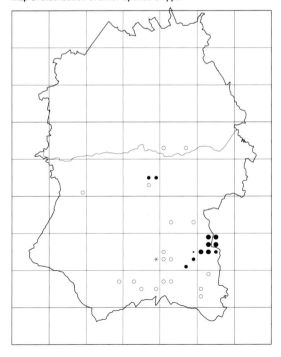

established thanks to the efforts of Ian Small and Dick Ryan. The population extends over an area in excess of 400 hectares (1,000 acres). In 1990 numbers reached the very high level of 1984, 75 individuals being counted in less than an hour. Many were seen in August 1991 (Piers Mobsby) but 1993 and 1994 were poor seasons (Ryan).

Although at least 19 colonies have been known to occur in the county, the large population at Porton Down is now the only survivor and the following sightings of individuals elsewhere are believed to have been vagrants from this site: a singleton on Cockey Down, south-west of Porton Down in August 1990 and a further two in August 1991 but none in the following three years (Mobsby); three on Figsbury Ring adjacent to Porton Down in August 1991 (Mobsby) and a damaged but fresh individual on Grovely Down in 1992 (David Simpson).

There are a few records from SPTA. The species was recorded from SPTA(C) at Wilsford Down in June 1974 (BRC) and from nearby Chirton Down in 1978 (BRC). Two or three were seen on Wilsford Down in 1987 and a further two on Chirton Down in 1989 (Avis and Ken Lloyd) but a breeding population has not been confirmed in this area.

The distribution map of sheep's-fescue, the only larval foodplant, shows that it occurs mainly on Chalk and Limestone in Wiltshire. It is widespread in central and southern parts of the county and it is therefore surprising that the silver-spotted skipper is now apparently restricted to Porton Down.

For a species that is on the edge of its range in England and that requires a very warm climate for survival, poor summer weather in the 1950s was probably the most significant factor causing its decline. The ploughing and destruction of downland, the reduction of stock grazing and the absence of rabbit grazing due to myxomatosis during this period were probably other major factors.

During the WBMS (1982–94) the silver-spotted skipper was recorded from 12 tetrads (1.2%). These, together with pre-1982 known and accepted records, have been plotted on the distribution map.

Future Prospects
It is probable that the present status of this species in the county will not change a great deal in the future unless man intervenes. Although natural colonisation of suitable downland remote from Porton Down is most unlikely it might, under certain conditions, spread temporarily to nearby areas such as Cockey Down. There appears to be no reason why it should not be present on several areas of downland in the remote part of south Wiltshire either side of the Ebble valley. There may be a few undetected colonies not far from the two over the county boundary in Dorset.

In 1994, Humphrey Kay was given permission to introduce six male and four female butterflies to a south-facing downland slope near Pewsey where silver-spotted skippers were last recorded in 1923 and which was considered to be a suitable habitat for the species. Natural colonisation from the nearest known colony on Porton Down, 30 km to the south, was considered to be impossible. Monitoring, and perhaps reinforcements, may show that this escarpment can once again support this rare county butterfly.

LARGE SKIPPER
Ochlodes venata (Bremer and Grey)

The generic name *Ochlodes*, given to the large skipper by Scudder in 1872, means 'turbulent' or 'unruly', a reference to the swift erratic flight of the species. The specific name *venata*, meaning the act of hunting or the chase, was given by Bremer and Grey in 1852. The name *sylvanus*, given by Esper in 1779, was in use for many years, meaning appropriately 'of the woods'.

The large skipper was probably described by Thomas Mouffet in 1634 and Christopher Merrett in 1666 although confusion with the very similar, but much rarer, silver-spotted skipper cast doubt on their identifications. It was first positively described by James Petiver in 1704 from specimens found on Hampstead Heath. He named the female 'The Chequered Hogg' and the male 'The chequer-like Hogg'. Moses Harris named it the large skipper in 1766 but subsequently 'Wood Skipper' was the name appropriately proposed by some authors. In 1853, the Rev Francis Morris wrote 'The habits of this kindred species are similar to the small skipper'.

The wings have mottled markings, as illustrated in Rob Turner's photograph of a basking female. The male's black sex-brand is more pronounced than that of the small skipper. It has the typical fast and darting flight of all members of the well-named skipper family.

The butterflies have frequently been observed nectaring on the flowers of leguminous plants, especially red clover (*Trifolium pratense*) and on rough hawkbit (*Leontodon hispidus*).

The white eggs are laid singly on the underside of grass leaves, most commonly on cock's-foot (*Dactylis glomerata*). After the caterpillar has eaten its eggshell it feeds on the leaves until partly grown, then hibernates until the spring when it continues feeding until pupating for a period of three weeks in the grass tussock.

The Flight Period
The first butterflies usually emerge in early June, before the small skippers, but both are on the wing during July. By the time the very similar, but much

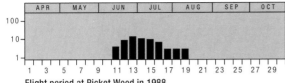

Flight period at Picket Wood in 1988

rarer, silver-spotted skipper emerges in August, the flight period of the large skipper is normally over.

Numbers peak towards the end of June and occasionally worn females are seen at the end of July and sometimes in early August. In Picket Wood between 1980 and 1994 the longest flight period was ten weeks in 1990 due to an exceptionally early individual being seen on 17 May. The shortest period was five weeks in 1993. The highest number of individuals counted on a weekly visit varied from 22 in June 1984 to three in June 1993.

The earliest county record, 6 May 1893, appeared in the Marlborough College List for that year, one in which many species emerged early. The latest record was 18 August 1991 in Picket Wood.

Measures of Abundance 1980–94 (Figure 5)

Large annual fluctuations have occurred at most of the monitored sites in Wiltshire. There were major declines in 1981 and at several sites in 1986 but numbers recovered and remained stable until 1991 when they plummeted to the lowest levels since monitoring began. A small recovery in 1992 was followed by further declines in 1993 when new low levels were recorded at several sites. In 1994 numbers rose to about average at most sites, except at Vagg's Hill where they fell sharply.

Status Before 1982

The first published Wiltshire record, in the 1865 Marlborough College List, stated 'common in most copses'. In all later College Lists it was referred to as common. It appeared in the Rev T B Eddrupp's 1899 list from near Calne and in E Cook's 1902 list from near Devizes.

Roy Pitman noted it at Odstock in June 1928. In 1936 he considered it to be generally very common in Wiltshire. In 1962 Baron de Worms said that it was still 'generally common, mostly in woodlands, throughout the county'.

Status Since 1982

The large skipper is a common and widely distributed species throughout England, Wales and south-west Scotland but is absent from Ireland and the Isle of Man. In Wiltshire, it is thinly distributed in areas of tall grassland along many wide grass verges and woodland rides.

During the WBMS (1982–94) the large skipper was considered to have been under-recorded. It probably occurs in most of the tetrads covering the county but was recorded from only 542 (57%).

Future Prospects

The large skipper will probably remain a fairly common and widespread species in the county as long as the areas of tall grassland that it favours can still be found.

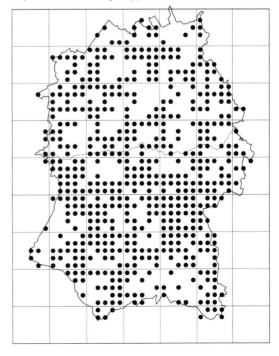

Map 9. Distribution of large skipper

DINGY SKIPPER
Erynnis tages (Linnaeus)

The generic name *Erynnis*, given to the dingy skipper by Schrank in 1801, is derived from the Furies who harried wrongdoers, hounding them from place to place, and refers to the butterfly's restless movement as if chased by the annoying goddesses. The specific name *tages*, given by Linnaeus in 1758, was the name of a boy with the wisdom of an old man who rose suddenly from the ground and instructed the Etruscans in the art of divination.

The dingy skipper was one of the 21 British species believed to have been described by Christopher Merrett in 1666. In 1704 James Petiver named it 'Handley's brown Butterfly', changed the name to 'Handley's brown Hog Butterfly' in 1706 and finally to 'Handley's small brown Butterfly' in 1717. Handley was one of a group of collectors known in the London area at that time who first recorded this species. It does not reappear in the literature until 1766 when Moses Harris called it the 'Dingey Skipper' in *The Aurelian*. This name, with a slight change of spelling, has been used ever since.

As its name suggests, this little butterfly is not colourful but, in fresh specimens, the markings in various shades of brown, as displayed on the female's wings in Ian Grier's photograph, are attractive. As it flies low over the vegetation with a fast fluttering movement it can easily be confused with two day-flying moths, the burnet companion (*Euclidia glyphica*) and Mother Shipton (*Callistege mi*) which are on the wing at the same time, often in the same habitat. However, its fondness for basking on bare soil and low vegetation gives the opportunity for closer examination of the hooked tips of the antennae which is a quick way to distinguish it from the moths.

The yellow eggs are laid singly on the upper surface of the leaves of common and greater bird's-foot-trefoil (*Lotus corniculatus* and *L. pedunculatus*) and sometimes on horseshoe vetch (*Hippocrepis comosa*). The caterpillar feeds on the young leaves of these plants until full-grown and then hibernates in a cocoon throughout the winter. It pupates in the following spring.

The Flight Period

There is normally only one generation, the butterflies being on the wing from about mid-May until late June. In some years a small, partial second generation may occur in late summer. In 1921 Steven Corbet stated 'it is interesting to note that a partial second brood occurred in early August near the village of Damerham in South Wilts'. This area is now in Hampshire and may have been Martin Down NNR. A second generation occurred in the wonderful summer of 1949 when a specimen was captured on 4 August (Reginald Jackson). Roy Pitman reported one at Old Sarum on 28 August 1957, the latest date known for the county.

During the WBMS there were three reports of second generation individuals. Two were in 1989, one individual at West Yatton Down on 25 July (Malvyn Potter) and one at Vernditch Chase on 30 July (Nick Wynn). While looking for Adonis blues on Pewsey Downs NNR on 19 August 1994 the author was amazed to find a very fresh dingy skipper basking in the warm evening sunshine, his first sighting of a second generation butterfly which gave him a rather strange feeling – that of seeing a butterfly so unexpectedly and 'out of season'.

No second generation butterflies have been seen at Bratton Castle Earthworks where the longest flight period during the years 1980–94 was eight weeks in 1985 and 1990 and the shortest was four weeks in 1986. The highest weekly number of individuals counted on the transect varied from 12 in May 1987 to three in June 1988 and 1994. The earliest sighting was on 2 May 1990 and the latest on 10 July 1985. A typical annual flight period at this site is shown below. Marlborough College reports include the incredible date of 11 April 1893, a year of very early emergence for many species. The next earliest was 1 May 1921, a year of excessive heat and drought.

Flight period at Bratton Castle Earthworks in 1992

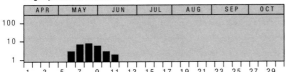

Measures of Abundance 1980–94 (Figure 6)

Numbers increased significantly at all sites in 1982 but the further large increase at Pewsey Downs in 1983 was exceptional. This was followed by a general decline until 1987 when, with the exception of Picket Wood, numbers increased significantly. Another general decline was followed by an increase in 1990, dramatically at Picket Wood where numbers had been decreasing steadily from the 1982 peak to such a low level that, by 1989, it was thought that the species was on the verge of extinction in the wood. However, the weather in 1989 and 1990, combined with ride widening and some tree felling which created sunnier and more open areas, were considered to be the reason for the upturn in 1990 but, in 1994, none was seen on the transect.

At Pewsey Downs and Bratton Castle Earthworks numbers fell in 1991, recovered in 1992 and have since fallen to low levels, here and at all sites, to considerably below the average values. The results from Boscombe Down, where monitoring began in 1989, were out of phase with those from other sites until 1992, since when they have followed the general trends.

Status Before 1982

The first Wiltshire record, published by the Rev Francis Morris in 1853, stated 'near Great Bedwyn and Sarum, Wiltshire; and in fact in most parts of England'. His source was probably J W Lukis who furnished several records for other species from these localities. In 1857, Henry Stainton stated that it occurred at Corsham. The 1865 Marlborough College report recorded it from Savernake Forest and Clatford (H A Evans), Great Bedwyn (T A Preston), Martinsell (J W Mills) and it was taken on 16 May 1866 (J E Hilliard). In the 1873 College List the dingy skipper was described as common and this status was maintained in all subsequent Lists until 1956. The Rev T B Eddrupp included it in his 1899 list from near Calne but it was absent from E Cook's 1902 list for the Devizes district and from Dr R V Solly's list of 1898–1901 from near Wylye.

Pitman recorded the dingy skipper from Farley in May 1928 and commented 'county full of life, collected 100 insects in last three days'. In 1936 he stated it to be 'common and widely distributed'. It was described as common in the Dauntsey School Fauna Lists from 1931 to 1948 and Bowmont Weddell reported it from near Westbury in June 1932. In east Wiltshire, where it was 'usually abundant', John Kempe noted that it was comparatively scarce in 1951. In 1962, Baron de Worms described it as 'common and widely distributed', repeating Pitman's statement of 1936 although probably by 1962 it was much more restricted in distribution due to the destruction of habitat during the 1950s.

Status Since 1982

The dingy skipper is now a local but widespread species over much of England and Wales but is much scarcer and more restricted in the north of England and in Scotland. It is the only skipper in Ireland where it occurs very locally. In Wiltshire it was always considered to be common but at the present time, although still widely distributed, it cannot be considered a common species except locally on some downland sites on the Chalk and Limestone. A few colonies are found in woodland rides and clearings and on some verges and embankments, especially along disused railway lines. The species has probably been under-recorded, especially in the south of the county, or has been overlooked unless deliberately searched for. The habitats in which colonies have been located in the county since 1982 are shown in Table 4.

Table 4. An assessment of the number of colonies in the county

Habitat/locality	Number of colonies			
	N Wilts	S Wilts	Total	%
Woodland rides and clearings	6	18	24	12
Grassland, excluding SPTA and Porton Down	22	67	89	43
SPTA(W) Imber	-	27	27	13
SPTA(C) Larkhill/West Down	-	30	30	15
SPTA(E) Bulford/Tidworth	-	12	12	6
Porton Down	-	12	12	6
Railway lines and verges	6	5	11	5
Total number of colonies	34	171	205	

Map 10. Distribution of common bird's-foot-trefoil

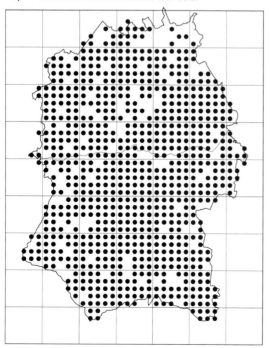

Map 11. Distribution of dingy skipper

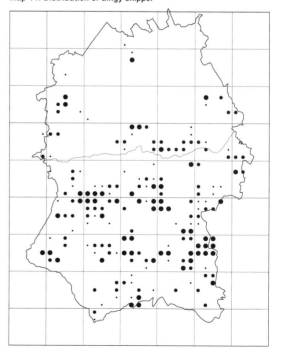

The number of colonies is difficult to assess accurately on the three areas of SPTA and at Porton Down due to the large size of each. The butterflies, although colonial to some degree, tend to spread out rather than remain in a discrete habitat. When estimating the number of colonies occurring on these areas of MOD land, it has been assumed that each record from within a 1 km square represented a distinct colony. This gave a total of 81 (40%) of the county total. This butterfly is commoner in the south than the north even if these 81 colonies are disregarded.

The dingy skipper appears to be very scarce north of a line from Corsham to Marlborough. There are four grassland colonies near Aldbourne and Baydon in the north-east (George Osmond *et al.*) and three in the Braydon Forest area. At least eight small colonies survive in the north-west: two in woodland clearings, three on railway and road embankments and three on limestone grassland near Castle Combe. There could well be others tucked away in this 'good butterfly country'.

The dingy skipper is a widespread species on downland north of Devizes and Pewsey, in the east at Ham Hill and in the Oxenwood area. It occurs in small numbers in Savernake Forest and on nearby disused railway lines. There are four colonies on grassland near Box, two in meadows near Winsley (Fuller), small vulnerable populations in most of the woodlands in west Wiltshire and at least two colonies in railway cuttings near Heywood (Nick Wynn) and Dilton Marsh (Fuller).

In the south-west, this species occurs on the downs north of Mere, on the grasslands of Cranborne Chase and on downland at Kingston Deverill. It is probably far more widespread on the chalk grassland north and south of the Ebble valley and on the downs around Coombe Bissett than is indicated on the distribution map. Many suitable areas of grassland and some woodlands in the area around Salisbury, including Pepperbox Hill and Langley Wood in the extreme south-east, support populations. Dingy skippers are widespread in Grovely and Great Ridge Woods but colony numbers are not clearly defined and it has been assessed that each wood contains two. During the WBMS (1982–94) this butterfly was recorded from 190 tetrads (20%).

The distribution map for comon bird's-foot-trefoil, the main larval foodplant, shows that it occurs much more widely in the county than the dingy skipper. The plant is able to grow in many habitats where other critical requirements of the butterfly are not found.

Future Prospects

Additional colonies will probably continue to be discovered, especially in the south of the county, while some of the present-day ones may become extinct due to further development and habitat destruction. Some of those in woodland may be lost if the woods become overgrown, dense and shady. Grassland populations could dwindle if the larval foodplants are smothered due to lack of suitable grazing management. Many of the grassland colonies are on MOD land, nature reserves, SSSIs or land that is too steep to plough and are, therefore, unlikely to suffer from extensive interference. This should mean that the status of the dingy skipper is unlikely to alter substantially and that it will probably remain a widespread and local species in most areas of the county.

GRIZZLED SKIPPER
Pyrgus malvae (Linnaeus)

The generic name *Pyrgus*, given to the grizzled skipper by Hübner in 1819, means a tower on a wall or a battlement, to which he presumably likened the chequered wing margin hairs. The specific name *malvae*, given by Linnaeus in 1758, was derived from the generic name of mallow (*Malvus*) which at that time was believed to be the larval foodplant.

The first recorded British specimen was caught by James Petiver on 30 April 1696 (11 May New-Style Calendar) in a boggy area of Hampstead Heath. When he published this record in 1699 he named the species 'Our brown Marsh Fritillary'. In about 1747 Benjamin Wilkes named it the 'grizzled butterfly' and between 1766 and 1775 Moses Harris called it variously the 'Grizzle', 'Gristle' and 'Gristled' but grizzled skipper has been the name accepted by lepidopterists for many years.

The wings of this little butterfly are dark brown, almost black in some specimens, speckled with white markings and with black and white bars on the fringes. It is fond of basking on stones and bare soil with wings wide open but, because of its small size and rapid darting flight, is easily overlooked or even mistaken for a large fly or one of the day-flying moths – common heath (*Ematurga atomaria*), Mother Shipton (*Callistege mi*) or burnet companion (*Euclidia glyphica*) – which are on the wing at the same time.

Individuals have been observed nectaring on the flowers of bugle (*Ajuga reptans*), as in Ian Grier's photograph, ground ivy (*Glechoma hederacea*), wild strawberry (*Fragaria vesca*) and horseshoe vetch (*Hippocrepis comosa*).

The greenish white eggs are laid singly, most commonly on the leaves of wild strawberry but, in the absence of this plant, barren strawberry (*Potentilla sterilis*), tormentil (*P. erecta*), creeping cinquefoil (*P. reptans*) and bramble (*Rubus fruticosus* agg.) may be used. The caterpillar feeds on the leaves of the chosen plant protected in a self-spun tent. It pupates when full-grown in a silken net low down in the vegetation until the following spring.

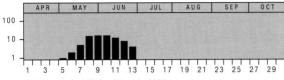

Flight period at Picket Wood in 1991

The Flight Period

The butterflies normally emerge in early May although some may be seen in late April in exceptionally early seasons. They remain on the wing until late June, occasionally into early July and, very rarely, a partial second generation occurs in August. This occurrence was not recorded in the county during the 1980s although the two butterflies seen on 26 July 1989 at Dean Hill in Hampshire close to the county boundary (Ches Carpenter) may have been individuals from a partial second generation.

At Picket Wood during monitoring from 1980 to 1994 the longest flight period was ten weeks in 1986 and the shortest was two weeks in 1989. The maximum weekly number of individuals counted on the transect varied from 17 in May 1982 to one in May 1989. The earliest sighting was 23 April 1982 and the latest 15 July 1986. One was seen at Boscombe Down on 19 April 1989 (Gerald Nicholls) but the earliest county date was 11 April 1893 listed in a Marlborough College report. The record in Bowmont Weddell's diary of a singleton in a wood near Trowbridge on 1 August 1941 is the latest and was almost certain to have been a second generation individual. A typical flight period pattern at Picket Wood is shown above.

Measures of Abundance 1980–94 (Figure 7)

This little butterfly occurs at very few of the monitored sites in Wiltshire and only Picket Wood, Somerford Common and, latterly, Bentley Wood East and Boscombe Down have had significant populations. There are considerable similarities between trends at these local sites and at sites nationwide monitored for the Butterfly Monitoring Scheme (BMS). The BMS data shows that, by 1994, the grizzled skipper had declined to only one fifth of its abundance in 1976.

There have been some dramatic fluctuations in abundance of the grizzled skipper at three monitored sites as shown in Figure 7. There was a steady decline in Picket Wood from 1978 to 1989 except for 1982 which was an excellent year for butterflies. In 1989, the grizzled skipper was very scarce at all sites, only one individual being seen in Picket Wood where it seemed to be on the verge of extinction. However, it made a remarkable recovery in the following two years at all sites, no doubt in response to good weather and, at Picket Wood it was also helped by management that increased the area of open and sunny habitats. This heartening recovery was short-lived. By 1994, values were considerably below the average at all sites, probably due to the poor spring weather of the previous few years.

Butterfly monitoring at Biss Wood, Ravensroost Wood, Picket Wood and Somerford Common indicate that the grizzled skipper is one of the first species to increase in abundance in response to coppicing in woodland.

Status Before 1982

The Rev Francis Morris was the first to record the grizzled skipper from Wiltshire. In 1853 he mentioned localities at Great Bedwyn and Sarum, presumably J W Lukis being his source. In 1857, Henry Stainton stated that it occurred at Corsham and it was listed in the 1865 Marlborough College report. A specimen was taken by J E Hilliard on 14 May 1866. In the 1873 College List, and all subsequent Lists until 1956, it was described as common. The Rev T B Eddrupp included it in his 1899 list from near Calne but it was absent from E Cook's 1902 list from the Devizes district and from Dr R V Solly's 1898–1901 list from near Wylye.

Roy Pitman recorded it from Farley in May 1928 and in 1936 stated 'common as the dingy skipper and met with in the same situations and at the same time of the year'. In the Dauntsey School Fauna List 1931–48 it was described as being 'fairly common in the area'. Weddell reported it from the Trowbridge area in June 1932, from near Slaughterford in May 1935 and at Cranborne

Chase in May 1940. In 1962 Baron de Worms described it as 'generally widespread in the county'.

Status Since 1982

The grizzled skipper's distribution in southern and central England is similar in many ways to that of the dingy skipper. However, it is rare in the north of England and in Wales and is absent from Scotland and Ireland. In Wiltshire, the two species are often seen together in the same habitats within woodland or on grassland although the grizzled has a greater affinity with woodland rides and clearings. In the past it was stated to be a common and widespread species and, although still widespread, it is by no means common. It occurs in small, discrete colonies and is seldom seen in more than ones and twos except in a few favoured woods where as many as a dozen may be counted at the peak flying time. Historical and more recent data suggest that all the skippers have been overlooked by recorders. Both the dingy and grizzled skippers need to be searched for and would not be expected to be seen on a casual country walk. An assessment of the number of colonies in the county during the WBMS 1982–94 is shown in Table 5.

Table 5. An assessment of the number of colonies in the county

Habitat/locality	Number of colonies			
	N Wilts	S Wilts	Total	%
Woodland rides and clearings	9	22	31	23
Grassland, excluding SPTA and Porton Down	8	33	41	30
SPTA(W) Imber	-	13	13	10
SPTA(C) Larkhill/West Down	-	21	21	15
SPTA(E) Bulford/Tidworth	-	13	13	10
Porton Down	-	8	8	6
Railway lines and verges	6	3	9	6
Total number of colonies	23	113	136	

The same criteria have been used as for the dingy skipper when assessing the number of colonies on SPTA and Porton Down. Although there are fewer colonies of grizzled skipper than of dingy skipper in the county, SPTA and Porton Down hold about 40% of the total for both species. However, the closer association of the grizzled skipper with woodland is evident from

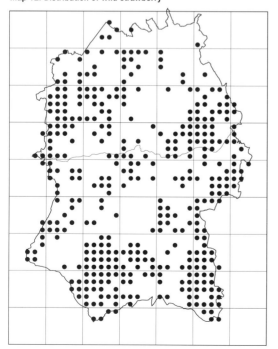

Map 12. Distribution of wild strawberry

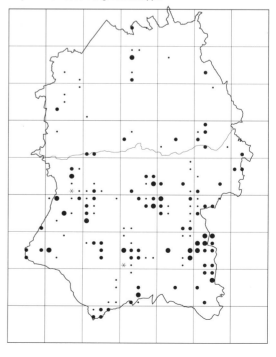

Map 13. Distribution of grizzled skipper

the percentage figure of 23 being double that for the dingy skipper. The total number of grizzled skipper colonies was a third fewer than those of the dingy skipper but the number of colonies along railway lines and verges was similar for both species.

Grizzled skippers are rare and localised in the north of the county and only at Somerford Common have there been sightings in double figures. Most of the other records were of one or two individuals. Several occurred in the early 1980s when the species was less scarce than in the 1990s. During the WBMS, there were records from two areas in the Cotswold Water Park; from woodland, but not meadows, in the Braydon Forest area; a disused railway line near Swindon; grassland at Hinton Parva and Sugar Hill near Aldbourne.

In the north-west of the county there were sightings, mainly of singletons, from six localities in the Box and Castle Combe areas. It was occasionally reported from downland north of Devizes and from Pewsey Downs NNR. It appears to be distributed very thinly throughout the Savernake Forest area, on adjacent disused railway lines and eastwards to Bedwyn Brail, Ham Hill and Oxenwood.

The grizzled skipper has been widely recorded across the centre of the county but rarely in double figures. There were some relatively strong colonies in woods in west Wiltshire in the early 1980s but most of these have now probably been reduced to very low numbers.

In the south of the county stronger populations survive in woodlands such as Grovely, Great Ridge and those on the border with Somerset. There are small colonies scattered over SPTA, Cranborne and Vernditch Chases and the adjacent grassland areas and in most woodlands to the east of Salisbury. A few individuals were seen at Clearbury Ring and

Pepperbox Hill in 1992, it was 'quite common' in Langley Wood in that year (Graham Smith) and it had a very good season at Dean Hill (Ches Carpenter). It appears to be absent from much of the downland in the south but suitable areas may not have been visited by recorders. During the WBMS (1982–94) the grizzled skipper was recorded from 153 tetrads (16%).

Although wild strawberry, the principal larval foodplant, is widespread in the county as shown by its distribution map, the butterfly's distribution is very local. It would appear that one of the secondary foodplants, probably creeping cinquefoil, is used on SPTA where the two strawberries are scarce or absent.

Future Prospects

The future for this species in the county is not encouraging and the declines observed on the monitored sites are probably a reflection of a general decline throughout the county.

Many of the woodland colonies in cleared areas and along the rides in young conifer plantations will now be in danger of extinction, as the trees mature and shade out the ground flora, unless the rides continue to be kept wide and open to the sun.

Some colonies were probably lost during the WBMS, as almost happened at Picket Wood, and some grassland populations are in danger if the vegetation is allowed to become too tall and dense. Several of the records are of very small populations that may be close to extinction. The number of individuals counted exceeded ten in only 20 of the 153 tetrads. Numbers will probably continue to decline further as habitats deteriorate, disappear, or become too small and isolated. Although possibly under-recorded, it is not anticipated that many additional sites for the grizzled skipper will be discovered.

WOOD WHITE
Leptidea sinapis (Linnaeus)

The generic name *Leptidea*, given to the wood white by Billberg in 1820, is derived from two words meaning 'thin' or 'delicate' and 'form' or 'appearance' in recognition of the delicate appearance of this slender-bodied butterfly. The specific name *sinapis*, given by Linnaeus in 1758, means 'mustard', which is not the caterpillar's food plant.

The wood white was first mentioned by Christopher Merrett in 1666 and referred to by James Petiver in 1699 as 'The small white Butterfly'. Moses Harris gave it the present name in 1766.

This is the smallest of the Pieridae family. Rounded wingtips, absence of black spots, long thin abdomen and sustained, but weak, fluttering flight distinguish the wood white from the small and green-veined whites and the female orange-tip.

The flowers of bugle (*Ajuga reptans*) and ragged-Robin (*Lychnis flos-cuculi*) are visited for their nectar, in addition to those of the larval foodplants. Peter Durnell's photograph shows a male nectaring on bramble (*Rubus fruticosus* agg.). The typical habitat is shown in John Grearson's photograph on page 43.

The pale yellow eggs are laid singly on the underside of the vegetative parts of tall specimens of meadow vetchling (*Lathyrus pratensis*), bitter-vetch (*L. linifolius* vars.), bird's-foot-trefoils (*Lotus* spp.) and tufted vetch (*Vicia cracca*) where they grow in open areas in woodland. The caterpillar hatches in two to three weeks and eats its eggshell before starting to feed on the vetch leaves. It pupates on an upright stem in a tussock of grass attached by a silken girdle.

The Flight Period

The butterfly emerges in late May and is on the wing until the beginning of July. In some years there is a small, partial second generation in August.

There is no information on flight periods or abundance from any Wiltshire sites. Of the few dated records, the earliest was 26 May 1978 at

A wide sunny ride in Somerford Common near Malmesbury where
most of Wiltshire's woodland butterfly species occur. The wood white
was introduced in 1973 and survived until 1981.

Somerford Common (David Brotheridge) and the latest 4 August 1956 in the woods at Whiteparish (Ian Heslop).

Records Before 1982

The earliest published Wiltshire record was that of the Rev Francis Morris in 1853 who stated 'rarely near Great Bedwyn and Sarum, as J W Lukis Esq has informed me'. The wood white was included in an exhibition of lepidoptera by W W Dayman at a meeting of the Marlborough College NHS in September 1865. The locality from which it was taken was not stated but in the 1865 College List the species was recorded from Sergeant Doel's (*sic*), Savernake Forest, Rabley Copse and the Great Bedwyn locality cited by Morris. On 21 June 1866 it was recorded by J H Johnson but no location was given. These are the only records from the Marlborough College reports.

Edward Newman's (1869) only reference to the wood white in the south of the county, 'common at Wilton, near Salisbury – W H Grigg' may have referred to Grovely Wood where the species was believed to occur until the early 1950s. Heslop reported it from Bentley Wood in the south-east prior to 1900. Roy Pitman did not mention this species from the Salisbury area in his diaries. In 1936 he stated 'no recent record has come to hand' and continued 'quite likely that it will be reported soon, as it is supposed to be increasing in several isolated locations in neighbouring counties'. In 1939 he was informed that it used to occur near Southbourne, Dorset, but he makes no further reference to this information.

Heslop saw two in woods at Whiteparish in July 1945, took one there in August 1956 and saw one in 1957 and another in 1959 in Blackmoor Copse where R E Haskell and J M Harris also recorded singles. These are the last records of the wood white from the south-east of the county. Sightings of these singletons may have represented small established colonies, were attempted introductions, had been released by breeders or they may have been wanderers from nearby colonies.

However, none was known in Hampshire or nearby in Dorset at the time in spite of Pitman's comments in 1936. In the early 1950s, a few wood whites were seen in Grovely Wood and in Verndich Chase on the Dorset border (Gerald Nicholls), the first recorded sightings from these two areas.

An anonymous BRC record for June 1974 from Somerford Common in the north of the county was the next reference to the wood white. At least six were seen there on 26 May 1978 when the colony that had been introduced in 1973 was flourishing (David Brotheridge). It was last recorded there in May 1981 when Caroline Peachey (now Steel) and Stewart Lane saw two whilst preparing the Invertebrate Site Register for Wiltshire. Nick Lear later informed the author that he understood that about a dozen adults were introduced in 1973 or 1974 from stock obtained in Buckinghamshire but this report has not been substantiated.

The wood white is a very local butterfly. There are approximately 90 woodland colonies in the south and south-west of England. It is more widespread in the Midlands and is frequent and widespread in Ireland. It is rare in the counties adjacent to Wiltshire. It has been absent from Avon for many years and from Hampshire since about 1931. It was last seen in the New Forest in about 1900. There are two colonies in Dorset, 40 km from the Wiltshire border, and a few in west Somerset but there are no recent records from the east of that county. The nearest colonies in Gloucestershire are probably 48 km away in the Forest of Dean and there are none within 25 km of the county boundaries with Oxfordshire and Berkshire. Wiltshire records have been rather infrequent and the wood white always appears to have been a rare species in the county.

Records Since 1982

Much to the author's surprise and delight a colony was discovered in Great Wood, 4 km south of Somerford Common. On 7 June 1984 three males were seen patrolling the main ride (Fuller) and on 17 June six were seen (John d'Arcy). Two were found in the wood on 23 June 1985 (Rob Turner

Map 14. Distribution of meadow vetchling
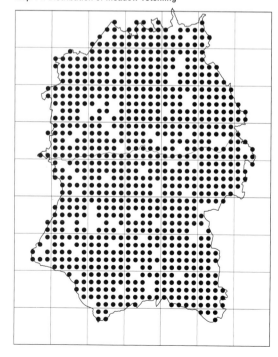

Map 15. Distribution of wood white
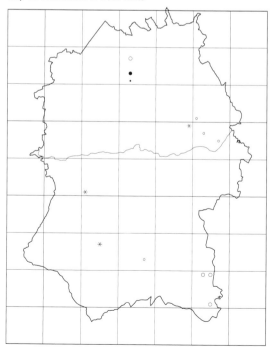

and Ian Grier), a singleton in 1986 (Nick and Nigel Wynn) and the last known sighting was of a singleton in 1987 (Anthony Tyers).

A male was identified on 3 August 1984 on a disused railway line near Savernake Forest (Colin Dodd) but a breeding colony was not located in the area although the date confirms that a second generation had occurred in a year that was excellent for butterflies.

A female was recorded in Great Ridge Wood on 31 August 1985 (Gordon Trebilcock). It is believed that this individual and, no doubt, four or five seen at the western end of Grovely Wood in 1990 (Malcolm Lyall) were from deliberately released bred stock. Both these woods are regularly visited by recorders and no wood whites have subsequently been seen in either.

The last sighting of a wood white in Wiltshire was in June 1992 when Jack Pile was surprised to find a female ovipositing in a ride in Grants's Farm Wood on SPTA(W). It can only be assumed to have been a vagrant from one of the Dorset or Somerset colonies some 96 km to the south-west. This would have been a long journey for such a small delicate creature.

John Heath commented in 1975 on the sightings of singletons as follows: 'In Monks Wood NNR a single specimen of the wood white was seen on 10 June ... This is the first record of this species within Huntingdonshire since 1923. No further specimens were observed subsequently. This species is well known to appear as single specimens remote from known colonies. The nearest locality for this non-migratory species is Salcey Forest, Northamptonshire, some 30 miles (48 km) distant'.

Future Prospects

It seems likely that the wood white is now extinct as a Wiltshire breeding species, adding this county to the considerable list of those from which it has been lost in the twentieth century. Many of the county's woodlands, including Savernake Forest, Braydon Forest, woodlands in mid-west Wiltshire, Great Ridge and Grovely Woods, woods in the south-east of the county and along the Dorset border as far as Cranborne Chase, have all been fairly extensively searched since 1984 but have failed to produce any colonies. Therefore, although records of singletons may continue to be made, it is considered very unlikely that a natural breeding colony will be discovered.

There were other records considered to be misidentifications, either due to the questionable date or to the unlikely habitat. These are not shown on the distribution map. All accepted records, including those from the BRC, have been mapped. During the WBMS (1982–94) the wood white was recorded from 4 tetrads (0.4%), the least frequently observed of any species.

Map 14 shows the distribution of meadow vetchling, one of the three larval foodplants that occurs widely across the county and which is usually quoted as the species' favourite. However, in addition to the presence of the foodplant, the wood white obviously has other requirements for its survival that the county does not offer.

CLOUDED YELLOW
Colias croceus (Geoffroy)

The generic name *Colias*, given to the clouded yellow by Fabricius in 1807, is the name of a promontory on the east coast of Attica, the site of a temple of Aphrodite, the goddess of love. The specific name *croceus*, given by Geoffroy in 1785, means saffron yellow. This species was illustrated by Thomas Mouffet in 1634 and named 'The Saffron Butterfly' by James Petiver in 1703 which perhaps influenced Geoffroy's choice of the scientific nomenclature. Benjamin Wilkes named it the clouded yellow in about 1741.

When seen at a distance this butterfly can be mistaken for a male brimstone but, at close range, its deep yellow colour becomes apparent. Its flight is more powerful and direct but, like its relative, its wings always remain closed when the butterfly is resting or feeding so that the dark-bordered golden yellow of the uppersides, seen on the butterfly with damaged wings in Ian Grier's photograph, is normally only visible in flight. There is a pale-coloured form of the female named *helice* which needs close examination to differentiate it from the two rare immigrants, the pale and Berger's clouded yellows (see page 192).

In years when this immigrant arrives in large numbers, fields of commercially grown clover (*Trifolium* spp.) and lucerne (*Medicago sativa*) are much sought-after both for nectaring and egg-laying. Adults also feed on wild plants including small scabious (*Scabiosa columbaria*) and red clover (*T. pratense*).

The yellowish-white eggs are laid singly on the top surface of the leaves of lucerne, clover and other members of the pea family. The caterpillar hatches about a week later and, after eating most of the eggshell, feeds on the leaves, completing its growth within a month if the weather is warm and dry. The chrysalis is attached to the stem of the foodplant by a silken girdle. The adult will emerge in about three weeks if the chrysalis has not been killed by cold or damp. Being a continually breeding species with no hibernation stage during its life cycle, it is very unlikely that it can survive the winter in Britain, except perhaps in very mild

The Flight Period

Each year, at least a few individuals of this fine immigrant species arrive in Britain from the continent where it is a fairly common butterfly. The first arrivals are occasionally seen in late May or early June but, in most years, they are not reported until the late summer and autumn. The earliest sighting of this species in Wiltshire was 22 April 1950 at Aldbourne by Miss M Foster. The latest was 24 November 1947 about which Roy Pitman wrote in his diary 'Mr Cox gives me a live *Helice* (*sic*) taken at Odstock yesterday, a fine insect freshly emerged but very feeble and was brought home sitting on a piece of bracken where it remained, surely a record date'.

Status Before 1983

In the 1865 Marlborough College report the clouded yellow was said to have been common in 1858. In June 1865 one was taken by J W Whitaker on Marlborough Common and another nearby by W W Melville on 9 October. Several were recorded in that autumn when the form *helice* was taken on Ogbourne Downs by W J Baverstock. In August 1868 it was abundant but in the 1873 College List it was stated not to be common. Its immigration status was not known at that time and it was believed that this species, together with the red admiral and painted lady, hibernated in the winter months.

The clouded yellow was included in the 1899 list of the Rev T B Eddrupp from near Calne and recorded from near Wylye between 1898 and 1901 by Dr R V Solly. One was seen in September 1912 at Alton Barnes by the Rev C A Sladen, the first during his 11 years there. The Rev D P Harrison, Rector of Lydiard Millicent, commented 'I knew 1922 was going to be a Clouded Yellow year for I saw five females in May and early June. In August I found some forty specimens in a clover field next to my house, all males. I did not see a single female the whole autumn' (WAM 1922). Others were reported that year from Winterbourne Bassett, Clyffe, Avebury, Milton Lilbourne and elsewhere in north Wiltshire.

Pitman's first diary (1928) coincided with a 'clouded yellow year' in which he saw the first on 4 July in Salisbury. By 18 August they were common in the area and on 12 September he took 41 on Laverstock Down commenting 'must be netted at first go, hopeless to give chase if missed first time'. By 15 September they were abundant, by which time he had taken 84. His final record of the year was on 4 October in Rampart Road, Salisbury, when his tally of captures was over 100. In August 1933 dozens were seen flying west at Shrewton by Major S Marples and, of 33 captured, six were the form *helice*. In 1936, Pitman stated 'rare in some years but occasionally common and in some districts the summer brood is abundant ... as in 1928 and 1933'.

Bowmont Weddell first recorded the clouded yellow from the Trowbridge area in August 1933 and in 1941 he saw many in a clover field at Hilperton. Twelve were still there on 3 September. It was included in the Dauntsey School Fauna List (1931–48) and was said to be 'found everywhere' in 1946. This was probably incorrectly dated and was a reference to 1947. Comments in Weddell and Pitman's diaries indicated that 1947 was by far the best year since records were first kept. Weddell said 'I write at the close of what must be the most remarkable season within living memory. Today November 5th, a Clouded Yellow was flying in my garden. They had propitious migrating conditions in May and June, and the subsequent fine spell allowed them to breed throughout August, September and into October. Every clover field in Wilts. must have produced its quota of scores or hundreds' (WAM). His earliest record for that year was on 28 May from Marlborough. Both forms were still flying at Tinhead near Westbury on 8 November.

Pitman's 1947 diary makes equally fascinating reading. On 7 October he commented 'must be the finest year ever for *croceus*, I have a wonderful series' and on 14 October 'have now taken well over 50 *helice* of varied forms, must surely be a record year for *croceus*'. On 25 October he enters 'took 15 *croceus* 3 females in Steven's field'. His earliest record was 3 June and his latest 24 November.

In the autumn of 1947 A S Wheeler, who was serving in the army at Devizes, made the following observations in a nearby clover field during his brief lunch-hours. His estimated numbers of the two forms seen in about two acres of the field are given below.

	C. croceus	f. helice
30 September	50	6
1 October	50	2
2 October	500	20
3 October	500	15
6 October	400	10
7 October	200	10
13 October	25	1
15 October	a few	10
21 October	0	6
6 November	0	1
8 November	3	0

These figures emphasise just how abundant the species was in that year. The percentage number of *helice* is of interest since many authors have given 10% as the normal figure. In 1962, Baron de Worms stated 'seen frequently in Wiltshire'.

The years 1877, 1947, 1983, 1992 and 1994, when the clouded yellow was abundant, have been well-documented but it was also seen in reasonable numbers in 1892, 1922, 1924, 1928, the early 1930s, 1941, 1943, 1949 and 1955. Several were seen in Wiltshire in 1984 but the exceptional year of 1983 was the best for the species since 1949. However, there are now more people recording butterflies than in earlier years so that comparisons with the past can be misleading. Years when the clouded yellow is abundant do not necessarily coincide with the arrival of two other, often common, immigrant species, the red admiral and painted lady. The year 1983 was very poor for the painted lady and in 1985, when large numbers of painted ladies and smaller numbers of red admirals arrived exceptionally early, very few clouded yellows were recorded.

Records Since 1983
Between 1983 and 1994, records for the clouded yellow were received every year, the lowest being of one only in 1988. All are included in Table 6.

Table 6. Total numbers of clouded yellows recorded in Wiltshire 1983–94

					Year						
83	84	85	86	87	88	89	90	91	92	93	94
234	31	5	9	10	1	23	5	4	179	6	137

In years when immigrant numbers are high, no doubt many are not recorded so that these figures only represent a small fraction of the total number of clouded yellows present. Nevertheless the figures do clearly indicate the three so-called 'clouded yellow years' 1983, 1992 and 1994. Until 1983 lepidopterists had begun to think that these 'years' were an event of the past because the previous invasion had taken place in 1947, 36 years earlier.

Map 16. Distribution of clouded yellow

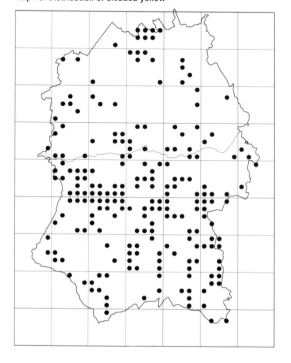

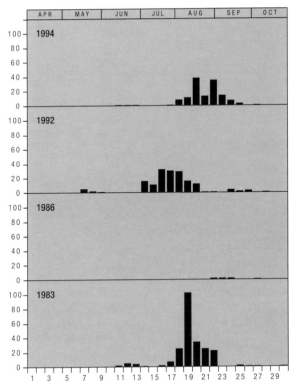

Comparative figures from the whole county for three 'clouded yellow years' and 1986, a more typical year

the number of records for the whole county were the highest. Figures for 1986, a typical year, have been included for comparison. However, according to Pitman's comments, 1983 'did not compare with the good years of 1948/9'. He probably meant 1947/8.

The 1992 invasion differed from those of 1983 and 1994 in that the first butterflies arrived a month earlier and were mainly confined to the western half of Britain. They quickly travelled north and by the end of May were being reported from the west coast of Scotland where the species had its best year this century. In Wiltshire, the first clouded yellows were sighted in early May and large numbers were seen in July and August, possibly the offspring of the earlier arrivals or another wave of immigrants. They were rarely seen on Wiltshire's monitored sites and were only reported from seven of the 19, the maximum being three individuals on one day at Pewsey Downs NNR (Dominic Ash). Very few were reported after mid-August although they were very common in the autumn along the south coast of England. In 1994, the flight period was similar to that of 1983, the first butterfly being seen in mid-June. Numbers peaked in mid-August but at much lower levels than in 1983. In all three years the late autumn high abundance levels of the 1947 season were not reached.

The clouded yellow may have been under-recorded during the WBMS (1982–94) in spite of the three years of high immigration. The distribution map is one of the few that tends to reflect recorder activity rather than species distribution. There were records from 207 tetrads (22%) but no doubt the butterfly had occurred in them all at some time during the 13 years.

In 1984 numbers were also above average and it was tempting to believe that some of the butterflies from 1983 had managed to survive the winter but this is considered to have been most unlikely. The 1992 invasion had followed relatively soon after that of 1983 and another in 1994 was completely unexpected. Comparative details of sightings in these three years (see diagram above) indicate that 1983 was the best. The duration of the flight period which lasted for 19 weeks was the longest, the maximum weekly count of 102 and

BRIMSTONE
Gonepteryx rhamni (Linnaeus)

The generic name *Gonepteryx*, given to this butterfly by Leach in 1815, is derived from two words meaning an angle and a wing, referring to the angular shaped wings of the species. The specific name *rhamni*, given by Linnaeus in 1758, refers to the generic name of buckthorn (*Rhamnus*), one of the two larval foodplants.

The butterfly was illustrated by Thomas Mouffet in 1634 and described by Christopher Merrett in 1666. James Petiver named it 'The Brimstone' in 1695, the first vernacular name to appear in the literature.

No other species can be confused with the brilliant sulphur-coloured males but the pale, greenish-white females are sometimes hard to distinguish from male large whites. When at rest or feeding, the wings are held tightly closed.

Nectar-producing flowers visited in spring include primrose (*Primula vulgaris*) and dandelion (*Taraxacum* spp.) and in summer, thistles (*Cirsium* and *Carduus* spp.) and knapweeds (*Centaurea* spp.). Anthony Tyer's photograph is of a male nectaring on lesser burdock (*Arctium minus*).

The eggs are laid singly in May and June on the underside of young leaves of buckthorn (*Rhamnus catharticus*) and alder buckthorn (*Frangula alnus*). The caterpillar emerges within two weeks, its presence being easily detected by characteristically damaged leaf edges. Many disappear before pupating but those that survive pupate in low vegetation, the adults emerging two weeks later.

Of all the British species, the brimstone probably lives longest as an adult, about half this period being spent in hibernation.

The Flight Period
On emerging from hibernation in the early spring, males roam widely over the countryside but females remain close to their breeding areas in woodland.

In Picket Wood the spring flight normally peaks during the second week of April. Adults of the new generation appear from late July and are rarely seen after mid-August.

In Picket Wood from 1980 to 1994, the longest flight period was 25 weeks in 1990 and the

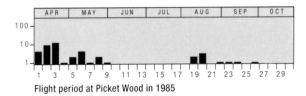

Flight period at Picket Wood in 1985

shortest 13 weeks in 1987. The highest number of individuals counted on a weekly visit varied from 12 in April 1985 to two in April 1981, 1989 and 1994. The earliest sighting was 7 March 1991 and the latest 23 October 1990.

Measures of Abundance 1980–94 (Figure 8)
There were marked fluctuations at most sites during the monitoring period.

High levels in 1982 were generally maintained until the dramatic decline in the very poor butterfly year of 1986. Numbers recovered during the late 1980s and early 1990s but fell at the majority of sites in 1993. Bentley Wood was the exception and showed a substantial increase to reach the highest value since monitoring began. In 1994, numbers declined to levels well below their average at most sites, probably as a result of the poor spring weather.

Status Before 1982
In Wiltshire, this was the first butterfly to be mentioned in the 1865 Marlborough College List. The first date given for a sighting was 6 March 1866 by E A King. In 1873 it was said to be very common and in all subsequent Lists it was described as common. It was included in the Rev T B Eddrupp's 1899 list from near Calne, in Dr R V Solly's 1898–1901 list from near Wylye and in E Cook's 1902 list from the Devizes area.

Roy Pitman took one on 4 March 1928 at Laverstock and found the species very abundant in the New Forest on 5 August, where he 'netted 5 in one strike'. In his 1936 report he said that it was 'generally common'.

In Bowmont Weddell's diaries (1932–82) for the Trowbridge area there are only three records of the brimstone, the first being on 11 August 1935. This surely did not reflect any scarcity of the species in the area during the 50-year period?

In the early 1960s Baron de Worms said that it was common in many localities.

Status Since 1982
The brimstone's national distribution correlates very well with the distribution of the larval foodplants, which are scarce in parts of Wales, Ireland and the north of England and absent from Scotland. In Wiltshire, most brimstones must breed on buckthorn, which is a common shrub, because alder buckthorn is very rare except in the south-east. During the years of the WBMS (1982–94) this species was recorded from 687 tetrads (72%).

Future Prospects
The main factor affecting the abundance of this species is likely to be the availability of the foodplants. The main threat could be the destruction of these shrubs when hedgerows are closely cut or grubbed-up and when woodland rides are trimmed. The brimstone is likely to remain a commonly seen but thinly distributed species.

Map 17. Distribution of brimstone

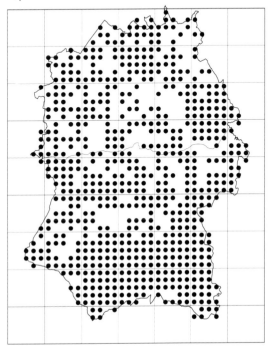

LARGE WHITE
Pieris brassicae (Linnaeus)

The generic name *Pieris* refers to one of the Muses (Pierides) who was supposed to live on Mount Pieris. Shrank divided the butterflies into five families and gave this name to the three common white species in 1801. The specific name *brassicae* was given by Linnaeus in 1758, a reference to the generic name of the larval foodplants.

The large white was illustrated by Thomas Mouffet in 1634 and described by Christopher Merrett in 1666. James Petiver named it 'The Greater White Cabbage-Butterfly' in 1703 and Adrian Haworth gave it the present name in 1803.

This white butterfly might be mistaken for a female brimstone in flight. Christine Tracey's photograph shows the underside.

Individuals of the spring generation nectar on primrose (*Primula vulgaris*) and red campion (*Silene dioica*) and those of the second generation on thistles (*Cirsium* and *Carduus* spp.) and knapweeds (*Centaurea* spp.).

The large batch of yellow eggs is laid on cabbages, Brussels sprouts and, in the wild, wild mignonette (*Reseda lutea*) and other members of the cabbage family.

The caterpillars hatch within two weeks and eat most of the eggshell before feeding in unison on the plants and stripping the outer leaves. A parasitic wasp (*Apanteles glomeratus*) lays its eggs under the skin of some caterpillars. The wasp maggots feed on the host's body-fat until finally killing it just as it is about to pupate. Those that have not been parasitised wander from the food plants in search of the dry, bare surfaces of fences, walls and tree trunks on which they pupate.

The Flight Period
Butterflies that emerge in early May are on the wing until early July. Two weeks later the second generation appears and continues flying into the autumn. In some years there is a small third generation. The whole flight period pattern is often complicated by the arrival of immigrants from the continent.

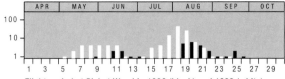

Flight period at Picket Wood in 1986 (black) and 1992 (white)

In Picket Wood from 1980 to 1994, the longest flight period was 25 weeks in 1990 and the shortest was 15 weeks in 1981 and 1984. The highest number of individuals counted on a weekly visit varied from 44 in August 1992 to two on various dates in 1980, 1984 and 1985. The earliest sighting was 24 April 1990 and the latest 8 October 1990. Two exceptionally early records, 6 March 1943 and 26 March 1928, appear in Marlborough College Lists.

Measures of Abundance 1980–94 (Figure 9)
As would be expected with a migratory species, there were some large annual fluctuations. The very poor years of 1980, 1984 and 1985 were followed by peaks in 1990 and particularly in 1992 when large numbers arrived on the east coast in late July and quickly moved westward into most of Britain. This species was voted 'Butterfly of the Year' in 1992 by several counties including Wiltshire. In 1993, numbers crashed from these exceptionally high values at all the monitored sites and in 1994 remained at levels which were significantly below the average.

Status Before 1982
The first published reference to the large white in Wiltshire was in the 1865 Marlborough College List but the first dated record was that of A Marshall on 30 April 1866. In the 1873 List it was described as abundant and in all subsequent Lists as very common. It was included in the Rev T B Eddrupp's 1899 list from near Calne and in E Cook's 1902 list from the Devizes area.

In the Salisbury area, Roy Pitman took one at Milford on 23 April 1928, the species being abundant throughout the year. In his 1936 report he stated 'abundant everywhere'. On 18 September 1939 he commented 'larvae and imagos are

swarming everywhere and serious damage is done in gardens. Have never before seen so many' and on 27 September he collected over 200 pupae from the side of a gasometer. On 28 May 1932 Bowmont Weddell recorded it from the Trowbridge area but did not refer to any particular abundance in 1939. In 1962 Baron de Worms described it as 'generally distributed and often abundant'.

Status Since 1982
This species is common and widespread throughout Great Britain and Ireland. It is found in all types of habitat but is especially associated with allotments, gardens and urban areas where brassicas are grown. During the WBMS (1982–94) the large white was recorded from 785 tetrads (83%) but probably occurred in them all.

In spite of it being a pest of many vegetable crops, with the result that chemicals are used against its early stages, the large white will probably continue to be a common species in most years.

Map 18. Distribution of large white

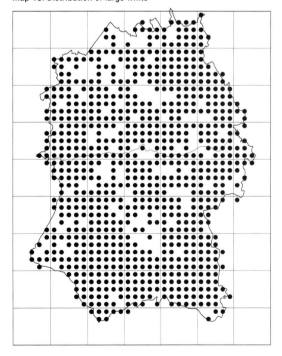

SMALL WHITE
Pieris rapae (Linnaeus)

The generic name *Pieris*, was given to the three common whites by Schrank in 1801 (see account for large white on page 52). The specific name *rapae*, given by Linnaeus in 1758, refers to the wild turnip (*Brassica rapa*), one of the larval foodplants.

The small white was illustrated by Thomas Mouffet in 1634 and described by Christopher Merrett in 1666. James Petiver named it 'The lesser white Cabbage-Butterfly' in 1703 and it was given its present name by Adrian Haworth in 1803.

Most small whites are smaller than average large whites. The males have a black dot in the centre of the upper wings as shown in Nick Wynn's photograph. Both species look similar when at rest with only the yellow undersides of the lower wings visible. The amount of grey on the wingtips is variable but never extends down the edge of the wing. Females are always more heavily marked than males and have larger spots. Although the markings are noticeably different from those of the similar-sized green-veined white, when seen in flight at a distance of three metres or more the two species are often difficult to separate.

In addition to the tall plants visited by large whites (see page 52), small whites nectar at smaller, lower-growing species including hawkbits (*Leontodon* spp.), clovers (*Trifolium* spp.) and field bindweed (*Convolvulus arvensis*). In prolonged hot dry weather they congregate in large numbers on patches of damp mud to obtain moisture.

The yellow eggs are laid singly on the underside of the leaves of members of the cabbage family both in the countryside, where two of the species most commonly used are garlic mustard (*Alliaria petiolata*) and charlock (*Sinapis arvensis*), and in gardens. The caterpillar emerges in about a week and eats its eggshell. The first generation caterpillars pupate on the foodplant but those of the second wander off to pupate on the bare surfaces of fences, walls and tree trunks.

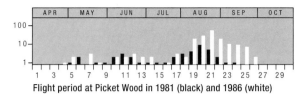

Flight period at Picket Wood in 1981 (black) and 1986 (white)

The Flight Period

The spring generation emerges in late April and early May, a few days before the green-veined white, and the second and third are on the wing from July until September. In most years the numbers are probably boosted by immigrants from the continent.

In Picket Wood during the years 1980–94 the longest flight period lasted for 24 weeks in 1990 and the shortest for 14 weeks in 1983. The largest number of individuals counted in a weekly visit varied from 55 in August 1986 to five on various dates in 1980, 1985, 1988 and 1991. The earliest sighting was 9 April 1990 and the latest 25 September in 1982 and 1991. The earliest Marlborough College record was for 5 March 1880.

Measures of Abundance 1980–94 (Figure 10)

Numbers are often swollen by immigrants resulting in large fluctuations in annual abundance. There were high levels in 1982, 1986, 1992 and 1994 at most of the monitored sites in Wiltshire, the decline in 1994 at Roundway Hill Covert being against the general trend. At most other sites the 1994 values were well above the average except at Vagg's Hill where numbers have failed to reach the high levels of the early 1980s.

Status Before 1982

The first published reference to this butterfly in Wiltshire was in the 1865 Marlborough College List. It was recorded on 20 April 1866 by L C Calley and described as very common in all subsequent Lists. It was included in the 1899 list of the Rev T B Eddrupp from near Calne and in the 1902 list of E Cook from the Devizes district.

Roy Pitman recorded the small white from Ugford on 4 April 1928 and, like the large white,

it was abundant throughout that year and was also a serious pest in 1939. In his 1936 report he stated 'abundant as the last [large white] and more often met with in the field'. It was the first of Bowmont Weddell's diary entries dated 24 April 1932. In 1962 Baron de Worms stated that it was reported from all parts of the county and was often very common.

Status Since 1982

The small white is a common and widespread species throughout Great Britain and Ireland and is usually more abundant than the large white. This is possibly because the caterpillars are solitary, well camouflaged, do not suffer so severely from the attacks of parasitic wasps and flies and because of the larger number of immigrants that arrive in some years.

During the years of the WBMS (1982–94) the small white was the most completely mapped species. It was recorded from 846 tetrads (89%) and, in spite of persecution of its early stages, it will no doubt remain a common species.

Map 19. Distribution of small white

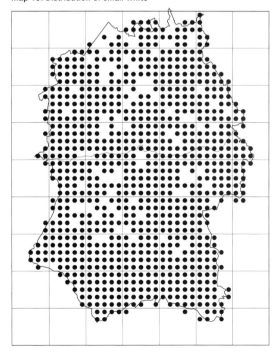

GREEN-VEINED WHITE
Pieris napi (Linnaeus)

The generic name *Pieris*, was given to the three common whites by Schrank in 1801 (see account for large white on page 52). The specific name *napi* was given by Linnaeus in 1758, a reference to rape (*Brassica napus*), a larval foodplant.

The green-veined white was illustrated by Thomas Mouffet in 1634 and described by Christopher Merrett in 1666. James Petiver named it 'The common white veined-Butterfly' in 1699. William Lewin was the first to name it the 'Green-veined White' in 1795.

The males have fewer spots and are less heavily marked than the females. Identification can easily be confirmed when the undersides can be seen as in Christine Tracey's photograph. In theory, this species should be distinguishable from the small white when on the wing but, unless the two are seen together and with the light at the right angle, uncertainty creeps in.

Green-veined whites may be seen nectaring on a wide range of plants including thistles (*Cirsium* spp. and *Carduus* spp.), knapweeds (*Centaurea* spp.), daisy (*Bellis perennis*), dandelions (*Taraxacum* spp.), ground-ivy (*Glechoma hederacea*) and wild basil (*Clinopodium vulgare*).

The female selects plants with care on which to lay her pale yellow eggs. Small rosettes or seedlings of wild members of the cabbage family growing in damp places are preferred. Water-cress (*Nasturtium officinale*) and cuckooflower (*Cardamine pratensis*) are used in wet meadows and hedge mustard (*Sisymbrium officinale*) and garlic mustard (*Alliaria petiolata*) in hedge bottoms and ditches. Eggs are laid singly but several may be deposited on the same plant. The caterpillar emerges within a week and eats most of its eggshell before feeding on young leaves only. It pupates in dense vegetation approximately three weeks later. The progeny of the second generation overwinter in the pupal stage.

The Flight Period

The first generation emerges in late April and early May. A second, and sometimes a third,

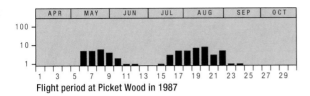

Flight period at Picket Wood in 1987

appear from late July to early September and usually in larger numbers than the first.

In Picket Wood during the years 1980–94 the longest flight period was 23 weeks in 1994 and the shortest was 16 weeks in 1983. The highest number of individuals counted in a weekly visit varied from 18 in August 1986 to four in August 1980. The earliest sighting was 22 April 1991 and the latest 2 October 1980.

There was an exceptionally early date of 4 March 1868 in a Marlborough College List, the next earliest being 27 March 1929. Perhaps early dates for this butterfly need to be treated with caution due to possible confusion with the small white.

Measures of Abundance 1980–94 (Figure 11)

Numbers declined during the generally dry hot summers of the late 1980s except on the Bentley Wood transect. There was a large increase in abundance in 1992 at all sites except at the Kennet and Avon Canal. Numbers then fell to considerably below their averages at most sites, Bentley Wood being the exception where numbers rose to high levels. Fluctuations in the abundance of this species are far less pronounced than for the large and small whites because there is no immigrant effect. However, there is some evidence that it becomes scarcer in hot dry seasons.

Status Before 1992

The first published reference to the green-veined white in Wiltshire was in the 1865 Marlborough College List. Following a recorded sighting by L C Calley on 22 April 1866 all subsequent Lists described it as being common especially in woods and marshes. It was included in the 1899 list of the Rev T B Eddrupp from near Calne, the 1898–1901 list of Dr R V Solly from near Wylye and the 1902 list of E Cook from the Devizes district.

Roy Pitman recorded seeing it in May 1928 in the Salisbury area and in 1936 described it as 'very common, at times abundant'. Bowmont Weddell saw three in the Trowbridge area in May 1932 and in the early 1960s Baron de Worms stated that it had been found in almost every area of the county.

Status Since 1982

The green-veined white is widely distributed and very common throughout Great Britain and Ireland, absent only from the Shetland Isles. It occurs in a variety of habitats but is probably more common in the countryside than in urban areas. It prefers damper areas of woodland, grassland, hedgerows and verges and occurs less commonly on dry open downland and grassland.

Observations of the green-veined white during the WBMS (1982–94) showed that it was widely distributed throughout the county. It was recorded from 700 tetrads (74%). This butterfly will probably remain a common species and continue to be passed by as a 'cabbage white' by the casual observer.

Map 20. Distribution of green-veined white

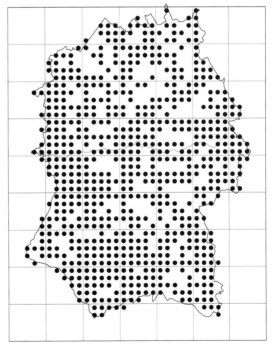

ORANGE-TIP
Anthocharis cardamines (Linnaeus)

The generic name *Anthocharis*, given to the orange-tip by Boisduval in 1833, refers to a flower and the character of grace, possibly because the males in particular lend grace to the flowers they frequent. The specific name *cardamines* was given by Linnaeus in 1758. It relates to the generic name of bitter-cress (*Cardamine* spp.) and cuckooflower (*C. pratensis*), the larval foodplants of the species.

The orange-tip was illustrated by Thomas Mouffet in 1634 and named by James Petiver in 1699 as 'The white marbled female (and male) Butterfly'. *Circa* 1747 Benjamin Wilkes was the first to use the name 'Orange-tip Butterfly'. The name 'Wood Lady', proposed by James Dutfield in 1748, proved popular with several writers but orange-tip (with or without the hyphen!) has prevailed.

The male is distinct in having a large area of orange near the tip of the forewings as shown in Ian Grier's photograph. The underside of the hindwings of both sexes is stippled with light olive which shows through the wings like a shadow on the upperside. Neither sex spends much time nectaring but there are records of butterflies visiting ground-ivy (*Glechoma hederacea*), bugle (*Ajuga reptans*), rape (*Brassica napus*) and honesty (*Lunaria annua*).

The greenish-white eggs are laid singly below the flowerheads of cuckooflower and garlic mustard (*Alliaria petiolata*). They turn bright orange within a few days and are one of the easiest of butterfly eggs to find. After eating its eggshell, the caterpillar feeds on the developing seed-pod. Pupation, which takes place within a month of the caterpillar hatching, lasts for more than ten months.

The Flight Period
Male orange-tips usually begin emerging in mid-April a few days before the females. The population peaks in mid-May and a few individuals may linger on into late June.

At Vagg's Hill during the years 1982–94 the longest flight period lasted for 11 weeks in 1989 and the shortest for seven weeks in 1993. The highest number of individuals counted in a week

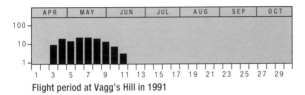

Flight period at Vagg's Hill in 1991

varied from 26 in May 1990 to eight in May 1982. In 1991 orange-tips were seen in abundance.

The earliest Marlborough College records were 24 March 1944 and 12 April 1921.

Measures of Abundance 1980–94 (Figure 12)

During the years of monitoring there were large annual fluctuations. From low numbers in 1982, they rose to a peak in 1985, fell sharply in 1986, climbed again in 1991 and then slumped to remain at low levels during the following three years. The recovery at Hartmoor in 1994 was against the trend.

The zero value at Kennet and Avon Canal in 1984 probably resulted from habitat damage in the winter of 1983 when the canal was dredged and the silt dumped on the towpath bank. By 1985, garlic mustard was as abundant as before the dredging work and orange-tips quickly repopulated the site.

Status Before 1982

The first published reference to the orange-tip in Wiltshire appears in the 1865 Marlborough College List. Following a recorded sighting on 22 April 1866 by A C Almack it was described in all subsequent Lists as common. It was included in the 1899 list of the Rev T B Eddrupp from near Calne and in the 1902 list of E Cook from the Devizes district. Roy Pitman 'took a nice lot' at Petersfinger on 6 May 1928 and in his 1936 report he described it as 'usually very common'. Bowmont Weddell recorded three in the Trowbridge area on 17 May 1932 and in the early 1960s Pitman described it as being 'well distributed in the county mainly in lush meadows, but of fluctuating abundance'.

Status Since 1982

The orange-tip is widely distributed over most of Great Britain and Ireland and has become more common in recent years, noticeably so in the north of England and parts of Scotland. It is an early spring species of unimproved flowery meadows, woodland rides and clearings, country lane verges and byways. The orange-tip was commonly found in many parts of the county during the 1980s and early 1990s possibly as the result of less intensive spraying and cutting along stretches of roadside verges where the larval foodplants grow. It probably occurred in all the tetrads covering the county but was less common than elsewhere in some urban areas and on the drier grasslands of Salisbury Plain, from where the records were often of wandering singletons only. During the WBMS (1982–94) it was recorded from 636 tetrads (67%).

Future Prospects

The status of this butterfly in the county is unlikely to change significantly provided that larval foodplants are allowed to survive on verges, along byways and in the few remaining unfertilised areas of damp grassland.

Map 21. Distribution of orange-tip

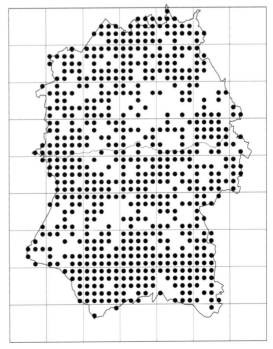

GREEN HAIRSTREAK
Callophrys rubi (Linnaeus)

The generic name *Callophrys*, given to the green hairstreak by Billberg in 1820, is derived from two words meaning beauty and the eyebrow, probably a reference to the metallic green scales on the frons between the butterfly's eyes. The specific name *rubi*, given by Linnaeus in 1758, comes from the generic name of the bramble, one of the secondary larval foodplants.

It was first referred to by Christopher Merrett in 1666. In 1702, James Petiver called it 'The holly under green Butterfly' and in 1795, William Lewin gave it its present name of green hairstreak.

The undersides of the wings of this little butterfly are green with a few white dots which sometimes form an indistinct broken line. In worn specimens the green scales are often missing and the wings then appear to be brown. It is difficult to detect because, in flight, the green colour is not apparent and when at rest the wings remain closed as shown in John Kerr's photograph. Males are territorial and spend much of their time camouflaged as they perch on the fresh green leaves of a chosen shrub before darting out with a rapid jerky flight in pursuit of passing insects to engage in battle with other males or in pursuit of females.

In Wiltshire, this species has been observed nectaring on a variety of herbs and shrubs including buttercups (*Ranunculus* spp.) wild strawberry (*Fragaria vesca*), rape (*Brassica napus*), ground-ivy (*Glechoma hederacea*), milkworts (*Polygala* spp.), common bird's-foot-trefoil (*Lotus corniculatus*), guelder-rose (*Viburnum opulus*) and privet (*Ligustrum* spp.).

The green eggs are laid singly in May and June in the axil of a fresh leaf or among the flower-buds of many plants including common rock-rose (*Helianthemum nummularium*), common bird's-foot-trefoil, vetches (*Vicia* spp.), dyer's greenweed (*Genista tinctoria*), gorses (*Ulex* spp.), buckthorn (*Rhamnus catharticus*) and dogwood (*Cornus sanguinea*). The caterpillar feeds on the young leaves but is also cannibalistic. It pupates in July in leaf litter and the chrysalis is attended by ants which cover it with fine soil. The pupal stage lasts for up to ten months.

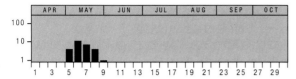

Flight period at Upton Cow Down in 1990

The Flight Period

The first butterflies usually emerge in early May although, in early seasons, they may be seen during the last week of April. They are on the wing until the first half of June but a few worn individuals sometimes survive into early July. The butterflies are only active in sunshine and when the minimum temperature is 13°C. Males tend to remain in their territories while mated females roam, flying close to the ground in search of opportunities for egg-laying. The flight period pattern at Upton Cow Down in 1990, an early season, is shown above. During the years of monitoring at this site from 1984–94 the longest flight period was six weeks in 1984; none was seen in 1987 or 1988. The maximum number of individuals counted on the transect on a weekly visit was 11 on 1 May 1990. The earliest recorded date for the county was 11 April 1991 at Boscombe Down (Gerald Nicholls) and the latest date was 6 July 1986 at Ham Hill (Jack Coates).

Measures of Abundance 1980–94 (Figure 13)

Index values from sites with small populations should be treated with a degree of caution since this method of monitoring may not be reliable due to the elusive habits of the butterfly. For example, none was seen at Bratton Castle Earthworks in the three successive years 1983–85, which were good for the species at most sites. Pewsey Downs NNR was the only Wiltshire site where significant numbers occurred during the 1980s but the reason for its apparent absence there in some years since 1991 compared with some large increases at other monitored sites is not known. Figure 13 shows that there were some large fluctuations from high levels in the early 1980s to low levels from 1986 to 1989, with two dramatic peaks in 1990 and 1993 at all sites except Pewsey Downs. With this exception, correlation between the graphs for the

five sites is good. Numbers declined in 1994 but not to the extremely low levels of the late 1980s. In the exceptionally good year of 1982, Godfrey Smith wrote of the abundance on SPTA(W), one of its strongholds in the county, 'numbers seen on the light green leaves of hawthorn bushes were such that the colour was changed to the distinctive green of the hairstreak'. In that year, marsh fritillary and Adonis blue were also abundant on the ranges. These population explosions, followed by periods of relative scarcity, have been known and commented upon by lepidopterists in the past. In the long term, these, as well as the less noticeable annual fluctuations, will be reflected by the figures from monitored sites.

Status Before 1982

In 1853, the Rev Francis Morris, who was the first writer to mention Wiltshire, stated 'near Great Bedwyn and Sarum' presumably quoting J W Lukis, his source for most Wiltshire records. In the 1865 Marlborough College List there was a record of a specimen being taken on 28 May 1864 at Clatford Park Farm by C R W Hardy. In the 1873 List it was described as 'scarce; Rabley and West Woods'. It was considered to be locally common in the 1935 and 1956 Lists. All four hairstreak species were missing from the Rev T B Eddrupp's 1899 list from near Calne, from Dr R V Solly's list of 1898–1901 from near Wylye and from E Cook's 1902 list from the Devizes district.

In the Salisbury area Roy Pitman took a green hairstreak on 3 June 1928 at Clarendon and saw one at Odstock on 6 June 1928. In his 1936 report he described it as being 'locally common and sparsely distributed, appearing very freely in South Wiltshire especially in wooded valleys'. It was described as fairly common in the Dauntsey School Fauna List 1931–48 but no localities were given. Bowmont Weddell reported it from Westbury in his first diary on 5 June 1932. In 1958 Ian Heslop wrote of the species in Blackmoor Copse, 'Often common but subject to considerable fluctuations in numbers'. In 1962 Baron de Worms described it as 'reasonably common throughout Wiltshire' and Dr John Eagles found it to be common near

Great Ridge Wood during the 1960s and early 1970s.

Status Since 1982

This is the most widely distributed of the five hairstreaks and is found in small local colonies throughout Great Britain and Ireland. In Wiltshire's neighbouring counties it is frequent in the Cotswolds in Gloucestershire, locally common on Cranborne Chase and Martin Down in Dorset, locally widespread in Hampshire but scarce in Berkshire and Oxfordshire.

Since 1982 the green hairstreak has been widely recorded from many parts of the county. An assessment of the number of known colonies is shown in Table 7.

There are many similarities between the distribution of this species and those of the dingy and grizzled skippers. Most of the criteria used for assessing the number of colonies for those two species have been used for the green hairstreak. There are 72 colonies, 39% of the total from Porton and SPTA, about the same proportion as for both the skippers. Even when these 72 colonies are disregarded, there are still many more colonies in the south of the county because of the much more extensive grassland-with-scrub habitat available. The percentage associated with woodland (12%) is the same as for the dingy skipper. Several records were sightings of a single butterfly and for most there was no proof of breeding. Although individuals do not appear to roam far from suspected breeding areas voluntarily, small sedentary butterflies can be blown considerable distances. For example, two noted in separate areas of Bentley Wood in 1983 were not proved to be breeding and it was considered that both were blown in from nearby downland colonies (Waring 1983) and some butterflies seen on downland sites and on SPTA may have been windblown. However, most records from these largely open areas are from sheltered valleys and hollows or on the edge of scrub and plantations where the butterflies probably manage to remain in their breeding areas. When assessing the number of colonies in these wide open areas, separate colonies have been assumed if records were more than 1 km apart.

In woodland, colonies occur in areas of scrub either within the wood, as at Knighton Wood, on wood edges as at Vincient's Wood near Chippenham and along rides within the wood provided they are open and sunny and have areas of short turf. A colony may be very local within a wood and easily overlooked. The assessment of woodland colonies in South Wiltshire assumes that there are three in both Great Ridge Wood and Grovely Wood although these large woods may

Table 7. An assessment of the number of colonies in the county

Habitat/locality	Number of colonies			
	N Wilts	S Wilts	Total	%
Woodland rides and clearings	7	16	23	12
Grassland excluding SPTA and Porton Down	21	54	75	41
SPTA(W) Imber	-	17	17	9
SPTA(C) Larkhill/West Down	-	32	32	17
SPTA(E) Bulford/Tidworth	-	11	11	6
Porton Down	-	12	12	7
Railway Lines and verges	5	9	14	8
Total number of colonies	33	151	184	

Map 22. Distribution of green hairstreak

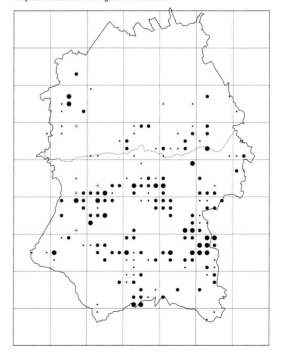

each contain only one, with its population being widely distributed.

The species appears to be very scarce in North Wiltshire. There are three chalk grassland colonies in the Aldbourne area in the east and ten on limestone grassland in the Castle Combe and Box region in the west. A singleton was recorded in 1989 at Hackpen Hill on the Marlborough Downs (David Brotheridge) and one, seen in a Corsham garden in 1984 (Tom Burnard), may have come from an undiscovered colony on the nearby railway line. Green hairstreaks have not been recorded from the Braydon Forest area where many of the woods and copses would appear to provide suitable habitat. This includes Somerford Common which has been monitored since 1984. There are several colonies on the downs north of Devizes and Pewsey and in the Shalbourne area in the east (Jack Coates). A singleton was seen in 1992 in West Woods (Sylvia Young) and there are populations in Savernake Forest and nearby disused railway lines (Humphrey Kay *et al.*).

Additional sites in South Wiltshire where the green hairstreak has been reported are a quarry on Whitesheet Hill, downs north of Mere and Ashcombe Bottom in Cranborne Chase. Most unimproved downland and the drove roads north of the Wylye valley support populations. In the extreme south-east there are colonies in Hound Wood, Bentley Wood, at Pepperbox Hill, near Franchises Wood and near Winterslow. It is often widespread and abundant on Porton Down (Ian Small) and was found on Boscombe Down and the nearby disused railway line in thousands in 1994 (Anthony Bedford-Russell). In some years it is common on the Salisbury Plain escarpment around Westbury and Warminster and there is an isolated colony on Cley Hill near Longleat. Very small colonies were present in Picket Wood (Fuller) and Black Dog Woods (Nick Wynn) in the 1980s but may now be extinct.

Future Prospects

The green hairstreak, like several other species which favour areas of grassland with scrub and sunny woodland clearings, has probably become much scarcer in the county in the last 50 years due to urbanisation, changing practices in forestry and agriculture and the general tidying up of the countryside. It is still widespread, especially in the south but has, no doubt, been overlooked in some areas. Nevertheless, the distribution map is believed to be a true representation of its county distribution. During the WBMS (1982–94) this butterfly was recorded in 177 tetrads (19%). Its overall status is not likely to change significantly although a few small, vulnerable colonies may become extinct and the size of others may be reduced if habitats deteriorate.

BROWN HAIRSTREAK
Thecla betulae (Linnaeus)

The generic name *Thecla*, given to the brown hairstreak by Fabricius in 1807, is that of a virgin and martyr commemorated by the Greek Orthodox Church. The specific name *betulae*, given by Linnaeus in 1758, refers to the generic name of birch. This is not the larval foodplant. This species was first mentioned by James Petiver in 1703. He named the male 'The brown double Streak' and the female 'The Golden brown double Streak' but he also suggested that they might be a single species. The present name, brown hairstreak, was first used for the male in 1710 by John Ray.

This is the largest of the four hairstreaks occurring in Wiltshire. Both sexes have two orange tails on the lower wings and bands of varying shades of orange interspersed with white streaks across all four underwings. Christine Tracey's photograph (above) is of a male and Nick Wynn's, on page 65, is of a female showing the prominent orange patches. This butterfly is unlikely to be seen in flight except in the tree canopy. The attitude of the wings when the

butterfly is at rest – fully open, partly open or fully closed – is dependent on the temperature.

Butterflies have been seen taking nectar from the flowers of bramble (*Rubus fruticosus* agg.), woolly thistle (*Cirsium eriophorum*) and creeping thistle (*C. arvense*) but the principal source of food is aphid honeydew.

The white eggs are laid singly on blackthorn (*Prunus spinosa*) growing in sunny woodland rides and clearings and along nearby hedgerows. They are usually deposited in the fork at the junction of a lateral shoot and a young twig as shown in C Tracey's photograph (inset on page 65). The partly developed caterpillar overwinters within the egg, emerging in late April or early May. It feeds on young leaves for up to two months and pupates low down in the vegetation.

The Flight Period
The butterfly emerges during August and is active throughout September and into early October if there is sunshine and the temperature exceeds

A female brown hairstreak displaying the orange markings on her forewings. These markings are much reduced in the male.
INSET *An egg in the typical position on a blackthorn twig.*

19°C. No flight period details are available for the two Wiltshire populations and, due to its elusive habits, the BMS is not a suitable method for assessing the abundance. Probably the best, but most time consuming method, is to search for and count the eggs during the winter months when they are fairly easy to see on the dark twigs in localities where the butterfly is known to occur.

The earliest of the few dated Wiltshire records was 3 August 1983 on the southern edge of Red Lodge Plantation (Paul Mapplebeck) and the latest was 15 October 1989 at Somerford Common (Roger Perkins).

Distribution
The brown hairstreak is widely distributed throughout southern Britain, its main strongholds being in north Devon, Somerset, south-west Wales, West Sussex and Surrey. There are a few other scattered populations in England and one on the west coast of Ireland.

At the time of writing there appear to be only two centres of population in Wiltshire. One is in the Braydon Forest area in the north of the county and the other is a population in the south straddling the Wiltshire/Hampshire border which covers the area around Cholderton, Tidworth and Porton Down. This population is believed to be centred in Hampshire but some females spread into Wiltshire when searching for egg-laying sites.

Braydon Forest
Remnants of this north Wiltshire forest on heavy clay survive as a group of woodlands and meadows between Minety and Brinkworth. They are linked by bridleways, footpaths and many hedgerows where blackthorn is frequent.

The first published record for the area appeared in Roy Pitman's 1936 report where Webb's Wood was listed. In 1964, Lieut Col Charles Cowan found females in two places between Wootton Bassett and Minety.

There were a few more records from this area during the late 1960s and several in the late 1970s when Dr Tom Tolman carried out extensive egg searches (BRC). During the 1980s, a few chance sightings of adults by recorders were reported. In the winter of 1984–85, Jeremy Fraser found 31 eggs in Somerford Common. Their distribution suggested that the colony was of a much lower density than in some other parts of the country where counts had also been made. In the winter of 1994–95, John Grearson organised a search and 17 eggs were found. In early 1989 the author set out to update Tolman's records and to establish the extent of the population. Most of Tolman's records were confirmed and a wider search revealed that this butterfly was using most woodlands and hedgerows in the area for ovipositing. Eggs were located from Flisteridge Wood in the west to Brockhurst Wood near Purton in the east. The most southerly egg was discovered under power lines in Flaxlands Wood. The northern limit was believed to be Upper Minety but, early in 1994, an egg was found on a blackthorn hedge at Ashton Keynes (C Tracey). This increased the known range of the brown hairstreak in the Braydon Forest area to 9 km from north to south and 8 km from east to west. During the winter of 1993–94 an egg was found over the border in Gloucestershire, the first record for that county (Matthew Oates).

Records of adults have been received during the last three or four years mainly from Somerford Common, Red Lodge Plantation and Ravensroost Wood. These are probably the three areas where the butterflies congregate and mate prior to the females dispersing into the surrounding area to lay their eggs. It is not known whether the area supports one widespread population or perhaps three or four overlapping colonies centred on the major woodlands.

Tidworth and Cholderton

This may have been the 'Sarum' locality referred to by Rev Francis Morris in 1853. However, Pitman was not aware of this locality when he stated in 1936 'rare in the county but easily overlooked'.

In his 1954 diary he stated that his colleague Dr Allan Davies 'has been to Tidworth for *Betulae* 'beating' and got nine larvae about half fed or less' and 'Davies has taken more female *Betulae* from near Shipton Bellinger'. Surprisingly, there are no further references to this species in his diaries. According to Cowan the brown hairstreak was certainly known in the area in 1964 when he wrote 'I saw only males near Tidworth in the well-known localities in South Wilts. and Hants'. Tolman searched this area for eggs in the late 1970s and 1980. Most of his findings have been substantiated in the last few years by Oates in Hampshire and by the author in Wiltshire. The distribution map shows that this population extends from near Everleigh to Porton Down, a distance of 18 km, and from Bulford Camp to Abbots Ann in Hampshire, a distance of 15 km. This population may consist of one or several colonies.

There have been some interesting sightings of adults. In 1987, a dead specimen was found in a garden conservatory at Newton Tony and in 1991 one was seen nectaring in the same garden (Daphne Graiff). In 1990, seven adults were observed on woolly thistles and, in 1991 in the same area, nine females were feeding on creeping thistles and a single male was seen low down on blackthorn foliage (Henry Edmunds). Observations of groups of this species are very rare.

A so-called 'master tree' may have been found in 1993 (Humphrey Kay). The author visited the site on 30 August and saw at least five adults near the top of 16 closely grouped small ash trees. Two brown hairstreaks were also seen at each of two isolated ash trees 30 metres away but none was seen along considerable lengths of blackthorn hedgerows. Similar numbers were seen in mid-August 1994. The author considers that this is a 'congregation area' for the butterflies in which several trees are involved. There may, of course, be similar places elsewhere where they gather amongst this widespread population.

The Marlborough District

Morris, who was the first to mention Wiltshire localities in 1853, stated 'near Great Bedwyn and

Sarum'. Presumably his source was J W Lukis. In 1860, William Coleman listed Wiltshire among 24 localities and in 1869 Edward Newman reported it 'as having been taken near Great Bedwyn and in West Woods'. Edward Meyrick recorded one female in the Marlborough district on 28 August 1873 and Neville Manders, aged 15, took one at Stype Wood on 31 August 1874. The last nineteenth century record from this area was that of a Mr Coleman who described it as being plentiful on 6 August 1880. He was the only recorder to mention the sighting of more than one individual. In 1982, 102 years later, Dr Peter Brough found eggs in Savernake Forest near the A4. However, independent searches by the author, Martin Warren and Jack Coates have proved unsuccessful and it is considered that the species no longer occurs in the neighbourhood.

Burderop Wood

Geoffrey Webber first recorded a brown hairstreak near Burderop Wood on 9 September 1978 and later found a single egg. In the winter of 1985–86 he found two more eggs and saw one adult in 1986. The author carried out unsuccessful egg searches in 1988 and 1989 and there have been no records from this area since those of Webber in 1986.

Other Localities in South Wiltshire

Pitman's records from Grovely and Barford St Martin, given in his 1936 report, have not been confirmed and no records of the species from the Salisbury area are included in his diaries from 1928 until 1983.

In 1958, Ian Heslop stated that he had taken caterpillars 'some years ago' at the southern end of Blackmoor Copse and he recorded the brown hairstreak from Whiteparish Common prior to 1957. In 1962 Baron de Worms gave Pitman as his source for records from near Redlynch in 1937 and 1957 but these were probably from Pitman's colleague Alfred Burras. None of these records has been substantiated during the WBMS in spite of the author's egg searches in apparently suitable habitat.

Future Prospects

The future for this species in the county, although not assured, may not be imminently threatened provided some very simple hedgerow management is understood and implemented by landowners in the two areas of population. Jeremy Thomas's detailed ecological study of this species has shown that eggs are laid on 2–3 year old twigs. Hedge trimming during the winter may therefore be catastrophic. It is now recommended that hedges are cut on a three year rotation after cutting of one third in the first year and another third in the two following years. Provided that this regime is adopted the brown hairstreak should survive in its two remaining localities but, if it is not, the future for the species is bleak.

During the WBMS (1982–94) it was recorded from 39 tetrads (4%) but from only 35 (3.7%) since 1987 and it is considered very unlikely that further populations will be discovered. The four tetrads for which the only records were between 1982 and 1986 are shown on the map as dotted circles.

Map 23. Distribution of brown hairstreak

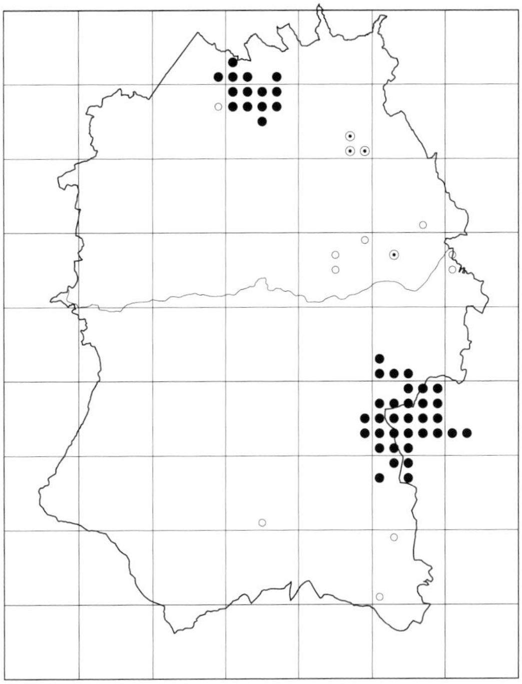

PURPLE HAIRSTREAK
Quercusia quercus (Linnaeus)

The generic name *Quercusia*, given to the purple hairstreak by Verity in 1943, is derived from the specific name *quercus*, which was given to the species by Linnaeus in 1758 and refers to the generic name of oak, the only larval foodplant.

The species was discovered by John Ray in Essex but was first described by his friend James Petiver in 1702 who named it 'Mr Ray's purple Streak'. In 1720 Eleazer Albin named it the purple hairstreak.

The purple is the commonest of the three woodland hairstreaks. The upper surface of the male's wings (see Ian Grear's inset photograph on page 69) alternates between appearing black and deep purple. The female is less colourful, deep purple being restricted to a patch on the lower half of the forewings as shown in Christine Tracey's photograph. The underwings of both sexes are silvery grey with a white streak crossing each. There is an orange eye-spot with a black pupil near the tiny black tail on the lower wing which can be seen in Graham Wall's photograph on page 69 of a male on an oak twig. Thomas and Lewington (1991) describe how males,

when they become active in the tree-tops, engage in 'prolonged aerial battles ... from below, they look like a handful of silver coins tossed into the sunlight'. With the aid of binoculars correct identification should not be too difficult.

Nectaring takes place in the tree canopy where honeydew, excreted by aphids, is so readily accessible on the leaves that the hairstreaks need do no more than walk to find a continuous supply, wearing down their tails as they go. In July 1983, the author observed ten feeding on aspen (*Populus tremula*) beneath oak trees (*Quercus* spp.). The leaves were stuck together with honeydew and the butterflies inserted their proboscides between the leaves to feed.

The greyish-white eggs are laid singly beneath oak flower-buds at all heights and on the sunny side of the trees. The caterpillar develops within three weeks and overwinters inside the egg, On emerging in April it eats part of its eggshell before boring into an opening flower-bud to feed. Later it spins a cocoon at the base of the bud from which

A male purple hairstreak among oak leaves on a lichen-covered twig.
INSET *A very fresh male displaying his purple-sheened wings in the sunshine.*

it emerges at night to feed on young leaves. Pupation has been shown to take place in ants' nests which Thomas suggests is likely to be the case for every purple hairstreak.

The Flight Period

The butterflies are on the wing from mid-July to the end of August, numbers usually peaking at the end of July. Even in areas where they are common, only one or two may be seen before the early evening when, if conditions are calm, warm and sunny, large numbers may be found flying erratically around the treetops, chasing one another and 'dancing' together.

During evening monitoring in Picket Wood near Westbury the longest flight period observed during the 14 years was nine weeks in 1992 and the shortest five weeks in 1989. The maximum weekly number of individuals counted on the transect varied from 204 in July 1992 to 44 in August 1988 and July 1993. The earliest date on which a butterfly was seen was 26 June 1992 and the latest 2 September 1991. The diagram shows a typical flight period pattern.

The dates of 30 May 1917 and 8 June 1887, stated in Marlborough College reports, are considered to be errors and the earliest accepted date is 30 June 1893, an exceptionally early year for many species.

Measures of Abundance 1981–94

Daytime transect walks are not suitable as a method for assessing the abundance of this species because of the butterfly's elusive habits. In a good season, the purple hairstreak population in Picket Wood, a 65 hectare (160 acre) woodland consisting of belts of oaks and conifers, probably numbers several 1,000 adults and yet, during a casual daytime

Flight period at Picket Wood in 1982

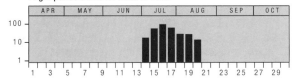

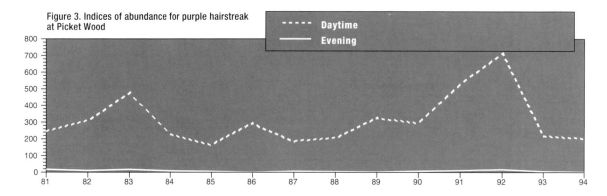

Figure 3. Indices of abundance for purple hairstreak at Picket Wood

- - - - Daytime
——— Evening

walk, seldom would any be seen. In order to assess the fluctuations in abundance of the population in this wood, early evening transect walks, starting at 6.30pm and lasting for about one hour, have been carried out since 1981 specifically to monitor this species. Timed observations of 30 seconds were made at strategic oak trees adjacent to the main ride.

The large difference in the apparent abundance of the species between daytime and evening transect walks is shown in Figure 3 and Table 8. The values suggest that there is a correlation between the two and it may be that for this hairstreak the daytime transect walk has some value even when only small numbers are involved. A period of 14 years is too short to be certain but, in the longer term, monitoring may show this to be true.

The annual fluctuations in abundance during the 14 year period have been large. Values ranged

from 166 in 1985 to 712 in 1992. In 1994, the value of 206 was significantly below the average 14 year value of 314.

Status Before 1982

The first published Wiltshire record of the purple hairstreak was that of the Rev Francis Morris who, in 1853, stated 'near Great Bedwyn and Sarum it likewise occurs, but not commonly there'. This entry was included in the 1865 Marlborough College List. On 23 August 1866 it was taken in West Woods. In the 1873 College List it was said to be very common, occasionally common in 1935 and quite common in 1956. Roy Pitman rarely mentioned the species in his diaries. An entry in 1928 stated 'Mr [Harry] Haynes says it can be taken at Castle Hill. A long-handled net is required as the insects fly high in the oaks'. In his 1936 report he described it as 'occasionally common in oak woods and fairly well distributed in the county'. Bowmont Weddell did not mention the purple hairstreak from the Trowbridge area in any of his diaries during the period 1932–78 although, no doubt, it was as common an insect in the local woodlands during that time as it is today. In 1962 Baron de Worms stated that it was generally common in oak woods.

Status Since 1982

The purple hairstreak is widespread over much of southern England and Wales but much more local in northern England, Scotland and Ireland. In spite of its general abundance in the south it has probably been one the most overlooked and

Table 8. Indices of abundance for purple hairstreak at Picket Wood

Year	Daytime	Evening
1981	17	244
1982	10	305
1983	17	478
1984	8	229
1985	5	166
1986	0	290
1987	6	186
1988	4	205
1989	2	324
1990	7	295
1991	12	534
1992	18	712
1993	6	218
1994	1	206

under-recorded of all British species, until fairly recently when its evening flight habit was more widely known, although it probably continues to be very under-recorded in many areas. This is certainly the case in Wiltshire if, as is suspected, the author's studies in the mid-west and other areas of the county are typical.

Touring suitable localities in the early evenings in July has shown this butterfly to be present, often in large numbers, in most of the tetrads around Trowbridge, Chippenham, Westbury, Savernake and Ramsbury. Colonies have been found on almost all mature oak trees inspected including isolated ones in hedgerows, those close to habitation and even in coniferous woodlands provided a few oaks are present. Many of the colonies on isolated trees, which are probably survivors from the time when the county was much more heavily wooded, have probably been self-contained on that same tree for many years. At every stop, butterflies could be seen flying around the treetops and, although positive identification was not always possible, there was no mistaking the hairstreak characteristics.

The butterfly has been recorded, usually in ones and twos, from other parts of the county where the author has not carried out evening surveys. There are populations in the Braydon Forest area, the wooded areas around Castle Combe and Bowood, in small woods and copses near Devizes, woodlands in the Warminster area and adjacent to the Somerset border.

It is probably abundant in the south-eastern corner of the county and far more widespread in woodlands on Cranborne Chase, on the Dorset border and along the Nadder Valley than the distribution map indicates.

It occurs widely in Grovely and Great Ridge Woods in the south. The lack of records from Salisbury Plain, the Marlborough Downs and the downland areas in the extreme south of the county where suitable oak is scarce, probably reflects the true absence of the species from these areas. The few tetrads in the Swindon area from which records have been received are unlikely to be a true reflection of the scarcity of the species there.

The map, although incomplete, does indicate the species' widespread distribution in the county.

The concentration of records in certain areas is mainly the result of recorder activity and the author's early evening observations. During the WBMS (1982–94) the purple hairstreak was recorded from 229 tetrads (24%).

Future Prospects

This species could become far more restricted to woodland in the future as the ageing oaks along lanes, byways and hedgerows disappear. Modern methods of hedge trimming are unlikely to help the situation. Unless there is oak regeneration nearby, isolated colonies are doomed to extinction since purple hairstreaks rarely stray from their home trees and are unlikely to colonise others more than about 50 metres away. Those hedgerow saplings which are allowed to survive are mainly of ash and elm, the faster growing tree species. Although purple hairstreaks are often reported from these trees where they are growing near oaks, they are being used for perching or for obtaining honeydew but not for breeding.

Map 24. Distribution of purple hairstreak

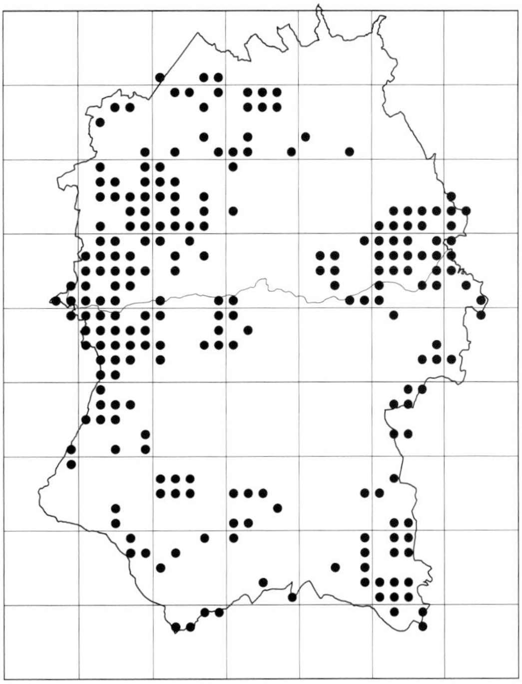

WHITE-LETTER HAIRSTREAK
Satyrium w-album (Knoch)

The generic name *Satyrium*, given to the white-letter hairstreak by Scudder in 1876, possibly means a satyr, a mythical being which engaged in voluptuous dances with the nymphs, referring to the sprightly flight of the butterflies. Alternatively, the name could be derived from a plant which was used as an aphrodisiac. The specific name *w-album*, given by Knoch in 1782, describes the white (*albus*) w-shaped line on the underside of the hindwing.

James Petiver first mentioned this butterfly in 1703 naming it 'The Hair-streak'. For the next 200 years the name of this species and that of the much rarer black hairstreak became intertwined and much confusion over identification ensued. It was not until 1896 that William F Kirby gave the species its present name.

The white-letter is the smallest, least colourful and the most elusive of the hairstreaks. This butterfly always rests and feeds with its wings closed. The underwings are dark brown and crossed by a single white streak which ends in a W pattern near the

bottom of the lower wings as shown in Guy Broome's photograph. The only bright colour is an orange band on the lower wings which is outlined with black, which extends into a tail.

This hairstreak, like the brown and purple, nectars mainly on aphid honeydew which it takes from the leaves in the tree canopy. It also takes nectar from herbaceous plants, creeping thistle (*Cirsium arvense*) and hemp-agrimony (*Eupatorium cannabinum*) being most frequently visited. Old individuals seldom have tails, these being worn away as the butterflies crawl over leaves and flowers to gather honeydew and nectar.

The sea-green eggs are laid singly, most frequently at the base of a bud, often a terminal flower bud, on elm (*Ulmus* spp.) but preferably on wych elm (*U. glabra*). They become dark brown within a few days. The fully developed caterpillar remains within the egg throughout the winter and hatches as the flower buds open in late March. At first it feeds on the flowers, then moves to the underside of the leaves as they open to chew holes between the leaf veins in a characteristic pattern. The chrysalis anchors itself by a girdle either to a twig or the underside of a leaf.

The Flight Period

The butterflies are on the wing during July and early August but are seldom seen, even near trees which are known to support a colony, except where a favoured nectar source is close at hand. They occasionally take short flights from the foliage before returning to rest or feed. From a distance the general appearance in profile is dark and triangular compared with the much brighter and more rounded shape of the purple hairstreak but worn specimens can be mistaken for purple hairstreaks and vice versa. Because of its elusiveness, no details of the flight period or levels of abundance are available. The earliest record of a sighting was 23 June 1976 (Barbara Cowley) but no location was given (WAM). The latest date was 31 August 1986 from Colerne Park Wood (Stephen Chamberlain).

Status Before 1982

The first published county record from Littlecote on 11 August appeared in the 1873 Marlborough College Report. In 1874 Neville Manders reported it from Stype, Marlborough and Thrup, the earliest being on 7 July. In the 1883 List it was stated to be 'moderately common, round the tops of trees' and in subsequent Lists it was described as locally common. In 1893 Charles Barrett wrote 'but its metropolis seems to be in Wiltshire, where Mr R C L Perkins has found it around Marlborough and Savernake in thousands'. Richard South repeated Barrett's comments in 1906.

In 1932, Bowmont Weddell bred white-letter hairstreaks in Trowbridge from local stock obtained by beating elm trees and catching the dislodged caterpillars on a sheet or 'beating tray'. He retained perfect specimens for his collection and released the rest into suitable habitat. This butterfly was probably one of his favourite species judging by the number of entries in his diaries concerning his breeding successes. His last entry was on 22 July 1969 when he saw one in his Trowbridge garden.

In the Dauntsey School Fauna List this butterfly was described as being fairly common in the area in 1934 which agreed with Roy Pitman's comments in his 1936 report: 'a very erratic insect, occasionally locally common as in 1934, when in some districts it swarmed. May be said to be well distributed in the county'. Pitman's first diary entry for this species was on 17 May 1946 and reads 'went for w-album larvae but wind spoilt beating, got about two dozen. Best trees are the Wych Elm with seed on'. His last reference to the species would appear to be in 1964 when he said it was disappearing in the Clarendon district due to the removal of wych elms.

In 1962 Baron de Worms quoted Weddell: 'fairly common in the county where wych-elm flourishes'. He added that the species was very plentiful near Lydiard Millicent in 1934 (P Harrison) and abundant in 1934 at Chute (Freer). From the mid-1930s to the mid-1970s there were records from the BRC and WANHS from widely separated parts of the county especially in the very hot, dry summers of 1975 and 1976 when there appears to have been a population explosion. Records for which no exact location was given have not been included on the distribution map. Many of these earlier records were of casual sightings.

Records Since 1982

The white-letter hairstreak is widely distributed in England and Wales as far north as Yorkshire. It is absent from Scotland and Ireland. It has always been a very local butterfly forming discrete colonies on groups of elms or on a single tree. Following the ravages of Dutch elm disease in the 1970s, it is probably much scarcer now than formerly although it is likely that it has always been under-recorded both in Wiltshire and elsewhere. Its former distribution, and its current status, are no doubt far from complete.

Details of all the records received from a total of 47 localities during the WBMS (1982–94) are given in Table 9. Sightings were mainly of singletons. In 1985, and in the years 1991–94 which were good for the species, small groups were seen at some sites although rarely in double figures. The white-letter

Table 9. Localities in which the white-letter hairstreak was recorded during the WBMS (1982–94), excluding 1982 and 1988, when there were no records for this species

Year	Number of localities	New localities in each year
1983	6	Black Dog Woods Chute Cadley Brown's Folly Slaughterford Red Lodge Plantation Cholderton
1984	4	Codford Marlborough Near Sopworth West Woods
1985	9	Savernake Forest Hazelbury Common Dunley Wood Sandridge Danks Down West Yatton Down Pinkney Picket Wood
1986	3	Colerne Park Wood Clanger Wood
1987	3	Lydiard Millicent
1989	3	Limpley Stoke Bentley Wood Somerford Common
1990	3	Nil
1991	10	Roundway Hill Covert Ravensroost Wood Distillery Farm near Minety Vagg's Hill
1992	11	Hodson Green Lane Wood KAC towpath at Bradford-on-Avon Near Green Lane Wood Zeals Bedwyn Common Coate Water Brokerswood Ditchampton
1993	14	Leigh Hill, Savernake Malmesbury Corsham Bradford-on-Avon Alderbury Near Blackmoor Copse
1994	10	Devizes Upper Minety Savernake Forest Newton Tony

Table 10. Distribution of white-letter hairstreak colonies

	North Wiltshire	South Wiltshire	Total
Pre 1982	23	22	45
1982–1994	34	13	47
Total	57	35	92

hairstreak was chosen as Wiltshire's 'Butterfly of the Year' in 1993 because of its greatly improved status.

There was a sighting at Roundway Hill Covert in August 1991, ten years and one day after the previous sighting there, and three adults were seen in 1994 (Beatrice Gillam). The 1989 record from Bentley Wood updates that of 1981 (BRC). The record from Picket Wood in 1985 (Nick Wynn) updates the author's 1978 sighting since when the species has been recorded from the wood in most years. A strong colony near the southern edge of Savernake Forest in 1985 was found when a non-entomologist took wych elm sprays home and found caterpillars on the leaves. These were identified as those of the white-letter hairstreak by Jeremy Fraser, who visited the location on 3 June and found six caterpillars on two trees about ten metres apart. In 1986, Martin Warren found numerous eggs and caterpillars in the spring and two adults on 4 August. In 1987, Guy Broome visited the colony and photographed a butterfly on brambles near the wych elms. In August 1993, at least six butterflies were observed in Red Lodge Plantation feeding on creeping thistles growing beneath young wych elms. In 1994, eggs were found on those trees which flowered profusely in the spring. Young caterpillars were located feeding among the flowers and on 11 June fully grown caterpillars and chrysalises were found (Gillam). The brief sighting of an adult on an elm-sucker hedge at Lydiard Millicent on 25 July 1987 (Ian Young) updates Harrison's record from this area 53 years earlier.

The approximate numbers of white-letter hairstreak colonies located in the north and south of the county pre and post 1982 are shown in Table 10. The increase since 1982 and the concentration of records in the north-west may be a reflection of recorder activity. However, the distribution map of the main larval foodplant, the wych elm, shows a concentration of this tree in the north.

Future Prospects

Following the drastic loss of elm trees in the 1970s, there was great concern among lepidopterists that this little butterfly would rapidly decline, possibly to the point of extinction. It was believed that flowering elms, especially wych elms, were essential for the young caterpillars and, without mature flowering trees, the species was doomed. Studies into its ecological requirements were initiated and it was discovered that colonies, although probably much reduced in size, were surviving on immature non-flowering elm sucker re-growth throughout the butterfly's range. It is a matter for debate as to how long this situation will continue since the elm re-growth, when roughly 12 years old, is reinfected with Dutch elm disease and many trees throughout the county were dying in the early 1990s. Caterpillars hatching from eggs laid on dying elms will obviously perish. Only eggs laid on younger elm growth that has not yet succumbed to the disease will have any chance of survival. Therefore, it seems likely that the future of this species depends on a succession of various-aged elm sucker re-growth so that the females are able to lay at least a proportion of their eggs on healthy elm. This is not, it would seem, a recipe for success, and yet the species has probably survived in this way since the mid 1970s.

Henry Edmunds recalled seeing a group of about twelve butterflies flying around the dying crowns of elm trees near Cholderton. Suddenly they gathered together above the trees and flew off to a neighbouring wood in which there were some healthy elms. It was as if they had somehow sensed that the trees were dying and that they had to go elsewhere to lay their eggs. This observation suggests that the white-letter hairstreak is not as sedentary as has often been stated and that, if it is able to survive on non-flowering elms, its future is not as bleak as had been predicted.

It is doubtful if the county status of this widespread and yet very local butterfly will ever be established unless a dedicated team of recorders is organised to search the widely scattered remaining elms for the egg and caterpillar stages, which are considered to be easier to find, for confirmation of the species' presence than relying on chance sightings of the very elusive adults. However, many suitable branches are well out of reach of even the most dedicated searcher!

During the WBMS (1982–94) the white-letter hairstreak was recorded from 46 tetrads (4.8%).

Map 25. Distribution of wych elm

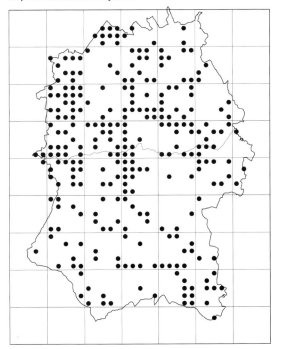

Map 26. Distribution of white-letter hairstreak

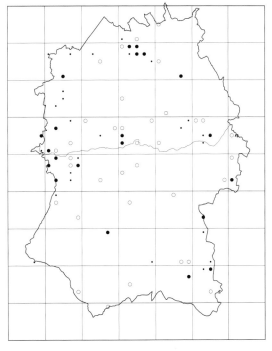

SMALL COPPER
Lycaena phlaeas (Linnaeus)

The generic name *Lycaena* was given to the small copper by Fabricius in 1807. Its derivation is not clear but it may come from a word meaning a 'she-wolf' or 'Lycia'. The derivation of the specific name *phlaeas*, given by Linnaeus in 1761, may originate from a word meaning 'to blaze up', referring to the ground colour of the butterfly's wings.

In 1699, James Petiver described it as 'The small golden black-spotted Meadow Butterfly' and in 1766 Moses Harris illustrated it as 'the Copper'. William Lewin named it the 'Small Copper' in 1795 and, although several other names were proposed, this is the name that has survived. This butterfly's habit of basking with wings wide open makes for easy identification. Graham Wall's photograph is of a female. Common fleabane (*Pulicaria dysenterica*) growing in damp places is the favourite source of nectar. Elsewhere, ragwort (*Senecio* spp.), yarrow (*Achillea millefolium*), marjoram (*Origanum vulgare*) and field scabious (*Knautia arvensis*) are commonly used. The female

lays her greyish-white eggs singly on leaves of common sorrel (*Rumex acetosa*) or sheep's sorrel (*R. acetosella*). The caterpillar emerges within two weeks and feeds on the young leaves. The chrysalis has yet to be observed in the wild but Thomas (1991) suspects that some may 'form an association with ants'.

The Flight Period
There are usually two generations but, in years when the weather is favourable, a third occurs in late September and early October. The first appears during late May and early June and the second, which usually occurs in much larger numbers, is to be seen from late July. Two flight period patterns in Picket Wood are shown in the diagram. That for 1980 is for a typical year and that for 1989 illustrates the population explosion in the late summer and autumn. During 15 years of monitoring in the wood, the longest flight period was 19 weeks in 1990 and the shortest was 6 weeks in 1987 and 1993. The maximum number

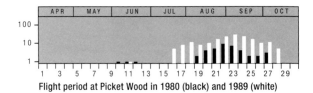

Flight period at Picket Wood in 1980 (black) and 1989 (white)

of individuals counted in a week on the transect varied from 29 in September 1989 to two in 1985. The earliest sighting was 13 May 1982 and the latest 8 October 1990. The earliest county record of 25 April 1869 appears in a Marlborough College List.

Measures of Abundance 1980–94 (Figure 14)

There were peaks in abundance in 1982 and 1984 and a very large increase in 1989. During that year, the small copper was extremely common throughout the county and there were certainly three, probably four, generations in some areas. It was chosen as the 'Butterfly of the Year' in Wiltshire. In favoured habitats numbers were phenomenal and Godfrey Smith, who has been observing butterflies in the county since the 1940s, said he had never known such a population explosion. Within two years numbers had slumped to very low levels at all monitored sites and, by 1994, they were well below average except at Picket Wood.

Status Before 1982

The first published Wiltshire record of the small copper appears in the 1865 Marlborough College List. J H Johnson also recorded it in May 1866. It was considered to be 'usually common' in all subsequent Lists. Roy Pitman recorded the small copper near Salisbury in May 1928. In his 1936 report he described it as 'very common in most parts of the county. Swarmed in 1933 until the last week of November'. Bowmont Weddell reported it near Trowbridge in May 1933 and in 1962 Baron de Worms described it as 'generally distributed and often common in the late summer'.

Status Since 1982

The small copper is widely distributed throughout Great Britain and Ireland. It is found in a variety of warm, dry habitats such as sunny woodland rides and clearings, flowery grassland, disused railway lines, waste places colonised by wild plants and some roadside verges. During the period of the WBMS (1982–94), the small copper was widely reported and it can still be considered a common, but thinly distributed, species and rarely abundant. It was recorded from 488 tetrads (51%).

Future Prospects

The small copper may become less common and more localised if the prevailing attitude for tidiness of some farmers, gardeners and local authorities continues to destroy its habitats and larval foodplants. However, it is obviously a resilient species and able to thrive when conditions are favourable as was shown in 1989.

Map 27. Distribution of small copper

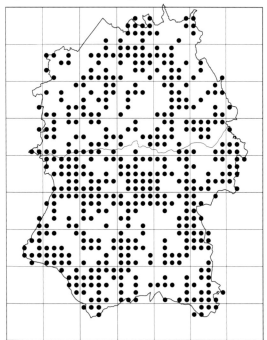

SMALL BLUE
Cupido minimus (Fuessly)

The generic name *Cupido*, given to the small blue by Schrank in 1801, refers to Cupid or Eros, the god of love. The specific name *minimus*, given by Fuessly in 1775, means 'the smallest'.

This butterfly was first illustrated by William Lewin in 1795 who named it the 'Small Blue'. Although the names 'Bedford blue' and 'little blue' have been used in the past the original name has prevailed.

The average wing-span of this, the smallest British butterfly, is about 22 mm but the size of individuals is very variable. For a few days after emerging, the uniformly dark upper side of the wings is fringed with white as illustrated in Richard Tambling's photograph, inset on page 79. The sexes are not easily distinguished although, unlike the dark brown of the female, the smoky-black wings of the male usually have some blue scales at their base. The pale silvery blue-grey underwings have tiny black dots, ringed with white, most of them arranged in a curving line parallel to the wing edges Ian Grier's photograph

(above) of a mating pair shows these underwing markings.

Males congregate in warm, sheltered spots to bask with wings half open, alert and ready to investigate passing insects in their search for virgin females. Although nectar is collected mainly from the three yellow-flowered members of the pea family, common bird's-foot-trefoil (*Lotus corniculatus*), horseshoe vetch (*Hippocrepis comosa*) and kidney vetch (*Anthyllis vulneraria*), the author saw about ten butterflies on privet flowers (*Ligustrum* spp.) in a disused chalk quarry in June 1985.

The greenish-white eggs are laid singly in kidney vetch flowerheads, the female carefully selecting the calyx of an unopened bud. By the time the caterpillar emerges, the seeds on which it feeds will have developed within the calyx. By late July, when the seeds begin to fall, the fully-grown caterpillar descends to the ground where it remains until April or May before pupating for about two weeks attached to a silk pad.

Kidney vetch, the only larval foodplant of the small blue, growing in profusion on Hadden Hill near Grovely Wood.
INSET *A freshly emerged butterfly showing the wings' fine white fringes.*

The Flight Period

Small blues emerge in mid-May and are usually on the wing until the end of June, numbers peaking in late May. They are not active unless the temperature exceeds 15°C. In favourable seasons there may be a small partial second generation in late July and early August, an occurrence observed at Bratton Castle Earthworks in only four of the 15 years of monitoring. Sightings were of singletons except in 1989 when second generation numbers peaked at higher levels than the first, a most unusual occurrence. The flight period pattern for a year in which a second generation occurred is shown below. At this site, the longest flight period recorded was ten weeks in 1989 and the shortest was four weeks in 1994.

Flight period at Bratton Castle Earthworks in 1982

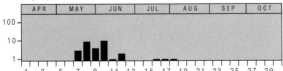

The maximum weekly number of individuals seen on the transect varied from 14 in May 1987 to one in May 1991. The earliest sighting was 10 May 1990 and the latest 4 September 1986, a very late date. The earliest known county date was 30 April 1990 at Boscombe Down (Stephen Palmer).

Measures of Abundance 1980–94 (Figure 15)

There have been some dramatic fluctuations in levels of abundance at the three monitored sites. They may be related to the erratic flowering of the kidney vetch, the only larval foodplant. During the early part of the flight period in May and early June the weather is often unsettled and cool and is probably a major factor contributing to the number of butterflies seen of this, and other, small and inconspicuous species. The peaks in abundance coincided at Pewsey Downs and Bratton Castle Earthworks in 1982 and 1987 but in most years there was little correlation between the values at the two sites. Numbers at all three sites were low in 1992 and rose in the following two years but, in 1994, were below the site averages at Pewsey Downs and Bratton Castle Earthworks but significantly above at Boscombe Down where the value was at its highest since monitoring began in 1989.

Status Before 1982

The Rev Francis Morris was the first to publish a Wiltshire record. In 1853 he listed many localities including 'near Great Bedwyn and Sarum, Wiltshire, in isolated places near woods, as J W Lukis Esq has informed me, as likewise near Amesbury'. It was stated to be 'abundant in Clatford Bottom' in the 1865 Marlborough College List and was recorded on 28 May 1866 by J H Johnson. It was included in the 1873 College List from Mildenhall and West Woods and in all subsequent Lists it was described as locally common.

It was included in the Rev T B Eddrupp's 1899 list from near Calne and E Cook's 1902 list for the Devizes district. The Rev C A Sladen found it generally distributed along the foot of the downs

at Alton Barnes in June 1901 and, later that year, in perfect condition in August. He commented 'must have been a second brood'.

Roy Pitman took specimens at Odstock in June 1928 and in 1936 he described it as 'common on the chalk downs, especially in south Wilts where a second brood is usual during August and September'. The Dauntsey School Fauna Lists of 1931–48 described it as fairly common on Salisbury Plain and Bowmont Weddell reported it from Bratton in June 1932. In 1962 Baron de Worms repeated Pitman's 1936 comments but, by 1964, Pitman considered that it was less common than formerly.

Status Since 1982

The small blue occurs mainly on the Chalk and Limestone in the south of Great Britain although there are a few, mainly isolated, colonies in the north of England and in Scotland. The populations in Ireland are mainly in coastal districts. In Wiltshire it is a widely distributed butterfly and often common in its favoured habitats, especially

Map 28. Distribution of kidney vetch

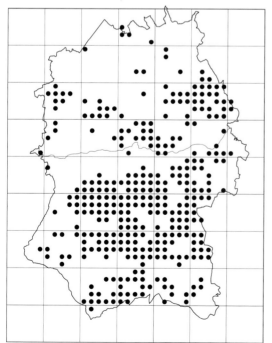

Map 29. Distribution of small blue

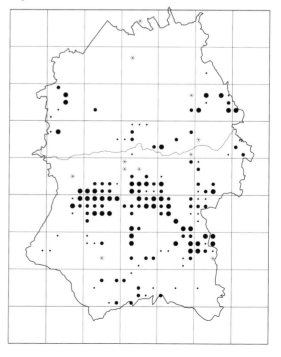

Table 11. An assessment of the number of colonies in the county

Locality	Number of colonies	%
North Wiltshire	30	16
South Wiltshire excluding SPTA and Porton Down	52	28
SPTA(W) Imber	35	19
SPTA(C) Larkhill/West Down	42	23
SPTA(E) Bulford/Tidworth	16	9
Porton Down	10	5
Total number of colonies	185	

on Porton Down and SPTA. As with several other species, the number of colonies on these large areas of uninterrupted chalk grassland is difficult to assess in some years. For example, in 1994 the butterflies were abundant and not restricted to specific sites but were found throughout both areas. It could be argued that there is just one large population at each which, in years of scarcity, becomes restricted to particularly favoured sites. Table 11 shows the estimated number of colonies known in the county since 1982 based on the assumption that, on Porton Down and SPTA, there is one colony in each 1 km square from which a record was received. This estimation indicates that 103 colonies (63%) occur at these two localities and highlights their importance for small blues.

Breeding colonies of the small blue are restricted to areas where its larval foodplant grows which, in its turn, is restricted to calcareous soils. Kidney vetch is widely distributed on Wiltshire's Chalk and Limestone. Its distribution and that of the small blue are very similar (Maps 28 and 29). Both are more frequent in the south than the north as shown in Table 11. Downland, such as that at Hadden Hill near Grovely Wood where the larval foodplant flourishes, is a typical habitat for small blues and is shown in Barbara Last's photograph on page 79.

On the Chalk, in the north-east there are nine colonies in the Aldbourne and Baydon area (George Osmond et al.), three near Shalbourne (Jack Coates) and several populations on the downs north of the Vale of Pewsey from Roundway Hill in the west to Martinsell Hill in the east. On the Limestone in the north-west, ten colonies have been found around Box and Castle Combe and two individuals were found on waste railway land at Chippenham in 1993 (John Tyler). In the south of the county, many grassland areas on the Chalk support the small blue and further colonies may be awaiting discovery.

In the south-west its apparent scarcity may be real since the most favoured sites have been well-visited and small blues have rarely been seen. In years when this butterfly is abundant, some occasionally wander from their colonies. These vagrants have been reported a long way from the nearest known colony. These long journeys are surprising for such a small, normally sedentary insect. The most remarkable records were the positive identification of two small blues on 27 July and one on 5 August 1989 at Somerford Common and one on 5 May at the Cotswold Water Park (Steve Covey). The nearest known Wiltshire colonies are at least 17 km distant but the larval foodplant grows within 4 km of both locations.

Future Prospects
Some colonies in the county have probably become extinct in the last 50 years due to habitat destruction, neglect or development. Two were known to have been destroyed during the WBMS in 1985 at Porton railway station due to development (Anthony Bedford-Russell). However, the small blue is a resilient species and, provided the kidney vetch continues to be a widespread plant, most of the colonies should survive. During the WBMS (1982–94) it was recorded from 156 tetrads (16%). Vagrants seen in 11 additional tetrads are included on the map.

SILVER-STUDDED BLUE
Plebejus argus (Linnaeus)

The generic name *Plebejus*, given to the silver-studded blue by Kluk in 1802, means 'belonging to the plebs', the Roman common people. The specific name *argus* was given by Linnaeus in 1758. Argus had 100 eyes and the name is a reference to the eye spots on the underside of the butterfly's wings. This butterfly may have been described by James Petiver in 1717 as 'The Small Lead Argus' but confusion with the names of other blue species has caused uncertainty. The first definite mention was that of Moses Harris in 1775 who gave it the name silver-studded blue which has survived to the present day.

This is the smallest of the bright blue butterflies which might be confused with the common blue where they occur in the same habitat. However, close inspection should make correct identification possible as the male's deep blue upperwings are bordered with black bands and have clear white fringes, shown in Peter Durnell's photograph on page 83. The silvery underwings are distinctive as is the orange band on the hindwing adjacent to a row of black eyespots containing the blue 'studs' which give the butterfly its name. Graham Wall's photograph (above), taken in the New Forest, clearly show these features. The female's upperwings are very similar to those of the brown argus while the background colour of the underwings is much browner and they have larger black eyespots than those of the male.

The white eggs are laid singly in July, most often on the woody parts of the larval foodplants, or on nearby plants, in areas that have been recently cleared or burnt and where there is bare earth amongst the vegetation. Various plants are used including heathers (*Calluna vulgaris*, *Erica* spp.), gorses (*Ulex* spp.), common bird's-foot-trefoil (*Lotus corniculatus*) and rock-roses (*Helianthemum* spp.). The eggs do not hatch until the following spring. The caterpillars only eat the tender young leaves and their sticky bodily secretions are very attractive to black ants (*Lasius niger*) which constantly attend them. Ants also attend the chrysalises, often burying them and occasionally

A male silver-studded blue on heather in the New Forest showing the black-bordered wings fringed with white. The markings of the female are very similar to those of the brown argus, without a trace of blue.

taking them into their nests. Silver-studded blues are very sedentary, remaining in small discrete colonies within the breeding areas except on some southern heaths where colonies consist of several thousand adults. The butterflies spend much of their time nectaring and crawling amongst the sparse vegetation. Their flight is short, fluttering and low over the ground.

In Great Britain, the silver-studded blue is mainly confined to southern heathlands, especially those in Dorset and Hampshire. A few colonies persist in Surrey, Sussex, parts of Suffolk, Norfolk and the south-west of England and one colony survives in north Shropshire. It is absent from the north of England, Scotland and Ireland and is very restricted in Wales.

The Flight Period

The butterflies usually emerge in late June on the New Forest heathlands and can be seen throughout July and most of August. No information is available on flight periods or abundance from any Wiltshire localities. The record in WAM for 3 June 1960 from the Salisbury Field Club, but without a locality being given, could have been of a sighting in Hampshire and is therefore not admissible as a Wiltshire record. The earliest acceptable date for a sighting in Wiltshire was 16 June 1989 when two males were seen at Landford Bog in the extreme south-east of the county (Humphrey Kay and Audrey Summers) and the latest date was 28 August 1991 when two males were seen nearby at Pound Bottom (Geoffrey Webber).

Records Before 1982

The first published Wiltshire record was that of the Rev Francis Morris who, in 1853, stated 'This fly is not uncommon near Sarum'. In 1860, William Coleman included Sarum in a list of 18 localities and, although it was not included in the 1873 Marlborough College List compiled by Edward Meyrick, then a college pupil, he stated that it was likely to be added. The report of a College Field Day to Stonehenge on 5 June 1893 Meyrick, who was by then a college master and president of the MCNHS, stated that 'the Silver-studded blue, which has not been taken nearer Marlborough was not uncommon'. In the 1921 List the species was recorded on 22 May by W P G Taylor, surprisingly without a comment by the compiler A W M Disney, since this was the first record for the Marlborough area. In the 1922 Report this fact was pointed out but no details of the location or the number captured were given. In all subsequent Lists, only the above record has been referred to with the additional comment 'once; Poulton Down'. The date is very early but it was noted that the season was one of 'excessive heat and drought, an extraordinary deficiency in the rainfall' and 'those species which should have appeared in June were 23 days early'. It is strange that enthusiasts such as Meyrick, Manders and Sladen, who seem to have scoured the area thoroughly, never came across this colonial species. This is the only record from the Marlborough area and is assumed to have been a case of mistaken identification and has not been mapped.

There was no mention of this species by Roy Pitman until his 1936 report in which he stated 'May be called rare as a Wiltshire insect ... However, on the Wilts-Hants borders near the New Forest it is locally common during July and August'. Bowmont Weddell did not mention the silver-studded blue in any of his 1932–78 diaries. Richard Thompson recalled taking a tatty male at Pepperbox Hill in the early 1950s which he assumed had been 'swept along the A36 by a lorry' from Plaitford Common a few miles to the south in Hampshire. In 1962 Baron de Worms listed most of the aforementioned records, adding 'near Collingbourne and at Bulford (Addison)'. These last two localities have not been mapped due to insufficient detail.

On 18 July 1975 a single specimen was caught and identified on SPTA(C) close to an area of heather (Rob Turner). This record has been mapped although there have been no further sightings from the area, to which access is limited. A singleton was seen in Picket Wood in 1979 (Godfrey and Michael Smith) but how it came to

Map 30. Distribution of heather

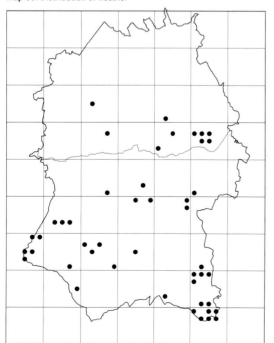

Map 31. Distribution of silver-studded blue

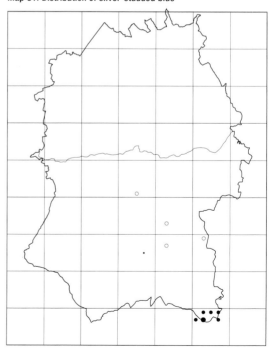

be there is a mystery. Neither this nor Thompson's record has been mapped since there is no evidence that colonies existed in these unlikely localities.

Records from the BRC have been scrutinised. Some have been rejected due to the suspect date, locality or record error. The entry for Great Durnford for 1981 (J M Guthrie) has been mapped although the record has not been confirmed. In 1980 or 1981 a small colony was known on the disused railway line near Newton Tony (Jim Buchanan). This record has been mapped but it is strange that there have been no reports from nearby Porton Down where a strong population might have been expected.

Records Since 1982

The silver-studded blue has always been very scarce in Wiltshire and, with one exception during the WBMS, it was only recorded from the New Forest heathland in the extreme south-eastern corner. In 1985, the author located colonies, with numbers fewer than five individuals in each, on Landford Common and near Lover. He also found a much stronger population near Pound Bottom on the Wiltshire/Hampshire border where, on 9 July, he counted 24 in 20 minutes.

All pre-1982 records were from calcareous sites and it is almost certain that none of these survive. However, in 1994 a singleton was caught, in order to identify it positively, on chalk grassland near Great Wishford (Steve Button). Whether this represented a small colony or was a vagrant is not known but none was seen during regular visits in the following weeks. If it was a vagrant it must have come from one of the New Forest populations 23 km to the south-east, a long journey for a very sedentary butterfly. If a colony is found on the Chalk it will be of national importance since, in the rest of England, all remaining populations are on heathland except for those on the Limestone on Portland Bill in Dorset and a few in Cornwall.

The map showing the distribution in Wiltshire of heather, one of the main larval foodplants, helps to explain why this butterfly is so rare in the county. The other heathland foodplants, cross-leaved heath (*Erica tetralix*) and bell heather (*E. cinerea*) are restricted entirely to the south-east corner. However, since other common and widespread foodplants are known to be used, particularly those that grow on Chalk and Limestone, it is perhaps surprising that the butterfly always appears to have been a county rarity.

Future Prospects

The two tiny colonies on Landford Common and near Lover are probably now extinct, having been eliminated by invading birch scrub and conifers. At Pound Bottom, where the species is probably part of a large Hampshire population, numbers are stable. The few individuals last reported from the Landford Bog WWT reserve in 1990, were probably vagrants from nearby areas or possibly the last remnants of a now extinct colony. Piers Mobsby has carried out a detailed study of the site and considers it unsuitable for the silver-studded blue. The status of the species in the county is unlikely to change and it will remain confined to one population in the south-eastern corner. During the WBMS (1982–94) it was recorded from seven tetrads (0.6%).

BROWN ARGUS
Aricia agestis ([Denis and Schiffermüller])

The generic name *Aricia*, an ancient town of Latium, is believed to have been given to the brown argus by Reichenbach of Leipzig in 1817. The specific name *agestis* was given by Denis and Schiffermüller in 1775. Its derivation is obscure but may have been a corruption of Argestes, the god of the north-west wind. James Petiver first described it in 1704 as 'The edg'd brown Argus' and in 1803 Adrian Hawarth gave it the present name of brown argus.

This is the only member of the 'blue' family which lacks blue coloration. The wings are uniformly rich brown with a narrow white fringe. The upperside has an inner border of orange lunules which are bolder on the larger females than on the males. At rest, particularly in worn specimens, both sexes may be confused with the female common blue. Richard Tambling's photograph is of a perching male. In flight, the reflection of sunlight on the pale underwings gives a silvery appearance similar to that of the small blue. Comparison of the pattern of the black dots on the underwings of this species and of the common blue can most easily be observed when the two are roosting together on grass flowerheads.

Nectaring has been noted at a variety of herbs in different habitats. Marjoram (*Origanum vulgare*) and devil's-bit scabious (*Succisa pratensis*) are particularly attractive where available but less specialised species are also visited including common bird's-foot-trefoil (*Lotus corniculatus*), black medick (*Medicago lupulina*), thistles (*Cirsium* and *Carduus* spp.) and knapweeds (*Centaurea* spp.). The greenish-white egg is usually laid on the underside of carefully selected fleshy leaves of common rockrose (*Helianthemum nummularium*) or, in its absence, on several species of crane's-bill (*Geranium*) including dove's-foot crane's-bill (*G. molle*). The caterpillar hatches within two weeks and eats part of the eggshell before chewing a hole on the underside of the leaf through which it enters to feed on the interior, creating distinctively shaped transparent patches. As it grows, it ceases mining and feeds on the whole thickness of the leaves. The

A landscape of ant-hills at Porton Down, the favoured haunt of many species of butterfly. The short sward and abundance of downland plants, in particular common rockrose, support large numbers of brown argus.

chrysalis is formed on the ground and is attended and buried by ants. Barbara Last's photograph (above) is of part of the so-called 'antscape' on Porton Down where abundant rockrose and a short sward make an ideal brown argus habitat.

The Flight Period

There are two generations in the life cycle of the brown argus. Butterflies of the first usually emerge in mid-May and are on the wing for about six weeks. The second, which is frequently in larger numbers, can be seen from mid-July and often well into September. The diagram below shows the flight period pattern at two sites, in 1990 at Upton Cow Down, a site which supports a strong colony

where the foodplant is rockrose, and in 1989 at Picket Wood, where the colony is small and uses one of the secondary foodplants. This species was abundant at Upton Cow Down in 1990 following the excellent autumn of the previous year and, untypically, the spring generation was larger than that in the autumn. At Picket Wood the spring generation was represented by the sighting of a singleton on only four occasions in 15 years.

During monitoring at Upton Cow Down (1983–94), the longest flight period was 18 weeks in 1990 and the shortest was nine weeks in 1983, 1986 and 1987. The maximum number of individuals counted on the transect during a weekly visit varied from 30 in May 1984 to two in August 1986. The earliest record was 1 May 1990 and the latest 25 September 1985. These appear to be the extreme dates for the county.

Measures of Abundance 1980–94 (Figure 16)

The fluctuations in abundance of the brown argus at four monitored sites show a fairly

Flight period at Picket Wood in 1989 (black) and Upton Cow Down in 1990 (white)

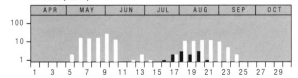

close correlation. The annual rises and falls in numbers of this species are similar to those of the wall, marbled white and small heath. During the early 1980s the levels of abundance were high but slumped dramatically in 1985. Numbers recovered in 1990 to peak at most sites but declined again during the next three years. There was an upturn in 1994 taking the values to above the average at all sites except Picket Wood where, in 1987, the brown argus was thought to be on the verge of extinction. Numbers fell below the observation threshold that year when none was seen. However, the removal of conifers and widening of the rides, combined with the good summer weather of 1989, helped to reverse the decline. In 1989 the brown argus was particularly common in the county and many individuals were positively identified in areas from which rockrose was absent. It is difficult to account for some of these sightings; those that represented colonies, rather than vagrants, were presumably using one of the secondary foodplants, a species of *Geranium*. This is illustrated by

comparing the distribution map of the brown argus with that of its principal foodplant, common rockrose.

Status Before 1982

In 1853 the Rev Francis Morris called this species the 'Brown Argus Blue'. The earliest Wiltshire record appears to have been his statement that 'this insect is common near Great Bedwyn and Sarum, Wiltshire, as J W Lukis, Esq has informed me'. In the 1865 Marlborough College List it was stated to be moderately common. It was recorded on 28 May 1866 by W J Pratt and in all subsequent Lists was described as common. It was included in the 1899 list of the Rev T B Eddrupp from near Calne; it was recorded from near Wylye between 1898 and 1901 by Dr R V Solly and appeared in the 1902 list of E Cook for the Devizes district. Roy Pitman recorded it from Homington Down near Coombe Bissett on 10 June 1928 and in his 1936 report stated it was 'common in most parts of the county'. In the Dauntsey School Fauna List (1931–48) it was described as being rare in the area, only being

Map 32. Distribution of common rockrose

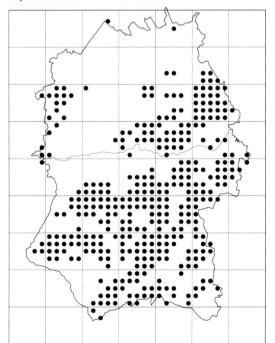

Map 33. Distribution of brown argus

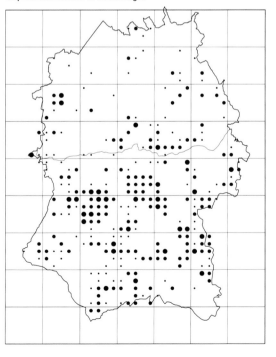

seen at Cheverell on 2 June 1934 and in the Manor grounds in 1945 and 1946. Bowmont Weddell reported it from Bratton on 4 June 1933 and in 1958 Ian Heslop stated that it 'occurred sparingly' at Blackmoor Copse. In 1962, Baron de Worms considered it to be 'generally common, mainly on downs, throughout the county'.

Status since 1982
This species is widespread in southern England, parts of East Anglia and the southern Midlands. It is more localised in the south-west of England and mainly restricted to the north and south coastal areas of Wales. In the north of England and Scotland it is replaced by the northern or Scotch brown argus *Aricia artaxerxes* (Fabricius). It does not occur in Ireland.

In Wiltshire its distribution is widespread and very similar to that of the dingy skipper, green hairstreak and other species for which unimproved grassland is the preferred habitat. An assessment of colony numbers has not been carried out using the method applied to some of the other species but it has been estimated that there are in excess of 250 in the county, about 100 of these being in the areas of Porton Down and SPTA. The distribution map clearly shows this concentration and also the abundance of populations in many areas in the south of the county on unimproved grassland, particularly north and south of the River Ebble and on the downs north of Mere.

There are woodland colonies in Great Ridge and Grovely Woods and in woodlands east of Salisbury, but the apparent absence of this species from the extreme south-eastern corner is surprising since, although the principal larval foodplant is absent, the secondary foodplants occur. The small populations in most of the woods in West Westbury and small grassland areas around Bradford-on-Avon thrive on one of the secondary larval foodplants. Although colonies are not numerous north of Salisbury Plain, there are a few in the Vale of Pewsey and several on the downs north of the Vale between Devizes and the Shalbourne area and one or two in Savernake Forest. North of this region the brown argus is uncommon and is most frequent on the Limestone in the Box and Castle Combe areas but does not occur around Malmesbury. There are a few small colonies in Braydon Forest, in the Cotswold Water Park and about a dozen in the Aldbourne area but only one is known north of Swindon (Steve Button).

Future Prospects
Although the distribution map includes all the records received, experience of the brown argus would indicate that it is often overlooked and is able to maintain itself in very small colonies and often in very small habitats. In 1989, as already mentioned, this species was seen in many unexpected localities and there could be several more awaiting discovery. There may be a slow decline in populations in the county in the future if grassland habitats are allowed to scrub over or are destroyed but it is certainly under no great threat at present. During the WBMS (1982–94) it was recorded from 281 tetrads (29%).

COMMON BLUE
Polyommatus icarus (Rottemburg)

The generic name *Polyommatus*, given to the common blue by Latreille in 1804, means 'many-eyed', an epithet of Argus, originally the family name for all blue butterflies. The specific name *icarus* was given by Rottemburg in 1775. Icarus, whose wings were attached with wax, tried to escape from Crete but flew too near the sun thus melting the wax. He fell and drowned in the Aegean or Icarian sea.

This species was probably illustrated by Thomas Mouffet in 1634 and described by Christopher Merrett in 1666 but James Petiver was the first to name it 'The little Blew Argus' in 1699. Identification of the blues caused the early aurelians many problems and names became confused. In 1775, Moses Harris finally called it the common blue, the name by which it is still known.

The upperside of the male's wings is the colour of bluebell flowers, fringed with white as shown in Ian Grier's photograph of a basking male. Normally the female's wings are brown with a varying amount of blue at the base of each and a line of crescent-shaped orange spots parallel to the wing edges. The undersides in both sexes are light brown with a pattern of black dots, ringed with white.

Males are very active and therefore attract attention as they flit from flower to flower or pursue other butterflies entering their territory. Females become more active when searching for egg-laying sites among low vegetation. Many plants are visited for nectar though there appears to be some preference for members of the pea family including common bird's-foot-trefoil (*Lotus corniculatus*), horseshoe vetch (*Hippocrepis comosa*), lucerne (*Medicago sativa*) and restharrow (*Ononis* spp.).

The greenish-grey eggs are laid singly and have been found on young leaves of seven wild leguminous plants but common bird's-foot-trefoil is the preferred species. On hatching, the caterpillar feeds on the leaves and most individuals pupate after about six weeks and give rise to a second generation.

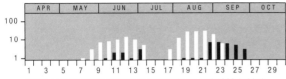

Flight period at Picket Wood in 1980 (black) and 1990 (white)

The Flight Period

The first generation is on the wing from the middle of May, throughout June and into early July. The second, which usually appears in larger numbers, is on the wing from late July, throughout August and, in favourable seasons, well into September. During the 15 years of monitoring in Picket Wood the longest flight period was 16 weeks in 1982 and the shortest, only five, in 1987 and 1993. The maximum number of individuals counted weekly on the transect varied from 41 in August 1984 to one in 1993. The earliest sighting was 16 May 1982 and the latest 30 September 1988.

The earliest record in a Marlborough College List was 2 May 1945.

Measures of Abundance 1980–94 (Figure 17)

Yearly fluctuations in abundance were similar at the six monitored sites and highlight the dramatic fortunes of the common blue during the 15 years. The wave pattern of the graphs is similar to that of several other species and reflects the importance of weather as a main factor governing the number of butterflies on the wing. There were peaks in 1984 and 1990 at all the sites. Numbers dropped dramatically in the following three years and rose again in 1994 but were considerably below the average at most sites.

Status Before 1982

The first published Wiltshire record occurred in the 1865 Marlborough College List and on 23 May 1866 it was recorded by R C Davis. In the List of 1873 it was described as being abundant and in all subsequent Lists as being very common. It was included in the Rev T B Eddrupp's 1899 list from near Calne, in Dr R V Solly's 1898–1901 list from near Wylye and in E Cook's 1902 list from the Devizes area. Roy Pitman took this species at

Petersfinger on 27 May 1928 and in his 1936 report stated it to be 'common, sometimes abundant, favourite haunts being rough flowery hillsides'. Bowmont Weddell recorded it from the Trowbridge area on 26 June 1932 and in 1962 Baron de Worms described it as 'common and widespread throughout the county'.

Status Since 1982

The common blue occurs throughout Great Britain and Ireland. It occurs in a variety of habitats where the larval foodplant occurs including downland, flowery meadows, sunny woodland rides and clearings, suitable roadside verges, wasteland and even some urban areas. During the WBMS (1982–94) it could still be described as common and widespread and was recorded from 618 tetrads (65%). Its future status is unlikely to change providing that the smaller fragmented breeding areas are not destroyed.

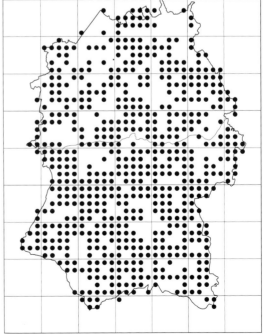

Map 34. Distribution of common blue

91

CHALKHILL BLUE
Lysandra coridon (Poda)

The generic name *Lysandra*, given to the chalkhill blue by Hemming in 1933, is the name of an Egyptian princess, the daughter of Ptolemy I. The specific name *coridon,* given by Poda in 1761, is the name of a shepherd in Virgil's Eclogues. In 1704 James Petiver listed this butterfly as 'The pale blue Argus' and in 1775 Moses Harris named it the chalkhill blue.

The chalkhill is the largest of the blues that occur in Wiltshire, slightly larger than its close relative, the Adonis blue. Its common name is derived from its sole habitat, chalk (and limestone) grassland. The delicate blue of the male's upper wings could be described as chalky blue, or almost white, as shown in Rob Turner's photograph. The wings on both sexes are fringed with white, the terminally dark veins extending as faint lines across the fringes. The outer edge of the forewings of the male has a dark band which is replaced by a row of dots between the veins on the lower wings. The female is inconspicuous both in colour and movement as she crawls among low-growing horseshoe vetch (*Hippocrepis comosa*) in search of egg-laying sites. She is very similar to the female Adonis blue, dark brown on the upperside with black spots along the edge of the lower wings which are edged with white, not blue as in the Adonis. Pale brown underwings, almost white in some males, are spotted with black dots ringed with white and are clearly illustrated in Peter Durnell's photograph of a nectaring male (opposite).

This species nectars both at the common chalk-loving plants such as knapweeds (*Centaurea* spp.) and scabiouses (*Knautia arvensis* and *Scabiosa* spp.) and at some of the more local species – carline thistle (*Carlina vulgaris*), wild basil (*Clinopodium vulgare*) and ploughman's-spikenard (*Inula conyza*). Sometimes males are attracted in large numbers to damp ground to take up moisture and minerals.

The white eggs are laid singly on horseshoe vetch or adjacent vegetation growing on sun-baked slopes in the vicinity of an ant colony.

A male chalkhill blue nectaring on black knapweed. The pattern of spots on its underwings is typical. In some individuals the spots occur as lines and streaks to produce the 'vars' so eagerly sought by Victorian collectors.

The caterpillar overwinters, fully developed, within the egg. It hatches in late March or early April and feeds at night on horseshoe vetch. It is attended by ants which feed on honey exuded from its honey-gland. The pupa is formed either in a cell made by the ants in the soil or within their nest. It secretes amino acids on which the ants feed. As the adult emerges ants surround it giving it protection as a 'reward' for the provision of food in its early stages (Thomas and Lewington 1991).

The Flight Period

The chalkhill and silver-studded are the only two blues which occur in the county that have a single generation. The chalkhill is the last to emerge,

Flight period at Pewsey Downs NNR in 1980

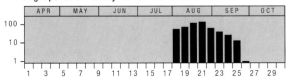

usually at the end of July. Their numbers peak in mid-August and, if the season is favourable, some individuals survive into early October. The diagram shows a typical flight period at Pewsey Downs NNR. During the 15 years of monitoring, the longest flight period was ten weeks in 1985 and 1992 and the shortest was seven weeks in 1981 and 1989. The maximum number of individuals counted on the transect in a weekly visit varied from 185 in 1982 to 46 in 1990. The earliest sighting on these downs was on 23 June 1870 (C A Sladen).

During the mapping scheme there were two exceptionally early records from Morgan's Hill, 30 May (Tom Burnard) and 12 June (Arthur Cleverly), both in 1984. The latest date was 26 September when there were records from Prescombe Down in 1986 (Martin Warren) and Whitesheet Hill in 1992 (Barry Checksfield). The latest county record was the sighting of a few fresh individuals on downland near Warminster on 1 November 1972 (Kit Lipscomb).

Measures of Abundance 1980–94 (Figure 18)

No clear overall picture of fluctuations in abundance is evident from the data shown in Figure 18 and there is little correlation between the sites. At Pewsey Downs, which has a large population, the 1985 value has been estimated and no value is available for 1993 which makes interpretation of the apparent decline in 1994 uncertain. At other sites, values increased in 1994 to take them well above their averages. The continuous increase at Boscombe Down since monitoring began in 1989 is exceptional. The fluctuations at Roundway Hill Covert, Bratton Castle Earthworks and Upton Cow Down are probably typical of many small colonies which manage to survive in marginal habitats throughout the county.

Status Before 1982

In 1853 the Rev Francis Morris was the first person to include Wiltshire in a publication in which 23 localities were listed. He stated 'It is not uncommon near Sarum, and also at Martin's Hill near Great Bedwyn, Wiltshire, where J W Lukis Esq has obtained it'. In 1860 William Coleman included Wiltshire amongst 17 localities. It was included in the 1865 Marlborough College List as occurring at Rainscombe Park (W J Baverstock). On 16 July 1868 it was taken at Alton Barnes by C A Sladen. In the 1873 College List it was said to be 'common on downs' and in subsequent Lists it was described as 'locally rather common'. In 1896 the Rev C A Sladen commented 'A great year for *L. coridon* on the range of chalk downs extending east from Devizes where I found it literally swarming; you could hardly walk without treading on a specimen, every flower of thistle and centaury had its two or three occupants. At Winsley I saw one male last year'. It was included in the Rev T B Eddrupp's 1899 list from near Calne, in Dr R V Solly's 1898–1901 list from near Wylye and in E Cook's 1902 list from near Devizes.

Roy Pitman reported the species from Old Sarum, near Salisbury, on 24 July 1928 and said 'a good locality which should be frequented often'. The chalkhill blue was obviously one of his

favourite species. He referred to it many times in his diaries especially when recalling how eminent lepidopterists of the day caught specimens of the many varieties for which Wiltshire was famous. He also documented the decline of the species due to the destruction of many of these 'happy hunting grounds' either by ploughing, being spoiled by development or because they were not grazed. However, in his 1936 report he was still able to say 'The Wiltshire downs are famed for this species where the rare forms and varieties are often met with. It is a locally abundant insect'. In 1957 he commented 'Continued ploughing of virgin downland has exterminated many colonies of blues. The absence of rabbits has allowed rank vegetation to stifle the flora. The use of weed killers, the spread of urbanisation and the re-afforestation with conifers are all taking their toll on the county's lepidoptera'. Two years later he commented 'Camp Hill completely ploughed beyond recognition. The chalkhill blue colony was famous throughout the country' and in 1961 'Still declining and gone from many

Map 35. Distribution of chalkhill blue

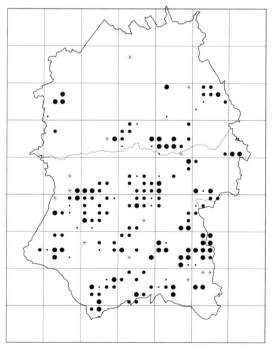

former haunts, 130,000 acres of downland ploughed since 1940'.

Bowmont Weddell recorded the species from Bratton on 27 July 1933 and there was a very early record from the Dauntsey School Fauna List for 10 June 1934. In 1962 Baron de Worms stated 'Wiltshire is especially rich in localities for this species, but a number of them have been destroyed by cultivation in recent years. Many rare aberrations of this insect have been taken in the County'.

Status since 1982

The chalkhill blue is still a widespread species in southern England where its distribution closely follows that of the Chalk and Limestone. It has become extinct in the east in some of the former areas within its range. In Wiltshire, due to the extensive areas of unimproved chalk and limestone grassland to which the larval foodplant is confined, this species is widespread and occurs in large colonies in some localities. However, there are many small self-contained colonies limited to much smaller areas of grassland than in former times.

Table 12 shows an assessment of the number of colonies recorded in the county during the WBMS. The colonial instinct of the chalkhill blue is weaker than it is in some other species which complicates any analysis. Vagrants, usually males, that appear from time to time in unlikely places such as Picket Wood, Bentley Wood and Somerford Common testify to this.

Table 12. An assessment of the number of colonies in the county

Locality	Number of colonies	%
North Wiltshire	26	17
South Wiltshire excluding SPTA and Porton Down	61	39
SPTA(W) Imber	13	8
SPTA(C) Larkhill/West Down	32	20
SPTA(E) Bulford/Tidworth	12	8
Porton Down	12	8
Total number of colonies	156	

This assessment indicates that 69 colonies (44%) occur on Porton Down and SPTA which highlights the importance of these areas for butterflies. On SPTA the chalkhill blue is not particularly abundant and is more or less confined to discrete areas where the larval foodplant is plentiful, but on Porton Down it is abundant over the whole area suggesting that there is possibly just one large population. In the north of the county there are four colonies on the Chalk near Aldbourne (George Osmond et al.), one near Clouts Wood (Mike Williams), two near Marlborough, three in the Shalbourne area (Jack Coates), a string of colonies on the downs to the north of the Vale of Pewsey from Tan Hill in the west to Martinsell Hill in the east and probably four separate colonies on the downs between Devizes and Cherhill.

There are five on the Limestone between Castle Combe and Box including a particularly strong one at West Yatton Down. The colony in the Winsley area reported by Sladen in 1896 has not been found in recent years. The distribution map shows that the chalkhill blue is widespread throughout the central area of the county and on many of the downs in the south where thousands have been regularly seen north of Mere (Michael Powell). Small populations have been found on Pepperbox Hill and Dean Hill (Ches Carpenter) in the south-east. During the WBMS (1982–94) vagrant males were recorded from 13 tetrads. Excluding these sightings, the chalkhill blue was recorded from 165 tetrads (17%).

Future Prospects

Some of the small colonies could be in danger of extinction if the management required to promote the growth and spread of the larval foodplant is not implemented. However, a large proportion of the populations are in no immediate danger because the land use of the sites where they occur is unlikely to change significantly.

ADONIS BLUE
Lysandra bellargus (Rottemburg)

The Adonis blue shares the generic name *Lysandra*, given by Hemming in 1933, with the chalkhill blue (see page 92). The specific name *bellargus* was given by Rottemburg in 1775 and is derived from two words meaning 'beautiful' and 'many-eyed'. The other specific name, *adonis,* given by Denis and Schiffermüller in 1775, was the name of a beautiful youth beloved of Aphrodite and was in use for many years. This butterfly may have been listed by James Petiver in 1717 as 'The Lead Argus'. In 1775 Moses Harris called it the 'Clifden Blue', a name derived from Cliveden in Buckinghamshire where the species had been taken. In 1906 Richard South named it the Adonis blue which was the scientific name in use at the time.

Approximately the same size as the chalkhill blue and a little larger than the common blue, the male Adonis, 'the beautiful', lives up to its name. As the sun catches its dazzling bright blue upper wings there can seldom be confusion with any other blue, the common being the most similar. When at rest, identification can be confirmed by checking that the dark ends of the veins, on both pairs of wings, are much more pronounced where they cross the white fringes than they are on the chalkhill. The females of the two species are almost identical and can only be separated by the black spots on the upperside of the lower wings which are edged with blue, not white as in the chalkhill. All these features are shown in Peter Durnell's photographs. The pattern of spots on the underside of both sexes of each species is also very similar though the pale brown background of the Adonis is usually slightly darker. The inset photograph by Graham Wall on page 97 shows the undersides of a mating pair.

Males spend much of their flying time searching for emerging females. After mating, the females rest in hot depressions among the short chalk or limestone grassland until their eggs are ready to be laid. The adults of the first generation nectar chiefly on horseshoe vetch (*Hippocrepis comosa*), one of the few early flowering plants available. When the second generation is on the wing there

A basking female Adonis blue. The area of blue scales varies between individuals, from being absent to almost completely covering the wing. INSET *A mating pair showing the attractive underside wing markings.*

are many nectar producing species in flower including common bird's-foot-trefoil (*Lotus corniculatus*), knapweed (*Centaurea* spp.), devil's-bit scabious (*Succisa pratensis*) and carline thistle (*Carlina vulgaris*). In dry weather, males may congregate on damp ground to obtain moisture and minerals as shown on the dust jacket of this book. They are sometimes attracted to decaying material and also dung.

The greenish-white eggs are laid singly on the underside of horseshoe vetch leaflets, the females flying low in search of small plants growing in hot spots among short vegetation. Caterpillars of the early summer generation hatch within three weeks and feed exclusively on horseshoe vetch, pupating a month later on the ground. The second generation adults are on the wing from mid-August to mid-September. The eggs laid by this generation hatch in about 40 days. The larval and pupal stages of both generations are constantly attended by ants which the caterpillars 'reward' for their protective behaviour with a supply of sweet secretions from

a honey-gland and microscopic pores. Caterpillars of the autumn generation do not complete their growth before they hibernate. They resume feeding at the end of March in the following year with ants in attendance. This fascinating relationship between the Adonis blue and ants is described in full by Thomas and Lewington (1991).

The Flight Period
The first generation emerges in mid-May, peaks in early June and a few individuals survive into mid-July. The second generation usually appears a month later and peaks at the end of August. In favourable weather conditions, a few butterflies linger on until mid-October. As with many species, there is considerable variation in emergence times, the males always being seen a few days before the less-conspicuous females. The earliest county record was from Boscombe Down on 8 May 1989 (Stephen Palmer, Gerald Nicholls) and the latest date was 15 October 1986 at Bratton Castle Earthworks.

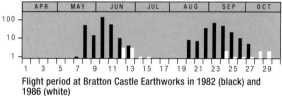

Flight period at Bratton Castle Earthworks in 1982 (black) and 1986 (white)

The well-known colony at Bratton Castle Earthworks has been carefully monitored by the author since 1980 and a considerable amount of information has been obtained about the colony's status. The flight period diagram for 1982 and 1986 clearly shows the range of variation in emergence times and abundance levels. During the monitoring period, the longest flight period for both generations was 16 weeks in 1984, 1990 and 1992. The shortest period was ten weeks in 1986 and 1993. The earliest date was 10 May 1990 and the latest was 15 October 1986. The maximum number of first generation butterflies on the weekly transect varied from 129 males in 1982 to two in 1986 and 16 females in 1982 to one in 1986. Second generation numbers varied from 55 males in 1994 to one in 1986 and 32 females in 1994 to one in 1986. The first generation was larger than the second in nine of the 15 years.

During the 1980s the data from Bratton Castle was compared with that from monitored sites near Swanage in Dorset and other sites in the south of England (Jeremy Thomas). The second generation at these more southerly sites was almost always the larger. Thomas suggested that, at Bratton Castle, the second generations were perhaps only partial and the pupae from the first generation overwinter until the following spring to produce larger numbers in the first generation. This suggestion has not been confirmed and, since 1992, the second generation has been the greater. This may be an indication that the life cycle of the colony is changing.

Measures of Abundance 1980–94 (Figure 19)
For many years the Adonis blue has been known to be a species whose numbers fluctuate violently. Figure 19 and the flight period diagram clearly show that this has been the case at Bratton Castle. It is remarkable that the Adonis blue survives

there because, until 1991, there had been no grazing and the vegetation was tall and dense over most of the area. At many other sites, the species had not survived under these conditions. It was feared that the frighteningly low value in 1986 was an indication of imminent extinction. The steepness of the earthwork banks in the main breeding area has resulted in only a thin covering of soil which allows the larval foodplant to flourish. The small patches of bare chalk that remain are another requirement of this warmth-loving species. It was reassuring to witness a very large increase in abundance in 1994, when the index value was well above the site's average for the first time since 1985, although below the maximum of 1982. Sheep grazing has recently been introduced which should create a much larger area of suitable breeding habitat and give the butterflies a greater chance of survival.

The colony at Upton Cow Down was always much smaller than that at Bratton Castle and confined to a small area which had become very overgrown and scrubby by the early 1990s. It is not known whether the colony has become extinct or has moved its base to more suitable locations on the Salisbury Plain escarpment. Recent grazing should improve the area and, provided that some butterflies have survived nearby, they may return. Numbers have plummeted at the Boscombe Down disused railway embankment since 1991 but there was a small revival in 1994.

Status Before 1982
North Wiltshire
Neither the Rev Francis Morris in 1853, nor Edward Newman in 1869, mentioned Wiltshire localities, probably because Marlborough College was the main source of their information and the Adonis blue was not recorded from that area until 1883. The species was not included in the 1873 College List but its compiler, Edward Meyrick, was of the opinion that it was 'likely to be added'. The first published Wiltshire record was that of E F Benson who took one on 2 June 1883. In 1894, Meyrick stated 'on 17 June the species was discovered by F C Hanbury to be established on

the grassy hillside between Manton Copse and West Woods, several specimens being taken and others seen. This is a curious and unexpected discovery'. In 1897 it was found commonly on the slopes of Oare Hill and by 1899 was described as locally common and recorded from the downs at Calstone and from the Devizes district by E Cook in 1902. In both 1921 and 1922 the Rev C A Sladen reported one from the present-day Pewsey Downs NNR. In the 1935 Marlborough College List it was described as locally rather common and Silbury Hill was included as an additional locality. In 1956, only Oare Hill and Walker's Hill were listed and, by 1962, it was stated 'has not been taken or certainly seen for several years, disappearing from the area'.

South Wiltshire

The Adonis blue was recorded from near Wylye by Dr R V Solly between 1898 and 1901, and from near Donhead St Mary by the Rev Canon Short in 1901. Roy Pitman recorded the Adonis blue from Clarendon near Salisbury in 1928 and, with Harry Haynes on Homington Down, he 'took as many as required on grass heads whilst looking for vars'. According to other diary entries, the Adonis blue, like the chalkhill blue, was a common species on the downs around Salisbury at that time. In his 1936 report he stated 'not so widely distributed as the last [chalkhill blue] but common, and at times in south Wilts abundant, especially in the second brood'.

Bowmont Weddell recorded the species from Bratton Castle in June 1932 and in several subsequent years. In the Dauntsey School Fauna List it was recorded from 'the Plain' in 1936 and from Bratton Castle in 1956. In 1962 Baron de Worms repeated several of these records and stated 'It is found in the County in the same localities as the last species (chalkhill blue), but has been exterminated from several by cultivation'. It would appear that the species began to decline in the late 1950s as a result of habitat destruction, lack of grazing, the introduction of myxomatosis and a series of generally poor summers. Quotations from the annual entomological reports in WAM,

compiled by Weddell, chronicle this decline. It should be noted that there were far fewer active recorders in the 1950s and 1960s. Most of the comments are based on the observations of a handful of lepidopterists and, with a few exceptions, refer to the colonies at Cotley Hill near Warminster, Bratton Castle and a few sites in the Salisbury area. However, there seems to be little doubt that, during the 1950s, 1960s and 1970s, the Adonis did not fare well at these sites. This was probably true elsewhere in the county.

Status Since 1982

The Adonis blue has always had a southern distribution in England. It is confined to chalk and limestone grasslands where its only larval foodplant grows in abundance. It became extinct in the Cotswolds in the 1960s and a total of only five colonies are now known from the Chilterns and the Berkshire Downs. A few colonies survive in Kent, Surrey, Sussex, Hampshire and the Isle of Wight and one small colony in Devon. In Somerset, a colony introduced in 1988 was surviving in 1994. A survey of the Dorset colonies in 1978 found that they were mainly small and limited to 32 sites. However, the situation improved during the 1980s (Thomas).

In 1982, at the start of the WBMS, the only known site in Wiltshire was at Bratton Castle. However, since then the Adonis blue has been reported from many sites from which it was believed to have become extinct and from several areas with no previous records. It is likely that this butterfly had persisted at most of its former known sites for several years but was overlooked when in very small numbers. Roy Stockley recalled that, prior to 1982, he knew of only two locations in the county where the Adonis could be seen but in 1983 he knew of about 30, mainly on or near SPTA(W). These appeared to have 'turned up' over the previous two years after an absence of at least eleven. He noticed that as the Adonis appeared to be increasing the chalkhill blue was declining. In his 1984 report, Godfrey Smith, the lepidoptera recorder for the SPTA(W) Conservation Group, stated 'Records of Adonis blue have shown a remarkable increase in the last two years. There is a well-established Adonis colony near Bratton but in the last two years there have been records of what appear to be newly-formed colonies from all over the Ranges with numbers in excess of 100 individuals in many areas by mid-August. Future records of these two species will be of particular interest since, prior to 1981, an Adonis blue was rarely seen except near Bratton'. Increases in abundance and number of colonies during the first half of the 1980s were probably due to the fine summers of 1982–84 when numbers built up and individuals wandered onto nearby downland. Additional grazing by rabbits and sheep at this time had helped to make formerly ungrazed downland suitable for the Adonis. The possibility of some introductions cannot be ruled out, but the only known introduction was that by Roy Stockley on Elm Hill, Warminster, where about 1,000 larvae were put down in 1983. The colony continued to thrive in 1991 (Simon Barker).

South Wiltshire

The distribution map clearly shows that the concentration of records is from SPTA(W). This emphasises the importance of the MOD Ranges for this species. Many colonies have also been found along the north-west escarpment of Salisbury Plain from Great Cheverell Hill west to Upton Cow Down near Westbury and south to Cotley Hill near Heytesbury. There is one isolated, strong colony on Cley Hill near Longleat. The species is uncommon on SPTA(C) and (E) numbers never having been recorded in double figures.

In the south-west, there are large populations on the strip-lynchets near Mere and on White Sheet Hill where a small colony also survives in a disused quarry. There may be two or three distinct colonies on south-facing slopes between Maiden Bradley and the Deverills. The only recent record was of two males seen by the author in 1986. Many colonies survive on the downs north and south of the Ebble valley between Berwick St John and Coombe Bissett and in grassland combes north of Tollard Royal. There are good populations on downland along the Wylye Valley near

Sherrington and Deptford and the Avon valley at Middle Woodford and Little Durnford. Small colonies also occur on the downlands adjacent to Grovely Wood. A small, isolated colony was discovered on the Hampshire border near Buttermere in the late 1980s and butterflies were last seen there in June 1992 (David Green).

The Adonis blue still occurs in small numbers at Boscombe Down (Gerald Nicholls) and there is one small colony on Easton Down at Porton (Dick Ryan). In some years a sizeable population has been counted at Figsbury Ring (Piers Mobsby *et al.*). In 1973, Pitman's comment concerning this site was 'an exciting report since they have not been seen for many years'.

In 1987 a large population was discovered on the south-facing bank of a cutting on the A303 which had been colonised by horseshoe vetch (Barbara Last *et al.*). It is a strange experience to see these rare butterflies pairing within a metre or so of the carriageway in the turbulence caused by heavy vehicles speeding by. Due to the strength of this colony, individuals were taken from it in 1990 to

Map 36. Distribution of Adonis blue

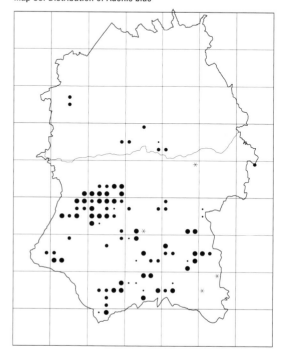

re-establish the Adonis blue in the Cotswolds from where it had disappeared in the 1960s.

North Wiltshire

The Adonis blue is much rarer in the north due to the relatively smaller areas of calcareous downland which support horseshoe vetch. It appears to be maintaining a precarious foothold on the Limestone. It occurred near Castle Combe in the 1940s (Charles Anderson) but was not recorded there again until 1985 when the author saw four males on Danks Down near Ford. Two were seen nearby at Rack Hill in 1986 (Norman Baldock) and 1993 (Simon Barker and Mike Williams) and a single male at West Yatton Down in 1991 (Jean Matthews).

Occasional records from the Chalk near Devizes at Beacon Hill, King's Play Hill and Roundway Hill Covert (Beatrice Gillam) could be of one widespread population or represent a few discrete colonies. There have been no reliable records from Morgan's Hill but singletons from Calstone and Cherhill Downs since 1984 (Geoffrey Webber *et al.*) and several males in 1994 (Gillam *et al.*) indicate the presence of a colony. The last record from Pewsey Downs NNR was in 1956, until a few males were seen in 1984 on the western slopes of the reserve (Fuller and Keith Payne). Adonis blues were not reported again until 1992 when they were seen for the first time on the transect established in 1979 (Albert Knott).

Table 13 is an assessment of the number of colonies in the county. The criteria used are those applied to several other species (see dingy skipper page 36).

This assessment is perhaps over-optimistic. A few records may have been misidentifications,

Table 13. An assessment of the number of colonies in the county

Locality	Number of colonies	%
North Wiltshire	6	7
South Wiltshire excluding SPTA and Porton Down	52	58
SPTA(W) Imber	23	26
SPTA(C) Larkhill/West Down	4	4
SPTA(E) Bulford/Tidworth	3	3
Porton Down	2	2
Total number of colonies	90	

sightings of some singletons may not have represented colonies and some of the very small colonies may now (1994) be extinct. Nevertheless, it is certain that Wiltshire and Dorset are the strongholds for this species in England. They probably support two-thirds of the colonies, Dorset having more of the larger and stronger populations. During the WBMS (1982–94) the Adonis blue was recorded from 90 tetrads (9.5%). Males, presumed to be vagrants, were reported from four further tetrads.

Future Prospects

No doubt the abundance of Adonis blue populations will continue to fluctuate widely resulting in local extinctions of some small colonies. However, in years of high abundance, re-population from nearby colonies is possible provided the habitat remains suitable. On most of the downlands that have strong colonies they are unlikely to be destroyed but the deterioration of some sites could be a threat. Requirements for the species' survival are now well-known as a result of studies carried out in the 1980s (Thomas). Provided that these are heeded, the Adonis blue should continue to be a Wiltshire speciality.

HOLLY BLUE
Celastrina argiolus (Linnaeus)

The generic name *Celastrina*, given to the holly blue by Tutt in 1906, is derived from a word used for a tree supposed to be the holly, one of the larval foodplants. The specific name *argiolus*, given by Linnaeus in 1758, means 'smaller than argus' which, at that time, was a reference to the common blue. This species was first described by John Ray in 1710 and listed by James Petiver in 1717 as 'The Blue Speckt Butterfly'. The name 'Azure Blue' given to it by Moses Harris in 1775 was used by many authors until Kane, in 1885, and Richard South, in 1906, called it the holly blue.

The holly blue is similar in size to the common blue and may be mistaken for this species especially by those who are not familiar with the different habitats of the two butterflies. The blue on the upperside of the male holly blue closely resembles that of the male common blue but is seldom seen clearly because, unlike the common blue, the butterfly closes its wings on alighting and flies at a greater height. When resting in dull weather the wings may be held partly open, as in Peter Creed's photograph on page 103, giving an opportunity to confirm the sex. The male is more or less uniformly lilac blue. The female is blue with a broad black margin on the forewings and black marginal dots on the lower wing edge. The second generation is more heavily marked than the first. Stephen Palmer's photograph shows the very pale underwings, speckled with tiny black spots, which distinguish this species from the other blues. Only the small blue also has pale underwings but it is much smaller.

Unlike the other blues, the holly blue is not restricted to a special grassland habitat by the caterpillars' foodplants and therefore the males do not defend territories and are not found in colonies. This is an elusive species, prone to crawling among shrubby vegetation rather than flying. The adults obtain food from four sources: nectar from flowers and aphid honeydew, moisture from wet mud and additional minerals from mammalian droppings. The main nectar

Holly blues are reluctant to open their wings except in weak sunshine.
This male, resting with its wings held partially open, allows details of
the upperwings to be seen.

source for the summer brood is bramble (*Rubus fruticosus* agg.).

The greenish-white eggs are laid singly in the spring at the base of holly (*Ilex europaeus*) flower buds. Holly is the only foodplant that has developing berries at this time of year. The caterpillars hatch in about two weeks and eat the top of the eggshell before boring into the bud and feeding on the contents of the developing berry. This generation pupates among the foliage attached by a silken girdle and the butterflies emerge two to three weeks later in July and August. The eggs of the second generation are laid on several shrubs which have ripening berries in late August and September. These include dogwood (*Cornus sanguinea*), spindle (*Euonymus europaeus*) and cotoneaster spp. but ivy (*Hedera helix*) is most commonly used. The caterpillars feed up quickly but the exact sites in which they pupate for the winter have not yet been found in the wild (Thomas and Lewington 1991). Adults emerge in the following April or May.

The Flight Period
The holly blue usually has two generations but, very occasionally, some of the pupae develop into adults to produce a small, third generation in late September or early October. The first generation is on the wing from mid-April to early June and the second from late July until the end of August. This butterfly flies in a fast but erratic manner around trees and bushes rather than over low vegetation. A blue butterfly seen during April and early May will be this species, even if not positively identified, since the common blue is seldom on the wing before late May or early June.

During 15 years of monitoring along a stretch of the Kennet and Avon Canal towpath

Flight period at Kennet and Avon Canal towpath in 1991

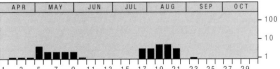

near Bradford-on-Avon, holly blues were recorded in eight years. The longest flight period was 16 weeks in 1991 and the shortest, only one week, in 1980. The maximum weekly number of individuals counted on the transect varied from five in 1991 to one in 1980. The earliest sighting was 13 April 1991 and the latest 7 September 1991.

The earliest date in a Marlborough College List was 2 April 1929 but, during the WBMS (1982–94), there were two records for 17 March 1990, from Bradford-on-Avon (Gwyneth Yerrington) and Cholderton (Henry Edmunds). The latest date was 14 October 1990 when the author watched a fresh female attempting to oviposit on ivy at Bradford-on-Avon. This was probably a third generation individual.

Measures of Abundance 1980–94 (Figure 20)
The abundance of this little butterfly fluctuated widely between 1980 and 1994. Annual variation in population size has been well-known for many years and commented upon by most writers. Various theories have been put forward to explain this phenomenon. Probably the most favoured is the parasitism of the wasp (*Listrodromus nycthemerus*) which preys exclusively on holly blue larvae. In 1994 Richard Revels carried out studies into the effects of the wasp and his results offer fairly substantial evidence that this parasitoid is the main controlling factor governing the abundance of the butterfly, although its survival is also affected by spring and summer temperatures.

Status Before 1982
At the time of the founding of the MCNHS in 1865 the holly blue population was probably in one of its scarce phases. It was not mentioned in a College List until 1869 when the entries read 'It was first discovered in Rabley Copse in some abundance, but since then single specimens have been taken ... By J B Fuller (26 April) ... and others' and 'Before this year this butterfly was quite unknown to our list, but it has now become singularly plentiful'. In the 1873 List it was

described as being 'common near holly', in the 1883 List as 'only once or twice since 1877', in Lists from 1892–1911 as 'rather uncommon', in 1935 'now sometimes common' and in 1956 'sometimes quite common'. It was taken by the Rev Canon Short at Donhead St Mary in 1901 and was seen in the Devizes area in 1902 by E Cook and in 1899 near Calne by the Rev T B Eddrupp.

Judging by the entries in Roy Pitman's 1928 diary, the holly blue enjoyed a good season. He saw one on 27 April and many more during the year. He commented that they were 'too elusive to net'. In his 1936 report he described it as 'Fairly common in some years; occurs spasmodically throughout the county, and often met with in town gardens'. The Dauntsey School Fauna List 1931–48 described the species as fairly common in the area. Bowmont Weddell first recorded it from the Trowbridge area on 22 July 1934 and in 1962 Baron de Worms stated 'Fairly common and widespread in the county, but very susceptible to fluctuation in numbers, and some years hardly seen'.

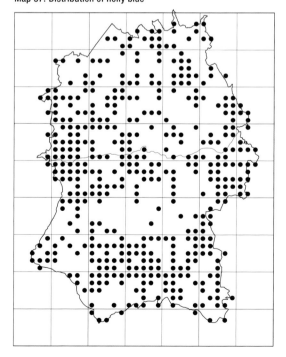

Map 37. Distribution of holly blue

Status Since 1982

The holly blue is widely distributed throughout southern England, Wales and East Anglia but it is more localised in the north. It is widespread but local in Ireland. The butterflies are rarely found far from cover and, in years of plenty, are seen along woodland rides and edges, hedgerows, in parks and gardens and often deep in the centre of urban areas wherever their larval foodplants, especially holly or ivy, are present.

Comparison between the holly blue distribution map and geology map of Wiltshire (page 3) shows that this species is absent from much of the Chalk, especially Salisbury Plain. During the years of mapping and monitoring (1980–94) there were two population explosions, one in the mid-1980s and the second, which was much larger and more noticeable, in the early 1990s. This species was selected as the county's 'Butterfly of the Year' in 1984 and 1990, although in 1984 its great abundance was not reflected at the monitored sites. None was recorded at any of these sites in 1994 and it may be a few years before we witness another population explosion. During the WBMS (1982–94) the holly blue was recorded from 444 tetrads (47%). The number of tetrads in which it was recorded was doubled during the years 1989–91 when butterfly numbers were very high. Its status in the county is unlikely to change but, no doubt, the violent fluctuations in abundance will continue to occur.

DUKE OF BURGUNDY
Hamearis lucina (Linnaeus)

The generic name *Hamearis*, given to the Duke of Burgundy by Hübner in 1819, is derived from two words meaning 'at the same time as' and 'the spring', both being references to the butterfly's flight period. The specific name *lucina* given by Linnaeus in 1758, was that of the goddess of childbirth, the bringer of light.

The first British specimen was taken by William Vernon in Cambridgeshire. The butterfly was known to James Petiver in 1699 and to John Ray in 1710 as 'Mr Vernon's Small Fritillary'. In 1766 Moses Harris called it 'The Duke of Burgundy, Frittillaria'. The name had apparently been in use for some time although how it came to be bestowed is not known. This name has survived, with the change of spelling, although in recent years 'fritillary' has been dropped since the butterfly is not related to that family.

This little butterfly is similar in size to the common blue but its coloration resembles that of the fritillaries. The inner third of the upperwings is dark brown. The outer two-thirds have a wavy pattern of tawny-orange and dark brown scales. The fringes are white as shown in Peter Durnell's photograph (above). The underwings are russet with white and black markings crossed by two white bands, visible in Beatrice Gillam's photograph on page 107 of a mating pair. Females flutter close to the ground vegetation and males defend their small territories in brief dogfights, launching themselves with a darting flight from a prominent perch. On downland sites this species may be confused with the dingy skipper and the day-flying moths burnet companion (*Euclidia glyphica*) and Mother Shipton (*Callistege mi*).

Nectaring has been observed on wild strawberry (*Fragaria vesca*), daisy (*Bellis perennis*), pignut (*Conopodium majus*), silverweed (*Potentilla anserina*) and buttercups (*Ranunculus* spp.). The shiny opaque eggs are laid in small batches on the underside of the leaves of primrose (*Primula vulgaris*) and cowslip (*P. veris*) growing among tall vegetation. The caterpillar hatches within three weeks and, after eating its eggshell, feeds on

A mating pair of Duke of Burgundy showing the attractive underwing markings. Very little activity occurs prior to mating, in contrast to the elaborate courtship rituals of some other butterfly species.

the leaves at night. Pupation takes place towards the end of July in dry grass tussocks or among chalk rubble on downland.

The Flight Period

The butterflies emerge in mid-May and are on the wing until mid-June. Occasionally a few linger on until July and, very rarely, a small, partial second generation has been seen in late July and August but there is no record of this having occurred in Wiltshire. A typical flight period pattern for Picket Wood is shown below. During monitoring at this site (1980–92) the longest flight period was seven weeks in 1990 and the shortest, only three weeks, in 1992. The highest number seen on a weekly transect varied from 16 in 1982 to three in 1992

Flight period at Picket Wood in 1987

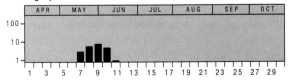

since when none has been seen. The earliest date was 4 May 1990 and the latest 25 June 1986. The earliest date from the Marlborough College Lists was 4 May 1933. During the WBMS (1982–94) the earliest date was 21 April 1989 at Dean Hill near Whiteparish (Ches Carpenter) and the latest 16 July 1986 at West Yatton Down (John Tyler). This was a very late date and one of only three records in the month of July.

Measures of Abundance 1980–94 (Figure 21)
The Duke, as this butterfly is affectionately known, is a small inconspicuous species flying only in warm sunny conditions which are often brief during the flight period. It spends much of its time perching on low vegetation and is easily overlooked especially when in low numbers. Correlation between the graphs for six monitored sites was reasonable from 1986 onwards. Values peaked in 1987 and 1990 but numbers were very low in 1988 and, since 1990, have declined alarmingly at all these sites. The weather was probably the main

reason for this decline but habitat deterioration could also have been a factor. At Bratton Castle Earthworks the introduction of sheep grazing in 1991 may have further reduced the number of cowslips which had always been scarce on the transect. It lies in a sheltered part of the earthworks and the butterflies may have been attracted to it for basking rather than for breeding.

At the woodland sites, conifers are being removed, rides widened and clearings created. In the long term, management will revert to the coppice system. Hopefully, these measures will save the Duke from local extinction although at Picket Wood they may have been implemented a little too late. Due to the deteriorating habitat and the poor weather during the flight period for this species in 1993 and 1994, it may have already become extinct. Although numbers rose significantly at Somerford Common in 1994 the index of abundance values were well below the 15 year average at all sites.

Status Before 1982
The first published Wiltshire record was that of the Rev Francis Morris in 1853. Among 15 localities he included 'though rather uncommon there, near Great Bedwyn and Sarum, Wiltshire'. The Duke of Burgundy was included in the 1865 Marlborough College List from 'Manton Copse and Rabley Copse, common in May; West Woods, W J Baverstock'. In subsequent Lists it was described as common in woods, although in the 1935 List as 'perhaps decreasing' and in 1956 as 'fairly common in most woods'.

Roy Pitman did not record the Duke of Burgundy in his 1928 diary but saw it in Grovely Wood in 1932 and at Farley in 1933. In his 1936 report he stated 'Fairly common in parts of the county, has to be looked for as it easily escapes detection'. Bowmont Weddell's entry for a record of the Duke from Bratton on 4 June 1933 reads '2 *lucina* and 70 eggs'. He listed the species, which was one he obviously enjoyed rearing, in most subsequent years. Although he visited the woods in West Wiltshire in the springtime over a period of 12 years to see the early fritillaries, it was not until

1943 that he recorded the Duke there. His diary for 16 May reads '2 *lucina* first time in woods'. In the Dauntsey School Fauna List (1931–48) the Duke was noted from the Salisbury Plain escarpment in 1933 and from the school area in May 1945 and 1946. In the SDNHS reports, Pitman recorded a 'slight increase in numbers' at Clarendon in 1957. In 1958 Ian Heslop stated that it was well distributed in Bentley Wood and in 1962 Baron de Worms summarised its status as 'quite common locally. Fairly common in woods and downs all over the County'. In 1966 Pitman noted 'a most definite increase in many localities', in 1968 'widely scattered on downland cowslips' and in 1975 'fairly well distributed around Winterslow'.

Status Since 1982
The Duke of Burgundy is now rare and locally distributed in Great Britain. The remaining populations are found mainly in central southern England. There are isolated colonies in the southern Lake District, on the north Yorkshire moors and in the Peterborough area in the East Midlands. It is now extinct in East Anglia and is absent from most of the Midlands, Devon, Cornwall, Wales, Scotland and Ireland. Wiltshire and Gloucestershire retain the majority of the strongest colonies. It is one of our most rapidly declining butterflies as was shown by Matthew Oates during his ecological and conservation study in the 1980s when he estimated that 250 colonies remained in England, many of them being very small and destined to die out unless urgent action was taken. For example, in Hampshire 68% of the county's colonies had been lost since 1950 and, of the remaining 21, ten were threatened with imminent extinction. During the WBMS (1982–94) the Duke was recorded from a variety of habitats and, as the distribution map shows, it was widely spread across the county but with concentrations on SPTA, in the Grovely and Great Ridge Woods area and south-east and east of Salisbury.

North and North-west Wiltshire
The Duke was scarce in the north of the county,

the largest population being at Somerford Common (John Grearson *et al.*). Singletons were recorded from near Aldbourne in 1987 (Humphrey Kay), the Cotswold Water Park in 1990 (Geoffrey Webber), Red Lodge Plantation in 1992 (Beatrice Gillam) and Ravensroost Wood in 1993 (Christine Tracey; see her photograph on page 111).

A small colony persists at West Yatton Down near Castle Combe (Maurice Avent *et al.*) but one located in Stanton Park Wood in 1984 (Fuller) is probably now extinct. A singleton was seen on Danks Down in 1985 (Fuller) and the surprising discovery of a small colony on the main railway line embankment near Chippenham in 1985 (Len Ingram) gives hope that there could be other inaccessible areas supporting small numbers. One butterfly was seen at Colerne Park Wood in 1986 (Harold Bennett) and two colonies were found near Alderton in the north-west in 1992/93 (Ivan Randall and Fuller).

Central and West Wiltshire
There are perhaps ten small colonies on the downs north of Devizes at Roundway Hill, Beacon Hill, King's Play Hill, Morgan's Hill, Calstone and Cherhill Downs and Knoll Down near Beckhampton (Gillam *et al.*). There was an isolated population on Etchilhampton Hill in 1984 which may now be extinct (Gillam). A singleton was seen in West Woods in 1987, the last record from Pewsey Downs NNR was of two seen in 1988 (Harold Crossley) and small numbers of butterflies were regularly recorded on Milton Hill until 1990 (Kay). Small colonies were reported from Rivar Hill in 1984 and Ham Hill in 1992 (Jack Coates) and Haydown Hill near Oxenwood in 1992 (David Green), all near Shalbourne on the Berkshire/ Hampshire border.

Picket, Biss, Green Lane, Norridge and Black Dog Woods in West Wiltshire supported small populations in the mid-1980s but the Duke is now believed to be extinct in all except Green Lane. There it maintains a precarious foothold in the area of scrub under the National Grid power lines where three were seen on the transect in 1994 (Roger Beckett).

Salisbury Plain
There are many populations on SPTA where, as for several other species, an assessment of the number is difficult. There were more records from SPTA(W) (Jack Pile *et al.*) than from SPTA(C) or (E) and particularly along the north-west escarpment of the Plain where colonies were reported stretching from Fore Hill near West Lavington to Bratton Castle Earthworks and Cotley Hill near Heytesbury.

South Wiltshire
The species continues to be seen regularly in clearings and rides in Grovely and Great Ridge Woods and adjacent grassland areas. There are strong colonies at Great Durnford and on the WWT reserve at Little Durnford (Piers Mobsby). A tiny colony survived near Boscombe Down in 1993 (Anthony Bedford-Russell) and a singleton was seen at Old Sarum in 1984 (Michael Stevenson). In 1987 at least four colonies were known on Porton Down on the Wiltshire side of the border with Hampshire (Ian Small) but in 1994 it was recorded from only one area (Dick Ryan).

The Duke of Burgundy is thinly distributed east and south-east of Salisbury. It has been recorded on all four transects in Bentley Wood which may indicate that there are four discrete colonies in the wood. Singletons have been seen from time to time in Blackmoor Copse. There is a relatively large colony on Dean Hill which straddles the Wiltshire/ Hampshire border (Ches Carpenter) but at nearby Pepperbox Hill the last record was in 1965 (Pitman). Colonies were found at Knighton Hill near Broad Chalke in 1985 (Peter Shallcross), at Langley Wood and Tollard Royal in 1986 (Oates), two individuals were found in Hound Wood in 1987 (Ted Gange) and a colony was found at Chickengrove Bottom in 1992 (Mobsby and Barbara Last). The species appears to be scarce south of the River Ebble. Small colonies were discovered on Sutton, Fovant and Compton Downs in 1990 and 1993 (Stephen Palmer), two butterflies were seen in Ashcombe Bottom in 1988 (Palmer) and a singleton near Win Green in 1991 (Diana Forbes).

Table 14. An assessment of the number of colonies in the county

Locality	Number of colonies	%
North Wiltshire	26	21
South Wiltshire excluding SPTA and Porton Down	51	40
SPTA(W) Imber	20	16
SPTA(C) Larkhill/West Down	17	14
SPTA(E) Bulford/Tidworth	8	6
Porton Down	4	3
Total number of colonies	126	

The only records from the south-west corner of the county were from a quarry on White Sheet Hill where a singleton was seen in 1992 (Keith Brown) and a male in 1993 (Fuller). This small population is a long way from the nearest known colony but systematic searches might reveal others on the adjacent Mere Downs and grasslands near the Deverills. An assessment of the number of colonies in the county during the WBMS is shown in Table 14.

The 126 estimated colonies were recorded from 124 tetrads and are shown on the distribution map. More than ten individuals were seen on a single visit in 11 (9%) tetrads, Somerford Common being the only location in the north of the county. Four tetrads are on SPTA(W) and five in the Salisbury area at Dean Hill, Great Durnford, Little Durnford Down, Grovely Wood and on a bank near Baverstock. The colony at Picket Wood is probably extinct and some of the others are by no means secure. Thirty-five (28%) tetrads represent sites where records were of singletons, mainly during the period 1984–86. Several of these have been visited since but the Duke of Burgundy was not recorded. Some are close to sites which have moderate-sized populations and single sightings may have been of vagrants from one of these. Others, such as those at West Woods, Colerne Park Wood and near Aldbourne were probably remnants of colonies which are now extinct. The author considers that several sites from which 'more than singletons' were reported, such as the West Wiltshire woods, no longer support colonies. Observers consider that the best areas for this species on SPTA(W) are deteriorating at an alarming rate (Pile *et al.*).

Map 38. Distribution of primrose and cowslip

Map 39. Distribution of Duke of Burgundy

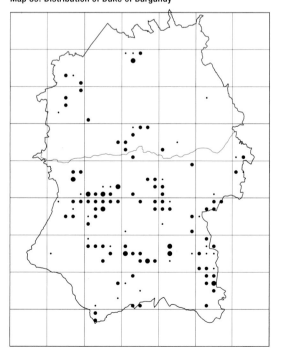

A scene in Ravensroost Wood, a WWT nature reserve in the Braydon Forest. The Duke of Burgundy was first recorded in 1993 in this rich butterfly habitat in the north of the county.

Future Prospects

The distribution map indicates this little butterfly to be in a much stronger position than is really the case and by 1994 the number of colonies may have been fewer than 90. In the early years of the WBMS it was regularly recorded from many sites although rarely in double figures. In recent years, records of the Duke of Burgundy have been considerably fewer and its future is by no means secure. Numbers in some of the stronger colonies may increase but it is considered likely that further extinctions will occur as habitats continue to deteriorate. Most woodland colonies will be seriously threatened unless ride widening and coppicing are continued. Some of the grassland colonies are likely to be shaded out by invading scrub. The species may become restricted to nature reserves where management for the Duke is implemented and to SPTA and Porton Down. Although both larval foodplants occur commonly in the county, as indicated on the distribution map, many of these plants are growing in habitats that do not have some of this butterfly's other critical requirements.

WHITE ADMIRAL
Ladoga camilla (Linnaeus)

The generic name *Ladoga*, given to the white admiral by Moore in 1898, was probably an invented word but it may have been taken from the lake of that name north-east of Leningrad, although this seems unlikely. The specific name *camilla*, given by Linnaeus in 1764, was the name of a Volscian princess. James Petiver was the first to mention this species in 1703. He named it 'The White Leghorn Admiral' from a specimen that had been collected in Italy and given to him. In 1710 John Ray recorded, but did not name, a specimen taken on 22 July 1695 in Essex. In 1717 Petiver used the name white admiral which has prevailed.

White admirals are somewhat elusive butterflies, particularly during the first weeks after emergence when they spend much of their time feeding on aphid honeydew and basking on the foliage in the woodland canopy. No sooner has the eye been attracted by white flashes floating through the dappled shade than the vision disappears leaving the observer wondering what he might have seen. It is only when a butterfly, probably a male searching

for females, glides and flutters along a woodland ride or into a clearing that it can be seen clearly. It resembles the purple emperor in flight but is considerably smaller. The upperside of the wings is dark, sooty brown crossed by broad, vertical white bands which, against a dark background, appear to cut the wings in half as shown in Graham Wall's photograph of a female feeding on bramble (*Rubus fruticosus* agg.). The pattern and colouring of the underside are unmistakable.

When her eggs are ripe the female descends from the canopy to search for honeysuckle (*Lonicera periclymenum*). Plants growing in shade produce few leaves and it is on these that the pale green eggs are laid. The caterpillar emerges within two weeks and feeds by stripping both sides of the leaf mid-rib. It overwinters when partly grown in a shelter made from a leaf and resumes feeding in the spring before pupating suspended from the plant. Bramble is probably the only source of nectar for this butterfly. Salts dissolved in dung are sometimes sipped.

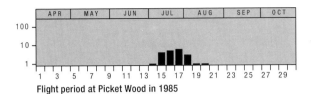

Flight period at Picket Wood in 1985

The Flight Period

Males usually emerge during the first week of July but, in early seasons, they appear two weeks earlier followed by the females a few days later. Numbers rise to a maximum in mid-July, some individuals lingering on into mid-August by which time their wings are very tattered, the result of feeding amongst the brambles. The flight period pattern for Picket Wood in 1985 is shown above. This is typical for the species. During monitoring at this site from 1980 to 1994, the longest flight period was eight weeks in 1980 and the shortest was in 1990 when none was seen. The maximum number of individuals counted on the transect in a week varied from 11 in July 1982 to nil in 1990. The earliest county sighting was 10 June 1992 in Blackmoor Copse (Philippa Daniel) and the latest was 25 August 1991 at Somerford Common (Kathleen Gifford).

Measures of Abundance 1980–94 (Figure 22)

There is close correlation between the graphs for four monitored sites. The white admiral, unlike most other woodland species, can tolerate and may prefer shady but not dense woodlands. It could be that the removal of conifers, coppicing, the clearance and widening of rides at these sites have not helped this species. However, all the woods continue to have considerable areas of shady habitat in which the females can find suitable egg-laying sites. Numbers were high in the mid-1980s but had crashed to very low levels by the end of the decade.

Dr Ernie Pollard studied the ecology of this species in Monks Wood in the 1970s and found evidence which suggested that the weather in June was a major factor determining the number of butterflies that emerged. A warm, dry month encourages rapid growth of the caterpillars, followed by a short pupal stage, thus reducing the period in which predation by birds might take

place. In cool summers these stages are vulnerable for a much longer period and fewer are likely to survive. In most years, the size of the population is also affected by a tiny parasitic wasp, *Apanteles sibyllarum*, which preys on the caterpillars.

The main reasons for large declines at the end of the 1980s were probably climatic. The exceptionally wet and cold July in 1988 must have prevented the females from egg-laying. This was followed by drought conditions in the next two years which, in several woodlands, caused desiccation of honeysuckle leaves resulting in the starvation of caterpillars. Numbers increased in the following two years to reach another peak at all sites in 1992 but since then the numbers have declined to low levels significantly below their averages.

Status Before 1982

The white admiral was taken by Edward Meyrick of Marlborough College on 29 July 1871. In earlier years the College was on holiday in July, and this was probably the reason why the white admiral had not previously been reported. In 1873 it was recorded from Loves Wood and from near Ramsbury. It 'turned up not uncommonly, having previously only occurred singly' at Stype Wood in 1874 (Neville Manders). In 1876 he stated 'a few years ago this was not known to occur here, but now unaccountably it is common enough'. The earliest published Wiltshire record was in Manders' paper, *Entomology of Marlborough*, read by him at a College meeting in 1879 in which he stated 'the first note we have of the white admiral is in 1868 at Ramsbury and in 1874 it was found commonly near Stype, from thence it is apparently spreading its range westwards'. By 1883 however it was 'not found within easy reach of Marlborough' and in the 1892 College List it was considered to be uncommon. In 1904 Manders published *Marlborough Butterflies* and wrote of the white admiral 'has apparently entirely disappeared from its old haunts, last seen at Knowle Wood on 4 August 1881. I think the insect is near its northern limit in our district, and that probably the wet summer of 1879 reduced its numbers to such an extent that it has been unable to maintain itself and has died out'. However, it was observed by W H Somerset near Ludgershall in 1905 so it was not entirely absent. The next record was in 1916 when several were seen in West Woods by H B Paten. By 1935 it was stated to be 'now locally rather common after being scarce for many years' and this status was maintained until the mid-1950s.

The white admiral's status changed yet again in the next decade. In the early 1960s it was scarce in the Marlborough area (R G Hartill) and in 1961 only one was recorded. In 1963 it was 'not found this year, the brambles in their breeding ride in the Forest have been bulldozed or cut down. We fear that one of the few remaining colonies in England may have disappeared' (N A Morgan). This may have been an over-statement, but the implication was that the species was rare. These accounts from the Marlborough area probably reflect the status of the species throughout north Wiltshire from the mid-nineteenth century until the 1960s.

In the south of the county Roy Pitman saw the white admiral in Whiteparish Woods in July 1932 and in his 1936 report he referred to it as 'locally common in woodlands throughout Wiltshire, but of recent years it has increased greatly in numbers. 1935 was a particularly good year, when many were observed miles away from woods and even flying along in the streets of Salisbury'. The Rev Walter Freer from Chute found it was numerous in Collingbourne Wood in the same year.

Bowmont Weddell recorded only singletons in the West Wiltshire woodlands from 1934 until 1939 when he saw four in Green Lane Wood. In June 1942 he stated that it was 'abundant but hard to take'. In 1951 John Kempe from Milton Lilbourne 'rejoiced to find it quite numerous in one East Wiltshire wood'. In 1962 Baron de Worms stated 'Fairly plentiful in recent years in most of the larger woods, has become increasingly common over the south of England latterly' (this last comment conflicts with the statements made concerning the butterfly's status in the Marlborough area at that time). In their annual reports during the 1960s and

Map 40. Distribution of honeysuckle

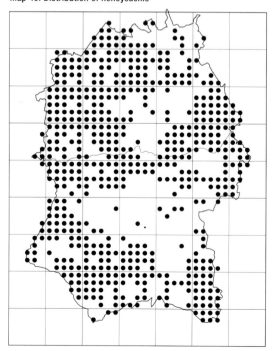

Map 41. Distribution of white admiral

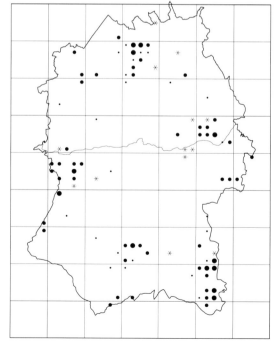

1970s Pitman and Weddell suggested that, in most years, the white admiral prospered. For example, in 1965 they stated 'well up to strength, very common' and in the mid-1970s 'numerous, numbers well up'.

Status Since 1982

During the WBMS (1982–94) the white admiral had two periods, the mid-1980s and the early 1990s, when numbers were high, and one period, 1988–90, of extreme scarcity. However, there is no indication that numbers are declining or that its range is retracting. It was recorded from 55 woodlands ranging in size from Bentley Wood (688 hectares) to Cheverell Wood (11 hectares) and in only 11 of these were more than ten individuals seen during a single visit. These woods are widely distributed throughout the county: Ravensroost, Red Lodge, Somerford Common and Great Wood in the north between Malmesbury and Swindon; Picket and Black Dog Woods in West Wiltshire are part of the old Selwood Forest; Whiteparish Common, Bentley Wood and Blackmoor Copse are remnants of Penchet Forest east and south-east of Salisbury; Bedwyn Common to the east of Savernake Forest and Grovely Wood on high ground between the rivers Wylye and Nadder north-west of Wilton. Smaller woods, where between two and nine individuals were seen on any one visit, may also have supported equally strong populations. During 1984–86, a period when white admirals were common, singletons only were seen in 19 of these woodlands.

Each may have been either a vagrant from a nearby woodland or from a small established colony within the wood. The white admiral is one of several species which are known to disperse from their favoured habitats in years when the species is common.

During the WBMS the white admiral was recorded from 81 tetrads (8.5%). The distribution map includes 13 tetrads in which probable vagrants were recorded from habitats outside woodland including a few from gardens in the countryside. Some of the sightings of singletons, such as those from the Bowood Estate and Great Ridge Wood, indicate the extreme scarcity of the white admiral in apparently good habitats. Perhaps these woodlands are not sufficiently shady or do not have honeysuckle growing with the necessary amount of vigour required to support the caterpillars. The larval foodplant is an indicator of acid and neutral soils and it is in woodlands on these soils that the white admiral occurs. The distribution map of honeysuckle shows that it is much more widespread than the butterfly but, in many of these locations, it grows in hedgerows or scrub habitats which are unsuitable for white admirals.

Future Prospects

There seems to be no reason why this fine woodland butterfly should not remain a widespread and frequent species in the county. The loss of bramble and honeysuckle from woodlands in which it breeds would obviously be detrimental.

PURPLE EMPEROR
Apatura iris (Linnaeus)

The derivation of the generic name *Apatura*, given by Fabricius in 1807, puzzled authors for many years and remains unsolved. The specific name *iris* was given by Linnaeus in 1758. Iris was the messenger of the gods and personified the rainbow, perhaps a reference to the variation in the purple colouring of the male's forewings when seen in different angles of light. In 1695 John Ray described a female captured in Essex. In 1704 James Petiver illustrated this butterfly and named it 'Mr Dale's Purple Eye'. In 1766 Moses Harris used the name purple emperor and, although several others have been suggested, this name has prevailed. The first published Wiltshire reference to the species was that of James Rennie in 1832 who included Wiltshire in a list of ten counties but without naming the localities. The next reference was in the 1865 Marlborough College List.

The male, which is smaller than the female, has a purple sheen on the wings but this can only be seen when they are at certain angles to the sun. The subtle colouring and startling eye-spots, found on the underside of the wings of both sexes, can be seen in Steve Day's photograph on page 117. The white markings on the upperside are very similar to those of the white admiral. The two species may be confused with one another, both being on the wing at the same time and in similar habitats, but the white admiral is smaller, much commoner and is more likely to be seen visiting flowers for nectar.

Both sexes remain for long periods in the canopy of tall trees, oak (*Quercus* spp.) being the most favoured, resting and basking on the foliage and feeding on aphid honeydew. Flowers are rarely visited for nectar but in the mornings fresh males descend from the treetops and alight on the ground to probe damp patches and puddles for moisture and minerals. Richard Tambling's photograph (above) shows a male basking on a stony track in Bentley Wood. Excreta, decaying matter and sap runs on damaged trees are also visited. Males are very 'inquisitive' and have frequently been reported alighting on skin and clothing in very hot weather probably in order to

A male purple emperor resting in oak foliage in the garden of a forestry cottage adjacent to Bentley Wood and Blackmoor Copse, perhaps contemplating entering the cottage, a frequent occurrence!

sip perspiration. After feeding, they soar into the canopy and establish territories around prominent trees waiting for the appearance of females. These trees are very important in the courtship ritual and may be used from year to year. They were referred to by Ian Heslop as 'master oaks' around which most of the butterflies' activity is observed. The males engage the females in mid-air and also contest the air-space with other males. Mating most frequently occurs high in the canopy but seldom on the master oak.

The female descends briefly when intent on egg-laying, an activity that rarely lasts more than ten minutes and usually takes place between noon and 2 pm on warm, sunny days. She lays six to ten green eggs within the shaded crown of 15–20 year old bushes. Goat willow (*Salix caprea*) is most commonly used but other willows including crack willow (*S. fragilis*) are occasionally found acceptable. The caterpillar usually hatches within 16 days and, after eating most of the eggshell, settles down to feed on the leaves. It hibernates on the twigs from early November until April and is fully fed by late June. The chrysalis is formed suspended from a leaf. The butterfly emerges about 18 days later.

Much has been written about the behaviour of this species by various authors, the most notable being *Notes and Views of the Purple Emperor* by Heslop, Hyde and Stockley (1964). Most of Heslop's studies and observations were carried out in Bentley Wood, Blackmoor Copse and woods at Whiteparish Common near Salisbury. His endeavours led to Blackmoor Copse being designated a nature reserve in 1956 mainly on account of its rich butterfly fauna. The wood is leased to the Wiltshire Wildlife Trust which manages it on behalf of the Royal Society for Nature Conservation (see Simon Smith's photograph on page 121). In the 1980s, a three-year intensive study of the purple emperor was carried out by Ken Willmott for the then World Wildlife Fund. Much of the information relating to its life history is the result of his work.

The attraction to this butterfly of bright reflective objects such as car windows, chromium trim and silver paper has been noted in Bentley Wood on many occasions. In 1964 Lieut Col Charles Cowan described how he watched a male that 'for fully three minutes skated along the warm radiator grille, intrigued by the dead flies, the caked mud, the engine smell or the AA badge. I also heard of one found dead inside a car parked there'. In 1969 Kit Lipscomb reported that between 13 and 24 July six males entered one of the forestry houses on the edge of the wood and, at another house nearby, he was told 'they were always coming in, so much so in fact that the windows were kept shut on sunny days to keep the butterflies out'. In 1970 Michael Blackmore watched a female glide down to his parked car and 'inspect' the bonnet before settling on brambles near the wing-mirror.

In 1978 J E Green told a lovely story illustrating the apparent 'tameness' of the male. 'It was feeding on a small piece of dry deer dung and was motionless apart from the rhythmic movements of the proboscis. Twenty minutes later I carefully picked up the dung and closely examined 'His Majesty' from various aspects. I stroked his wings in the hope that he might open them but he just kept feeding with wings closed, even when gently pushed. I noted the orange kneecaps, the purplish bands and orange tips of the antennae knobs and even spots on his eyes. The passage of a cloud over the sun, and suddenly he was away with powerful flight'.

In 1991 a male entered a car in Bentley Wood car park and remained for half an hour on the seat where salmon sandwiches had been lying (Tambling). In 1993 a tattered female was rescued from the pond in Blackmoor Copse (Sue Walker) and a male was attracted to the protective sun-cream on a friend's hand where it sat for a brief period (David Peart).

The Flight Period and Measures of Abundance
Purple emperors are normally on the wing from early July to late August but this is an elusive species and there are probably many more present in a habitat than are actually observed. In spite of its size and appearance it is very rarely seen by the casual observer. For this reason no details are available for compiling a flight period diagram or an index of abundance graph. The earliest sighting in Wiltshire was 10 June 1893 at West Woods (A C Hanbury). This was a year when many species appeared earlier than normal. In the twentieth century the earliest sightings were 26 June 1960 and 1976 near Salisbury (Roy Pitman). The latest record was 6 September 1956, probably from Bentley Wood (Heslop).

Distribution
This fine butterfly, one of our largest and most evocative to many lepidopterists, is confined to large, mature ancient woodlands mainly in the south Midlands and central-southern counties of England. Until the 1960s there were populations in Warwickshire, Lincolnshire, East Anglia, Kent and parts of Wales but the purple emperor is now believed to be extinct in all these regions. An isolated population in Nottinghamshire is the most northerly in England. The present strongholds are the woodlands on the Surrey/Sussex border, north Hampshire and Berkshire, the New Forest and south-east Wiltshire. In Wiltshire the purple emperor breeds, and is regularly seen, in three woodland areas and there are occasional records from elsewhere.

South-east Wiltshire
There are many records from woods in the area east and south of Salisbury which has been well-known for many years for its purple emperor populations. Pitman recorded three individuals in Clarendon Wood in 1929 but in his 1936 report he described it as 'Generally rare'. He listed six localities in the south of the county and added 'possibly many others but owing to its habit of flying and settling high up on oak trees it is often overlooked'. Baron de Worms reported it from Bentley Wood in 1941 and woods near Whiteparish in 1944 and 1945. Heslop rarely gave localities of sightings but he also recorded it from these woodlands in most years from 1941–59. In 1955 he noted 'numerous, every copse and spinney in south Wilts seem to be

occupied'. Several were reported from the Redlynch area in 1954 (Alfred Burras).

The purple emperor was seen in Hound Wood in 1981. In 1984 there were 62 sightings in Bentley Wood between 13 July and 17 August (Mike Read). In the mid-1980s as many as six males were attracted to a greenhouse at Tinney's Firs, Redlynch. They entered through the ventilators, kept very calm, did not flutter and crawled onto the observer's hand (Gerry Mundey). In 1986 a fine female was watched by the author for many minutes as she rested on an oak in Langley Wood. This species enjoyed a good summer in Bentley Wood in 1992 when it was seen in many parts of the wood, several often being seen in a day (Barry Fox). In 1993 and 1994 purple emperors were regularly seen in a garden close to Bentley Wood and Blackmoor Copse and males entered the house, in particular the upstairs bathroom (Walker). In 1994 up to a dozen were counted in a day at the peak flying time in Bentley Wood (Barry Fox).

Great Ridge Wood

Captain Reginald Jackson reported the purple emperor from Great Ridge and Stockton Wood in the early 1950s. Soon after moving to Codford in 1948 he was told that Great Ridge Wood was 'an excellent spot for a rare form of the red admiral which responds to raw beef'. This was presumably a reference to the purple emperor. There appear to be no records from the mid-1950s until 1978 when one male was found on the ground (David Simcox), another was seen a few days later (Chris Thomas) and there was an anonymous record for 1979 (BRC). These were the last sightings from a wood that was visited by many recorders during the WBMS (1982–94).

Grovely Wood

There was an anonymous record from Grovely Wood for 1979 (BRC). The butterfly was widespread at the eastern end in 1983 (Roy Stockley) and five were seen in 1986 (Michael Stacey). Singletons were noted in 1989 (John Tubb) and 1991 (Michael Stevenson), and in 1992 four or five were seen above a single oak. Two were observed above the same tree, probably the master oak, in 1993 and 1994 (Gordon Mackie).

South-west Wiltshire

The purple emperor occurred in Wardour Woods in about 1967 (Stacey) and a worn male was caught at Tuckingmill near Tisbury in 1984 (Peter Thompson). The only confirmed breeding colony in Dorset in 1984 (Thomas and Webb 1984) was in a Cranborne Chase woodland. In 1987 the author was informed (Tony Copley) that a reliable observer knew of the species from the Wiltshire side of the border but the record was not submitted. North of the Chase there were pre-1936 records from the Dinton area (Pitman) where a male was observed for 45 minutes in 1984 (Stephen Palmer) and a female was seen in 1994 (Jim Buchanan).

West Wiltshire

Bowmont Weddell did not record the purple emperor in his diaries (1932–78) from any of the woodlands in this area and Stockley found no evidence of the species being present during the 1960s. The earliest record was of a male on an ivy-covered wall at Neston in 1969 (Mervyn Tyte). In 1971 a female was seen ovipositing in Picket Wood (Michael Hale) and probable singletons were seen in 1982 (Rob Turner) and 1985 (Wendy Clark *et al.*) None has been seen by the author during 17 years of intensive monitoring. The only other records were from Norridge Wood in 1976 (Stockley) and Black Dog Woods where a forester, who had positively identified it, reported it in 1986 (Martin Warren). At Norton Bavant, in the Wylye valley, a single male was seen in a garden in 1989 and several individuals in 1990 (Helen Baker *et al.*). The butterflies involved in these observations may have been remnants of small populations that had become extinct, or they were vagrants.

East Wiltshire

There have been a few records from Chute Cadley near the north Hampshire border (Jim Buchanan). In 1984 he related how he had seen three purple emperors in the previous eight years and in the following years he saw single females in 1985 and

1987, a pair in 1989 and one male feeding on butterfly bush (*Buddleja davidii*) in a garden in 1992 at Conholt Park where the colony is probably based. A male was seen in Buttermere Wood in 1991 (David Green). The species is fairly common and widespread in this area in woods in Hampshire near the county boundary.

Marlborough Area

The 1865 Marlborough College List stated 'Has been taken in Savernake Forest' (W J Baverstock) but the only record from the Forest was for 1881 when a female was caught. The purple emperor was recorded from Stype Wood in 1873 and in the 1887 List it was said to be 'rather common' there. In 1879, Neville Manders commented 'Stype, situated on very high ground, yet swampy, and covered with oak trees, is the domain of the Purple Emperor'. He said of Savernake 'the worst locality, contrary to general expectation, is the Forest, there are fewer insects to be found there than in any wood I know'.

On a single day in 1881 several were seen around a small oak on the edge of Henswood but none was seen there during the following 20 years (Coleman). The only record from West Woods was in 1893 and the last College record was in 1914 but the locality was not given.

In 1947 a singleton was seen in Savernake Forest (Dick Godfrey) but it was not until 1977 (WAM) that the species was reported there again. Since then the purple emperor has been recorded annually, usually as singletons at the southern end near the Column. Although it was stated to be common in 1983 (Stockley) and 1987 (Wayne Fennell) other recorders searched in vain in 1990 in spite of baiting with chicken meat and ripe bananas (Humphrey Kay *et al.*). Keith Andrews' experiences of the species in the Forest contrast with those of most other recorders. On 12 July 1989 he counted 33 including females ovipositing on willows and a group of three males and one female at a sap run. Males were attracted to his car on three occasions and, in 1994, over 20 individuals were seen during a week in July including three males circling together around parked cars. In

nearby West Woods the only recent record was that of a single male in 1984 (Bryan Pinchen). In 1988 a group of people saw two for several minutes at Bedwyn Common and a female was observed ovipositing (Sylvia Young *et al.*). A lethargic female seen in a garden at Marden in 1989 was presumably a vagrant from the Marlborough area 15 km to the north-east (Kate Ashford-Brown *et al.*).

Braydon Forest

The first record of the purple emperor was of a male at Seagry Wood, Startley, near Malmesbury in 1954 (John Tyler). In 1964 Ian Heslop stated 'I have been most interested ... to see the purple emperor ... in central Wilts. and in North Wilts. (exemplified by the relics of the ancient forest of Braden); in the latter in particular it having been unknown hitherto'. He gave no further details. The record in WAM 1978 from Somerford Common is now thought to have been of a white admiral (David Brotheridge). The last record from the Common was of a female seen in Blackberry

Map 42. Distribution of purple emperor

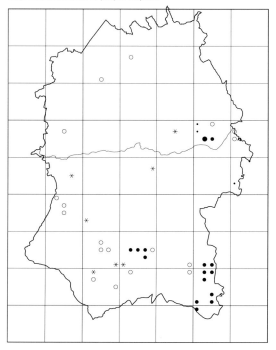

A recently coppiced area in Blackmoor Copse, a nature reserve leased and managed by the WWT. This is a favourite habitat of the purple emperor and woodland fritillaries.

Lane in 1980 (Ron Hatton *et al.*). Since 1980 most of the woodlands have been visited frequently by recorders. It is considered that the purple emperor no longer occurs in the area.

During the WBMS (1982–94) the purple emperor, including those assumed to have been vagrants, was recorded from 27 tetrads (3%). Before 1982 it was recorded from an additional 18 tetrads.

Future Prospects

The purple emperor's future in its stronghold in the south-east of the county is probably secure. Its status has not changed a great deal since the days of Heslop and Pitman. It is now well-established in Grovely Wood and Savernake Forest and perhaps in other woodlands nearby. There are three or four discrete populations in these woods from which vagrants occasionally wander. Records of butterflies from the Dinton area may represent another small population or they may have been vagrants from Grovely Wood.

Provided suitable stands of the larval foodplants are maintained in some of the county's larger woodlands the status of the species is unlikely to change a great deal.

RED ADMIRAL
Vanessa atalanta (Linnaeus)

The generic name *Vanessa*, given to the red admiral by Fabricius in 1807, was Dean Swift's pet name for Esther Vanhombrugh to whom he wrote his poem *Cadenus and Vanessa*. The specific name *atalanta*, given by Linnaeus in 1758, refers to the famous beauty and athlete who raced her suitors and killed them if they lost.

The butterfly was first illustrated by Thomas Mouffet in 1634 but surprisingly it was not listed by Christopher Merrett in 1666. In 1699 James Petiver used the vernacular name 'Admiral' as if it were already in current usage and, in about 1792–1813, Edward Donovan added the prefix 'Red'. An alternative name, 'the alderman', found favour with some writers but red admiral has prevailed.

The red admiral is a large, readily identifiable, butterfly. The most striking feature is the broad scarlet band. This feature can be seen in Ian Grier's photograph. With wings closed, the underside pattern provides excellent camouflage for the butterfly when roosting on tree trunks.

The males tend to establish and patrol a territory in pursuit of females. Once mated, the female lays her pale green eggs singly on the tips of young nettles (*Urtica* spp.). The caterpillar emerges in about a week and feeds on the leaves. The larval and pupal stages each last for three weeks. By late summer both sexes are occupied with feeding. Although red admirals are commonly associated with the butterfly bush (*Buddleja davidii*) and over-ripe fruit in gardens they also nectar at many wild flowers. In some years, groups of a dozen or more may be seen feasting at late summer flowers and ripe fruit which sustain them well into the autumn.

The Flight Period
The first arrivals from the continent are usually seen in Great Britain in May and June. From July, the offspring of these butterflies, and probably additional immigrants, occur throughout the summer and autumn in a succession of generations until they perish at the onset of cold frosty weather.

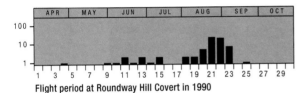

Flight period at Roundway Hill Covert in 1990

the Trowbridge area on 18 September 1933. In 1962 Baron de Worms described it as 'Plentiful and widespread in the county in most years' and continued 'there is evidence of a return migration of the offspring in the late summer as in 1959 when it was in thousands in the West Country. Very few instances of hibernating are known'.

When the weather has remained mild, a few are known to have survived hibernation particularly in the Salisbury area. The earliest record was at Whaddon on 7 January 1983 (Roy Pitman) and the latest was in Swindon on 30 December 1991 (Rob Turner).

Three distinct flight periods at Roundway Hill Covert in 1990 are shown above. During the years 1981–94 the longest flight period was 16 weeks in 1990 and the shortest, one week only, in 1988. The maximum number seen in a weekly visit was 22 on 28 August 1990 nectaring on hemp-agrimony (*Eupatorium cannabinum*).

Measures of Abundance 1980–94 (Figure 23)
As would be expected of a migratory species, annual numbers have fluctuated dramatically at the monitored sites. In 1988 and 1991 the red admiral was a scarce butterfly and only one or two were seen at several of these sites. Red admirals were very common throughout the county in 1982, 1989, 1990 and 1992 and this abundance was clearly reflected at the monitored sites but, in 1994, numbers were below or equal to the average.

Status Before 1982
The first published Wiltshire record occurs in the 1865 Marlborough College List. In the 1873 List it was described as common and in all subsequent Lists as usually common. Pitman reported it from his garden in Salisbury on 24 April 1928. This proved to be a very good year for immigrants, his final sighting being on 18 October. In his 1936 report he stated 'Very common in some years, dependent upon spring immigrants ... twice reported as hibernating in Wilts, which is an unusual event'. Two years later, on 24 January 1938, he saw one 'fly out of the hedge at mid-day'. Bowmont Weddell recorded his first from

Status Since 1982
In most years the red admiral is a common and widespread butterfly across southern Britain, more thinly distributed in the north of England and in Scotland, and in years when numbers of immigrants are high, they reach most of the mainland and many of the northern islands. During the period of the WBMS (1982–94) the red admiral no doubt occurred in all the county tetrads at some time as it roamed across the countryside but, in spite of its size, attractiveness and cosmopolitan nature, it was reported from only 606 tetrads (64%).

Map 43. Distribution of red admiral

PAINTED LADY
Cynthia cardui (Linnaeus)

The generic name *Cynthia,* given to the painted lady by Fabricius in 1807, is derived from that of a mountain on the island of Delos. The specific name *cardui*, given by Linnaeus in 1758, refers to the generic name of thistles which are the main larval foodplants. This butterfly was illustrated by Thomas Mouffet in 1634 and in 1699 James Petiver called it the painted lady, apparently a name already in general use.

When painted ladies alight, the wings are usually held wide open revealing the striking pattern of pink, white and black illustrated in Peter Durnell's photograph. Butterflies are most frequently seen nectaring on purple and pink flowers especially knapweeds (*Centaurea* spp) and thistles (*Cirsium* and *Carduus* spp.) in the wild, and ice plant (*Sedum spectabile*) and butterfly bush (*Buddleja davidii*) in gardens.

The pale-green eggs are laid singly on a leaf of a tall thistle and occasionally on other plants including nettles (*Urtica* spp.). The caterpillar hatches within a week and spins a silk pad on the underside of the leaf on which it feeds. Finally a tent of leaves is made in which the chrysalis develops. The adult usually emerges within a month of the egg being laid. Several generations may occur in hot summers but, as the weather deteriorates, all caterpillars, chrysalises and remaining adults perish.

The Flight Period

There is no evidence that the species can over-winter in Great Britain in any of its life stages. Painted ladies arrive from North Africa in small numbers in early June. Larger numbers follow throughout the summer. They frequently visit gardens and other places which have nectar-producing flowers.

Painted ladies arrived exceptionally early in 1985 and 1992. During the large influx in 1985, one was recorded on 4 April at Edington near Westbury (John d'Arcy), but the earliest twentieth century record was 1 April 1990 at Mere (Michael Powell). The only known earlier record is an entry

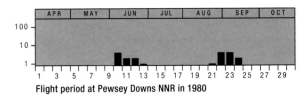

Flight period at Pewsey Downs NNR in 1980

for 17 March by E L Hesketh in the 1870 Marlborough College List.

The 1992 early invasion was a little later than that of 1985 and numbers reported were fewer. The first sighting in 1992 was 20 April on SPTA(W) (Rob Turner). The flight period at Pewsey Downs NNR in 1980 is shown above. During the years 1980–94, the longest flight period was 17 weeks in 1982 and the shortest, only one week, in 1981. In 1984 and 1989 none was seen. The largest number counted on a weekly visit was eight in August 1982.

Measures of Abundance 1980–94 (Figure 24)
The correlation between the fluctuations at four monitored sites is very close. Large fluctuations have frequently been commented upon and are normal for this species. Whereas it is unusual for no red admirals to be seen in a season, this is often true of the painted lady. In 1984 none was seen from ten monitored sites. It might have been expected that the annual fluctuations in abundance of this species and of the red admiral would be in phase but this has not always been the case. Although both peaked in 1982 and 1985 they were completely out of phase in 1988 and 1989; synchrony returned from 1990–93. In 1994 the number of painted ladies increased at all the sites whereas those for the red admiral fell at most of them.

Status Before 1982
The first published reference to the painted lady in Wiltshire appeared in the 1865 Marlborough College List where it was said to have been common in 1862, 1864 and 1865. In subsequent Lists it was described as 'irregular in appearance, sometimes common'. Roy Pitman recorded it at Odstock on 6 May 1928 and he saw and took many more in that year. His last sighting was on

3 October, also at Odstock. In his 1936 report he said it was 'occasionally common, like the red admiral, in habits it differs, preferring open down and flowery slopes. Does not hibernate'. Bowmont Weddell reported it on 22 July 1933 from the Trowbridge area. In 1962 Baron de Worms described it as 'often abundant in the county in years of immigration'.

Status Since 1982
In 1982, 1985, 1988, 1990 and 1994 the painted lady was a common butterfly and in 1985 it was selected as Wiltshire's 'Butterfly of the Year' on account of its early arrival and large numbers in the spring. No doubt it occurred in all the county tetrads in years of high abundance. During the WBMS (1982–94) it was recorded from 442 tetrads (46%).

Map 44. Distribution of painted lady

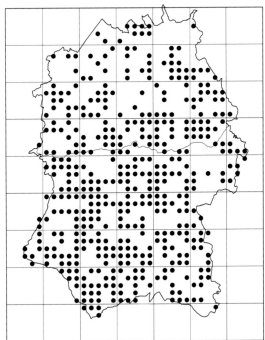

SMALL TORTOISESHELL
Aglais urticae (Linnaeus)

The generic name *Aglais*, given to the small tortoiseshell by Dalman in 1816, means 'beauty' or 'beautiful'. The specific name *urticae* given by Linnaeus in 1758 refers to the generic name of nettles, the larval foodplants. It was illustrated by Thomas Mouffet in 1634 and mentioned by Christopher Merrett in 1666. James Petiver called it the 'Lesser' or 'Common Tortoiseshell' from 1699. The present name was first used by Benjamin Wilkes in about 1741.

Anthony Tyers' photograph of an individual basking on the ground shows the exceptionally long, silky hair-scales on the inner part of the lower wings. Males hold territories near nettles (*Urtica* spp.) growing in full sun to await virgin females. Mating takes place within the protecting nettlebed. Small tortoiseshells take nectar from willows (*Salix* spp.) and dandelions (*Taraxacum officinale*) in spring and from many wild and garden flowers in summer and autumn. Ice-plant (*Sedum spectabile*) and butterfly-bush (*Buddleja davidii*) are important sources for large

numbers of butterflies before they go into hibernation.

The pale-green eggs are laid in large clutches, layer upon layer, on the underside of the youngest nettle leaves. The caterpillars feed together until full-grown, when they leave the nettlebed singly to pupate for a period of about three weeks.

The Flight Period
The small tortoiseshell emerges from hibernation as early as February if the weather is favourable. The offspring of these early butterflies are on the wing from the end of June and produce a second generation which may be seen until late autumn. Spring numbers usually peak during the second week of April but the time of the second generation peak varies depending on weather conditions.

In Picket Wood from 1980 to 1994 the longest flight period was 19 weeks in 1980 and the shortest was seven weeks in 1986, 1988 and 1993. The maximum number of spring generation

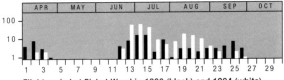

Flight period at Picket Wood in 1980 (black) and 1984 (white)

butterflies seen on any one weekly transect walk was eight in April 1980 and, of the later generation, the maximum was 62 in July 1984. The earliest sighting was 8 March 1990 and the latest 13 October 1987. Butterflies seen before March and after late October are likely to have been disturbed from hibernation. Two flight period patterns at Picket Wood are shown above. That for 1980 is probably typical for most open woodlands. The year 1984 was one when the butterfly appeared in great abundance.

Measures of Abundance 1980–94 (Figure 25)
There were some very large fluctuations of this often common species at the six monitored sites. The close correlation between the figures indicates that weather was probably the main factor affecting the number of butterflies seen. There was a gradual decline in numbers between the early 1980s and the early 1990s but there were peaks in 1982, 1984 and 1987. Numbers were low in 1981, 1983, 1986 and 1993 but recovered at most sites in 1994. In 1982 and 1991 this species was chosen as the county's 'Butterfly of the Year'. In spite of a moderate recovery in 1994, numbers at all sites were below average values.

Status Before 1982
The first known published Wiltshire record of the small tortoiseshell was in the 1865 Marlborough College List. In all subsequent Lists it was described as very common. Roy Pitman saw it in the Salisbury district in February 1928 and in his 1936 report stated it to be 'usually abundant everywhere'. It was first mentioned by Bowmont Weddell from the Trowbridge area on 29 February 1948. In 1962 Baron de Worms described it as 'a very common insect all over the county'.

Status Since 1982
The small tortoiseshell is found throughout Great Britain and Ireland. It is a very mobile species and is attracted to patches of nectar-rich flowers including thistles (*Cirsium* and *Carduus* spp.) and teasel (*Dipsacus fullonum*) that have colonised disturbed ground. In recent years, the general view of many recorders was that the small tortoiseshell was no longer a very common species. However, for most people this colourful insect is probably the most frequently seen and is known by name even by those who have no particular interest in butterflies. No doubt it occurs in every tetrad in Wiltshire but, during the WBMS (1982–94), it was recorded from only 819 (86%).

Future Prospects
In a few localities this species may suffer from the effect of nettles being sprayed rather than cut but, provided large stands are available in sunny, sheltered situations, the small tortoiseshell should continue to be a familiar and welcome sight.

Map 45. Distribution of small tortoiseshell

LARGE TORTOISESHELL
Nymphalis polychloros (Linnaeus)

The generic name *Nymphalis*, given to the large tortoiseshell by Kluk in 1802, refers to nymphs often made brides against their will by a lascivious god. The specific name *polychloros*, given by Linnaeus in 1758, comes from the Greek words for 'many' and 'colour'. This species was first illustrated by Thomas Mouffet in 1634 and was named 'The greater Tortoise-shell Butterfly' by James Petiver in 1699. Most later writers called it the 'Great', 'Greater' or 'Large' tortoiseshell.

The large tortoiseshell is now a very rare species in Britain and its present status is uncertain. Many lepidopterists doubt its existence as a resident breeding species and believe that the few sightings recorded each year are either of immigrants from Europe or bred specimens that have escaped or been released. Misidentification of this species for the similar, closely-related small tortoiseshell and comma is easily made by observers who do not have a clear, close-up view. Size alone cannot always be diagnostic because individuals of the two common species are sometimes larger than

normal. The large tortoiseshell is similar in size and shape to the peacock and has softer orange colouring than the bright markings of the small tortoiseshell and comma. The blue crescents on the wing edges are fewer and less noticeable than those on the small tortoiseshell. These differences can be appreciated by comparing Jean Matthews' photograph with those of the other two species.

In 1986, Roy Stockley, who had studied the ecology of this species and mastered the difficult breeding techniques, described his findings to the author as follows. The butterflies emerge from hibernation, which they probably spend in hollow trees in the wild, in late March and early April. Mating occurs soon after emergence (at the time he had four mated pairs under observation), the male dying soon afterwards. The female probably does not move far after mating for a period of two to three weeks. The spring flight period is very short during which time the female lays her yellowish eggs in large batches, usually on terminal twigs in the crowns of elms (*Ulmus* spp.) and occasionally on willow (*Salix* spp.), poplar (*Populus* spp.), aspen (*P. tremula*), cherry (*Prunus avium*) and pear (*Pyrus communis*). On hatching about three weeks later, the caterpillars remain together, spinning silken webs and feeding on the leaves until ready to pupate. Then they fall to the ground and search for suitable pupation sites. It is believed that many caterpillars and chrysalises are killed by parasitic wasps. The butterflies emerge in July and enter into hibernation very early. Those seen in late September or October probably die.

Most recorded observations have been of butterflies either in flight, resting or basking in the sunshine. Flowers are rarely visited but privet (*Ligustrum* spp.), willow and bramble blossom (*Rubus fruticosus* agg.) are known to be attractive. In Wiltshire gardens there have been sightings of large tortoiseshells nectaring at butterfly-bush (*Buddleja davidii*), aster (*Callistephus* spp.) and French marigold (*Tagetes* spp.).

The Flight Period

No details are available to compile a flight period diagram. The earliest Wiltshire record was 17 March 1882 (H Dobie) reported in a Marlborough College List and, in more recent times, Roy Pitman received a record from Bentley Wood on 26 March 1964 (George Forster). The latest sighting was recorded in the Dauntsey School Fauna List for 20 October 1938 and one was seen on 12 October 1980 at Bradford-on-Avon (Joan Ward). All records since 1982 have been of late summer individuals.

Measures of Abundance

No information is available from any monitored sites either in Wiltshire or the rest of Great Britain.

Status Before 1900

The first published Wiltshire record was that of the Rev Francis Morris in 1853 who stated 'It occurs also near Great Bedwyn and Sarum, Wiltshire'. Henry Stainton's correspondent at Corsham did not record it from that area in 1857 when it was considered to be 'not generally common'. In the first Marlborough College List

of 1865 it was stated to be 'occasionally met with' and to have been taken twice and seen once. It was seen on 29 April 1866 (H W Hockin) and caught on 18 April 1868 (C A Sladen). In the 1873 List, Edward Meyrick stated that it was 'not rare generally' but in the 1892 List he stated 'formerly not scarce, not since 1882'. Between 1865 and 1900 a total of 27 sightings, all of singletons, were reported but there was no mention of the species' early stages. It is probably reasonable to assume that the situation in the Marlborough area reflected the position in the remainder of the county indicating that the large tortoiseshell was either very elusive, very rare or perhaps both. In 1896 J W Tutt wrote 'It is most uncertain in its appearance being occasionally very abundant and then exceedingly rare for many years'. This summed up the experiences of most of his contemporaries.

Status From 1900–1980

During this period there were only seven singletons reported in the Marlborough College Lists, the last being from Wilton Brail in 1944. The large tortoiseshell was included in E Cook's 1902 list from the Devizes area but no details of its status were given. In July 1921 one was taken near Cripplestyle, Damerham, which was then in Wiltshire, by Steven Corbet who commented 'never common here'.

One was seen on the wing in the Milford district of Salisbury on 18 September 1928 (Pitman). In 1931 he reported five in August from near Redlynch but these may have been near the home in Hampshire of his friend, Alfred Burras, and may not have all been seen on one occasion. Singletons were reported from Lydiard Park in 1932 and Old Sarum in 1934. In his 1936 report he commented 'Now getting very scarce in the county. Former haunts are apparently deserted'. Bowmont Weddell's diaries (1932–78) contain no reference to the species. The Dauntsey School Fauna List for 1931–48 includes a singleton in October 1938 and 1940 and another in September 1943.

Richard Thompson, who lived in Salisbury from 1936 until the mid-1950s, recollected his father capturing a tattered large tortoiseshell near a very large elm tree in the city. He did not add this individual to his collection in the hope that he would catch a much better specimen later, but no more were ever seen.

There were a few records of singletons from WANHS and SDNHS reports during the years 1947–75. In 1962 Baron de Worms included several of the earlier records, his last being those from Old Sarum and near Shaftesbury in 1948 (Pitman). His references to Marlborough College records which stated 'Seen in numbers' and 'often in Savernake Forest where it was especially common in 1933' are not borne out by the College reports. He concluded 'Very rare now in Wiltshire, though formerly quite numerous'.

Ian Heslop reported singletons from Blackmoor Copse in each of the five years 1954–58. In 1956 several were seen near Pepperbox Hill and Whiteparish, and one at Coombe Bissett. In 1958 he commented 'There is considerable evidence that since this, our rarest resident British species, abandoned its principal colony in Suffolk, it has

been trying to establish a new colony in the area within a radius of 15 miles from the edges of Southampton Water. The sparse Sussex colony is stable. The separate Somerset and Dorset colonisations appear to have failed'. A further 17 years were to elapse before another sighting was made when he saw one in Bentley Wood on 24 July 1965 and commented 'the large tortoiseshell still contrives to lead a somewhat exiguous existence in the area between Salisbury and Southampton'.

In 1973 Pitman noted 'A very exciting report of this species in Hampshire in a local paper. Soon be on the danger list. Few reports over the last few years and no breeding records'. The final record for this period came from Blackmoor Copse via Pitman in 1975 when he said 'seen several times by Reg Stacey and his friends as it took several flights around the tops of the bushes and occasionally alighted to bask in the sunshine'.

During this 80 year period, there were 38 reports of large tortoiseshells, nearly all being of singletons.

Map 46. Distribution of English elm

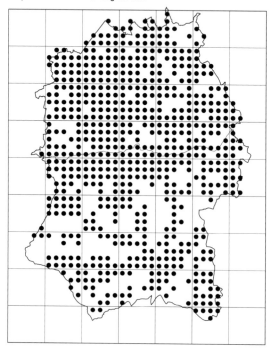

Map 47. Distribution of large tortoiseshell

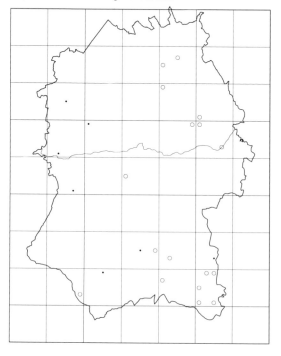

Status Since 1980

The large tortoiseshell was widespread during the latter half of the nineteenth century mainly in southern England and the Midlands. It was seldom considered to be a common species except in 1902, the early 1930s and from 1945 to 1948 when it was sometimes seen in large numbers. Its last stronghold was in East Suffolk where it was generally common until 1954 but then rapidly declined to become nationally rare. Possibly the reasons for large fluctuations in abundance were similar to those experienced by the holly blue. Due to a combination of unfavourable factors, it failed to recover from its scarce status in the early 1950s.

During the WBMS (1982–94) the 14 sightings of single adults gave the large tortoiseshell the status of being a Wiltshire butterfly and all these sightings are described below although some of the records were not confirmed. There were no reports of caterpillars or chrysalises which might have produced a breeding population. There were also a few uncertain sightings which have not been referred to.

In a hillside garden in Bradford-on-Avon a single large tortoiseshell was recorded from July onwards each year from 1980 to 1986, except in 1982 (Ward). There were many mature elm trees on the hillside during the 1970s where a breeding population could have survived as is suggested by these annual observations. In 1983 and 1987 singletons were seen in the nearby Country Park (Peter Wheeler) further substantiating this suggestion. The sighting in 1987 was the last from the area in spite of frequent searches by the author in subsequent years. The observation of a singleton, basking on a quarry bank at Beggar's Knoll near Westbury on 9 August 1982 (Ian Grier), coincided with the escape of a few adults from stock that had been bred in the town (Nigel Wynn).

In 1985, recorders who are familiar with butterflies and who were fortunate that the large tortoiseshells gave them time in which to make their identifications, made the following observations. One seen basking on a post at Lackham College near Chippenham on 23 July (Ward), one basking on raspberry canes in a Winterslow garden on 11 and 12 August (Cynthia Jones) and one seen on asters and French marigolds in a garden near Tisbury (Sadie Cooper via Peter Shallcross). One was seen at West Yatton Down on 14 July 1990 (Maurice Avent) and the last sighting in the county was of one at Little Langford Down near Grovely Wood in 1992 (David Simpson).

All these records have been included on the distribution map if sufficient location details were available, even though they may not have been confirmed. During the WBMS the large tortoiseshell was recorded from seven tetrads (0.7%). There were records from only 17 tetrads before 1980 which could be a true reflection of the species' former scarcity. However, in a county where there was an abundance of the main larval foodplants until the 1970s [see distribution maps for English elm (*Ulmus procera*) on page 130 and wych elm (*U. glabra*) on page 75], this species would have been expected to be much more common. Perhaps, due to its elusive behaviour, it was overlooked by earlier lepidopterists but this can now only be speculation.

Future Prospects

From the history of the large tortoiseshell in the county over the last 130 years it appears most unlikely that a naturally occurring breeding population will be found. Singletons may continue to be reported occasionally either as rare immigrants or bred specimens and further misidentifications will no doubt continue to be made.

PEACOCK
Inachis io (Linnaeus)

The generic name *Inachis*, given to the peacock by Hübner in 1819, was the name of the River God whose daughter Io was seduced by Zeus. The specific name *io* had been given by Linnaeus in 1758. This butterfly was illustrated by Thomas Mouffet in 1634 who wrote 'it can be called Queen of All'. In 1699 James Petiver called it 'The Peacock's Eye' and *circa* 1741 Benjamin Wilkes abbreviated this name to the peacock butterfly.

'Peacock' is an obvious reference to the likeness of the 'eyes' on the butterfly's wings to those on the tail feathers of the similarly-named exotic bird. The black undersides of the wings give excellent concealment during hibernation, which is spent in out-buildings, hollow trees, woodpiles and other dark places. John Grearson's photograph is of a female. In the spring, the males defend their territories along hedgerows and the rides and edges of woodland flying out to investigate any dark-coloured insect that passes by. Pairing occurs at this time. The females lay their pale green eggs

in batches on the undersides of nettle leaves (*Urtica* spp.). The gregarious caterpillars can easily be seen amongst their silken webs as they feed together. The larval and pupal stages together last for about eight weeks.

The Flight Period

Peacock butterflies start emerging from hibernation in late March, their numbers building up to a peak in the last two weeks of April. At this time of year nectar sources are scarce and most of the butterflies are attracted to woodlands where willows (*Salix* spp.) and primroses (*Primula vulgaris*) provide much of their food. The next generation emerges at the end of July and numbers rise quickly. Large groups of butterflies may be seen feeding avidly on nectar-rich flowers prior to entering into hibernation towards the end of August, or later if food is still available. In Picket Wood they disappear about two weeks after numbers have reached their peak. By this time thistles (*Cirsium* and *Carduus* spp.), teasel

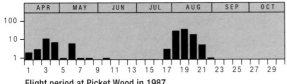

Flight period at Picket Wood in 1987

(*Dipsacus fullonum*) and hemp-agrimony (*Eupatorium cannabinum*) have finished flowering and some butterflies disperse to visit gardens where nectar is still available. The flight period in the wood in 1987 is shown above, and is probably typical of most woodlands in Wiltshire. During the 15 years of monitoring, the longest flight period was 24 weeks in 1990 and the shortest was 13 weeks in 1993. The maximum number of individuals counted weekly on the transect varied from five to 21 in the spring and 11 to 70 in the summer. The earliest county record was 11 January 1983 at Coombe Bissett (SDNHS) and the latest was 29 October 1993 in Salisbury (Ted Gange).

Measures of Abundance 1980–94 (Figure 26)
Results from monitored sites show few extremes and some similarities in the annual fluctuations. In the mid-1980s, numbers were lower than in the early 1990s, the poorest year being 1986. They were at their highest at most sites in 1992 but fell back sharply in 1994. The figures do not separate spring and summer generations but the numbers of the latter are almost always the larger. As peacocks are very mobile and roam widely, those counted at a site may not be residents but itinerants in search of sources of nectar. Sites with plenty of thistles, teasel, hemp-agrimony and knapweeds (*Centaurea* spp.) are likely to have the largest populations.

Status Before 1982
The first known published Wiltshire record was in the 1865 Marlborough College List and in all the subsequent Lists it was described as being common. Roy Pitman recorded it on 21 February 1928 in the Salisbury area and in his 1936 report he described the butterfly as common. It appears that Bowmont Weddell did not consider such a common

species worth noting for there is no mention of it in his diaries (1932–78) from the Trowbridge area. In 1962, Baron de Worms described it as being 'generally distributed throughout the county'.

Status Since 1982
The peacock occurs throughout England and Wales and is probably spreading further north in Scotland and Northern Ireland. Its eye-catching appearance has made it familiar to many people who see it in their gardens in late summer and autumn feeding in preparation for hibernation. Its success in the future may depend largely on this source of food and on waste places where nettles are allowed to grow. During the WBMS (1982–94) the peacock was widely distributed and was recorded from 713 tetrads (75%).

Map 48. Distribution of peacock

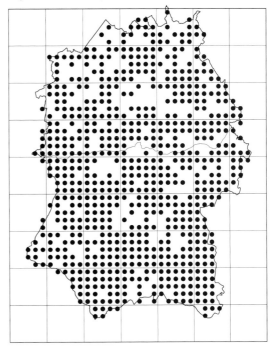

COMMA
Polygonia c-album (Linnaeus)

The generic name *Polygonia*, given to the comma by Hübner in 1819, is derived from two words meaning 'many' and 'an angle' and refers to the jagged edges of the butterfly's wings. The specific name *c-album*, given by Linnaeus in 1758 refers to the white (*albus*) c-shaped mark on the underside of the hindwings. It may have been illustrated by Thomas Mouffet in 1634 although his woodcut is not clear. In 1710 John Ray gave a full description but no name. In 1717 James Petiver used four names, the 'Silver', 'Pale', 'Jagged-wing' and 'Small' comma. It would appear that comma was already established and this name has survived.

The distinctive features are the jagged wing profile and the white comma mark on the underside of the hindwings. It could be mistaken for a woodland fritillary or tattered small tortoiseshell when in flight but when seen at close quarters, as in Richard Tambling's photograph, identification is not difficult. The pale green eggs are usually laid singly on the upper surface of the leaves of nettles

(*Urtica* spp.), hop (*Humulus lupulus*) and elm (*Ulmus* spp.). The larval and pupal stages together last for about nine weeks.

The Flight Period
The comma usually emerges from hibernation in late March when pairing takes place. The first generation is on the wing during July and August and the second from late August until well into the autumn. The diagram shows the flight period pattern in Picket Wood in 1982 where the longest flight period was 23 weeks in 1990 and 1991 and the shortest was four weeks in 1981. The maximum number of individuals counted weekly on the transect varied from one to 11 in the spring and two to 12 in the later generations. The earliest sighting was 7 March 1991 and the latest 26 October 1983 but these are not extreme dates for the county.

Roy Pitman saw a comma in the Salisbury area on 23 January 1969 and in 1982 he saw 'a few' on 15 November on rotting apples with small

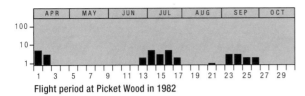

Flight period at Picket Wood in 1982

tortoiseshells and 31 red admirals. The latest county record was 21 November 1968 at Blackmoor Copse (Kit Lipscomb).

Measures of Abundance 1980–94 (Figure 27)

There have been large fluctuations in abundance at monitored sites in Wiltshire. Figure 27 shows the close correlation between the four sites. Numbers were high in the good season of 1982, fell in 1984, rapidly increased in 1986 and 1987 but crashed in the late 1980s. Numbers peaked in 1991 but then fell back and, in 1994, the comma was a scarce species.

Status Before 1982

In the second half of the nineteenth century the comma was a rare butterfly in Wiltshire. There were only 12 records from the Marlborough area (1863–1920). The first published record was that of one captured near Ramsbury by E H Manders in 1863. Edward Meyrick was 'astonished to see a fine specimen at Marlborough in 1895'. In the period 1905–18, the Rev Percy Harrison, Rector of Lydiard Millicent, saw only 'an odd specimen' until July 1918 when he saw about 35 in a local wood. From 1922 onwards, it was described as fairly common in the Marlborough area, several being seen together rather than singletons. By the mid-1930s the comma was a fairly common resident in the county. Roy Pitman saw several near Salisbury in 1928 and in his 1936 report he stated 'Very rare until about 1920 when it began to establish itself in various parts of the county'. Bowmont Weddell reported it from the Trowbridge area in 1934 and, in 1962, Baron de Worms stated 'has become increasingly common in the county since about 1928. Since the early 1930s has spread all over the south of England'.

Status Since 1982

The comma is now widespread and generally common in Great Britain south of a line from the Humber to the Mersey. It is absent from Scotland and Ireland. In the spring it occurs in a variety of habitats, particularly sunny woodland rides and clearings and along overgrown hedgerows. It is rarely seen on open downland. Later in the year it also becomes an urban insect, visiting gardens to search for nectar-producing flowers and to obtain the juices from rotting fruit. In late autumn, the blossom of ivy (*Hedera helix*) is particularly attractive to both this species and the red admiral. During the WBMS (1982–94) it was shown to be a widespread but thinly distributed species and was only recorded from 397 tetrads (42%).

Future Prospects

There appears to be no evidence of a decline in abundance or a contraction of range but, bearing its history in mind, it could become scarce again sometime in the future.

Map 49. Distribution of comma

SMALL PEARL-BORDERED FRITILLARY
Boloria selene ([Denis and Schiffermüller])

The generic name *Boloria*, given to both pearl-bordered fritillaries by Moore in 1900, is derived from *bolos*, a fishing-net, describing the markings on the underside of the hindwings. The specific name *selene* given by Denis and Schiffermüller in 1775 refers to Diana, goddess of the moon. The small pearl-bordered fritillary was thought to have been one of the species described by Christopher Merrett in 1666 but amongst the early aurelians there was, like today, confusion surrounding the identification of the small fritillaries. In 1710 John Ray positively described this species. In 1717 James Petiver called it the 'April Fritillary', Benjamin Wilkes named it the 'Small Pearl Border Fritillary' in about 1741 and in 1803 Adrian Haworth altered the latter to the present name.

The two small fritillaries, the small pearl-bordered and the pearl-bordered, are so similar in appearance that a detailed description of the difference between the pattern on the upper wings is of little use for field identification. The undersides

are less similar, the small pearl-bordered having more pearl markings and darker patches of brown. These can be seen in Steve Day's photograph on page 137 of one nectaring on marsh thistle (*Cirsium palustre*) in Bentley Wood. Ian Grier's photograph (above) shows a pair basking in Great Wood.

The cream-coloured egg is laid singly on, or close to, violet leaves (*Viola* spp.). The caterpillar hatches after two weeks, eating the eggshell before feeding on the leaves. It hibernates when half grown and pupates from late April hanging among the woodland vegetation.

The Flight Period
Small pearl-bordered fritillaries occasionally emerge in late May but are more usually seen at the beginning of June. The flight period at Picket Wood in 1981 is typical for the species. Numbers peak quickly in mid-June and butterflies are rarely seen after mid-July. Occasionally there are reports of a small partial second generation and singletons were seen in Bentley Wood eastern clearing in

A small pearl-bordered fritillary nectaring in Bentley Wood. The dark brown patches and silver 'pearls' are more numerous on this species than on the pearl-bordered fritillary (see page 141).

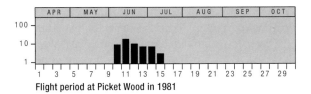

Flight period at Picket Wood in 1981

August 1989 and 1990. Seven weeks was the longest flight period observed at Picket Wood and occurred in four of the 14 years of monitoring. The maximum number of individuals counted on the transect during any one visit was 18 on 13 June 1981. The earliest sighting was 22 May 1990 and the latest 16 July 1983. There is an incredibly early date of 30 April 1893 in a Marlborough College List. This was an exceptional year for many species which emerged early in extreme drought conditions.

Measures of Abundance 1981–94 (Figure 28)
During the first three years of monitoring at Picket Wood (1978–80), the two small fritillaries were not distinguished from each other. By 1981

the author had sufficient experience of the two to enable identification to be determined with reasonable certainty even when the butterflies were flying. This small wood was a very good butterfly habitat in the late 1970s and early 1980s when woodland fritillaries were commonly seen. The sad story of this species at Picket Wood since 1981 is clear from Figure 28. Although there appeared to be signs of a recovery in 1987, numbers fell alarmingly during the next two years. In 1989 the few butterflies found were restricted to a small area of marginally suitable habitat and, in spite of extensive conifer removal and ride widening, the valiant efforts of conservation volunteers and contractors came too late and the last small pearl-bordered fritillaries were seen in 1991. It was suggested that the drought at that time hastened their end (Nick Wynn), since it has been known for many years that damp areas of woodland are preferred by this species. Unfortunately, monitoring has recorded the decline of this species to local extinction.

137

Blackmoor Copse is an ancient deciduous woodland which had become overgrown. Few open sunny areas remained by the early 1980s. Coppicing, ride-widening and butterfly monitoring began in 1984. Although monitoring was spasmodic in the first five years, estimated data indicated that the small pearl-bordered fritillary was scarce and the few seen were probably wanderers from Bentley Wood. However, in 1989 monitoring was more comprehensive and the butterfly appeared to have responded to the management. It became much more abundant, numbers stabilising at the higher levels until 1994.

The original character of Bentley Wood was changed from that of an ancient woodland in the 1950s by clear-felling large areas and replanting with conifers. By the early 1980s the conifers were rapidly shading out much of the ground flora in many parts of the wood. In 1983, Paul Waring established two butterfly transects and in 1986 Barry Fox resurrected one of them. During the next two years three more were established in appropriate areas of the wood. Small pearl-bordered fritillary numbers have fluctuated greatly over the last few years and, in spite of the removal of conifers from some areas, the wood is still too shady for most butterfly species to reach their full potential. It is hoped that continued opening-up of the wood will create additional suitable habitat in this stronghold for this species in the county.

Picket Wood, Blackmoor Copse and Bentley Wood were all designated SSSIs, mainly due to the richness of their butterfly fauna, particularly the woodland fritillaries.

Status Before 1982

The first person to refer to the species from Wiltshire was the Rev Francis Morris in 1853. He wrote 'It occurs near Great Bedwyn and Sarum, Wiltshire'. Presumably his source was J W Lukis. In 1857, Henry Stainton reported that it occurred commonly at Corsham. It was included in the 1865 Marlborough College List as 'Savernake Forest, abundant' and was recorded on 1 June 1866 by A C Hilton. In all subsequent College Lists until 1956 it was described as 'common in woods'. Roy

Pitman recorded it from the Bentley Wood area on 27 May 1928 describing it as 'prolific, took as many as needed'. In his 1936 report he stated 'common in most woods, likes open spaces'. The Dauntsey School List (1931–48) reported it as being common in Manor and Erlestoke Woods in 1945. Bowmont Weddell reported it from woods in the Trowbridge area in 1933 and from the Sutton Veny woods in 1936. In 1962, Baron de Worms repeated many of these records and stated 'of much the same distribution in the county as the last species', a reference to the pearl-bordered fritillary which he described as 'very common in most years in the woods of the county'.

Evidence suggests that a decline in numbers had already begun by the late 1950s and, although it is apparent that the small pearl-bordered fritillary had previously been a very common woodland species, it was becoming local and scarce.

Status Since 1982
South Wiltshire
The two separate small colonies known from Porton Down between 1985 and 1987 (Ian Small) are probably still extant. Besides Bentley Wood and Blackmoor Copse already referred to, three were seen at Hamptworth Common in 1987 (Malvyn Potter) and two were positively identified from several small fritillaries seen at Whiteparish Common in 1987 (Patricia Woodruffe). Good numbers of small pearl-bordered fritillaries were seen in Langley Wood in the extreme south-eastern corner of the county in 1992 (Graham Smith).

Great Ridge and Grovely, the two large woods in the south of the county, have had strong colonies. The last record from Great Ridge was that of six seen in 1989 (Barbara Last) and, since its status of being plentiful in Grovely in 1989, records have only been in single figures (Stephen Palmer, Gordon Mackie).

West Wiltshire
A few individuals were seen in woods on the Somerset border near Gare Hill and Longleat between 1985 and 1987. The status of the species in this area, which is infrequently visited, is

uncertain. A singleton was seen over the county border in Somerset in 1990 (Barry Checksfield), a small colony was found in a clearing in Stourton Woods in May (Wynn) and a stronger colony nearby in Somerset (Wynn). A small remnant colony found in Green Lane Wood in 1990 (Richard Wells) has not been confirmed since 1991. Some of the small fritillaries intermittently seen on the western edge of Pomeroy Wood on the Vagg's Hill transect may have been this species (Audrey Brown). The last sighting was of a singleton in 1992. One small colony which survives in Black Dog Woods, where seven individuals were seen in one hour in 1994 (Wynn), is now the only known colony in this part of the county.

North Wiltshire
A small colony was known in Savernake Forest in 1984 (Keith Andrews) but has not been observed since. The small pearl-bordered fritillary survives at Somerford Common but numbers have not reached double figures since 1983 when it was seen in abundance (Paul Mapplebeck). Since 1985, singletons only have been recorded on the transect (John Grearson). It is probably still present in Great Wood where it was the commonest species of butterfly seen in May in 1988 (Fuller and John d'Arcy) and where several were counted in June 1990 (Rob Turner). These are the only records from the north of the county.

Future Prospects
This butterfly is scarce in southern Britain. It has almost disappeared from most of the woodlands in East Anglia, the south-east and the Midlands.

It is now generally accepted that the change in woodland management from the coppice system to either neglect or felling and replanting with conifers and the loss of adjacent grassland have been the reasons for the turn-around in the fortunes of this and several other mainly woodland species. It was described as a common woodland insect in most areas, including Wiltshire, until about 40 years ago. However, during the WBMS (1982–94) the small pearl-bordered fritillary was recorded from only 25 tetrads (2.5%) and was found to be very

local and restricted in distribution. The decline, which accelerated in the last ten years, has reduced the status of the species to that of a county rarity. Of the total of 18 colonies recorded, those at Picket Wood, Green Lane Wood and Savernake Forest have almost certainly become extinct and the status of several others is probably very vulnerable. Urgent conservation measures are needed to ensure that this lovely little fritillary remains a county species.

The necessary management in Picket Wood was eventually carried out but was probably 'too little too late'. The colony had reached low numbers in a deteriorating habitat and, combined with unfavourable weather at the time of emergence, led to the demise of the butterfly. The wood now appears to have some suitable habitat for this species, but natural recolonisation is very unlikely due to its distance from the nearest extant population. Re-establishment from stock taken from other colonies may be necessary, both here and at other woodlands, if this species is to remain on the county list.

Map 50. Distribution of small pearl-bordered fritillary

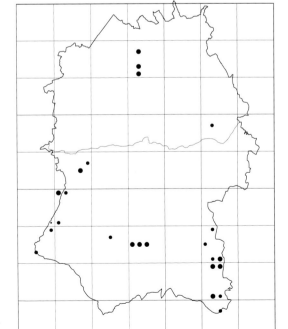

PEARL-BORDERED FRITILLARY
Boloria euphrosyne (Linnaeus)

The origin of the generic name of the pearl-bordered fritillary can be found on page 136. The specific name *euphrosyne*, given to this butterfly by Linnaeus in 1758, is the name of one of the three Graces who personified elegance and beauty. James Petiver was the first to give a name to this species in 1699 when he called it 'The April Fritillary'. In 1766 Moses Harris changed the name to 'Pearl Border Frittillaria'. With a slight change in spelling, this name came into general use and has survived to the present.

The difficulties of correctly differentiating between this species and its close relative, the small pearl-bordered fritillary, are explained on page 136. They can be appreciated by comparing details of the wing markings in Ian Grier's photograph (above) and Steve Day's on page 141 with those on pages 136 and 137.

The adults remain within a discrete area of a wood nectaring on bugle (*Ajuga reptans*) and other spring-flowering species. On warm, sunny days the males glide low over the vegetation in search of virgin females. After mating, the females remain hidden until the eggs are ready to be laid on, or close to, violets (*Viola* spp.) growing in warm, dry pockets. The caterpillars hatch after two weeks and feed on seedlings and young violet leaves until September. They hibernate and resume feeding in the first warm days of March prior to pupating in late April amongst dense vegetation.

The Flight Period
The pearl-bordered fritillary is usually on the wing from the second week of May until the third week of June. It is very unusual to see it in July although a partial second generation is occasionally reported.

The flight period for 1985 at Picket Wood, showing peak abundance at the end of May, is typical for the species. During monitoring at this site (1981–94) the longest flight period noted was seven weeks in 1984 and 1987 and the maximum number of adults seen on any one visit during a

A mating pair of pearl-bordered fritillaries in Picket Wood in 1985 where, sadly, the species is now extinct. The pearl border on the hind wings is clearly visible.

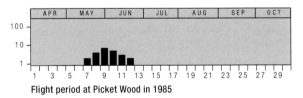

Flight period at Picket Wood in 1985

transect walk was 18 on 13 May 1982. The earliest sighting was 4 May in 1984 and 1990 and the latest 25 June 1986. The earliest date given in a Marlborough College List was 21 April 1893, this being the only April date during the 98 years 1865–1962.

Measures of Abundance 1981–94 (Figure 29)
The indices of abundance from seven transects at four monitored sites in Wiltshire 1981–94 show that there were large fluctuations. The results of monitoring at Wyre Forest on the Worcestershire/ Shropshire border, are included in Figure 29 for comparison. The population at Wyre is strong and has also fluctuated considerably. There were high peaks in abundance in 1982, 1987 and

1990–91 but, since 1991, there have been large annual declines at all sites and the pearl-bordered fritillary is now at a low ebb. There is reasonable correlation between the graphs for Picket Wood and Somerford Common, two sites in the north of the county, where the peaks in 1990 were much smaller than those at the southern sites and values fell to zero in 1994. Extinction has probably occurred at Picket Wood where management may have been too late to save this species. One or two were seen at Somerford Common but not on the transect. If it survives there, it could soon be the only colony in the north of the county. Values at Bentley Wood and Blackmoor Copse have also declined since 1992 and butterflies have only been counted in double figures on the two transects in Bentley Wood clearings.

Status Before 1982
The first published Wiltshire record of the pearl-bordered fritillary was that of the Rev Francis Morris in 1853 who included 'near Great

Bedwyn and Sarum, Wiltshire' amongst a list of localities and described it as very plentiful in many places. In 1857 Henry Stainton reported this species from near Corsham. It was listed as abundant in the 1865 Marlborough College List and was recorded on 16 May 1866 by C E Powell. In all subsequent Lists until 1956 it was described as 'common in woods'. Roy Pitman recorded it as 'prolific, took as many as needed' on 27 May 1928 from Farley. In his 1936 report he stated it was 'much more common than the last [small pearl-bordered] and met with in the same places'. Bowmont Weddell reported it in May 1933 from woods in the Trowbridge area, near Slaughterford in May 1934, near Sutton Veny in June 1936, Gare Hill in June 1939 and in Cranborne Chase in May 1940. In the Dauntsey School Fauna List (1931–48) it was stated that few were seen in the Manor Woods until 1943, when it became very common, and that it was also common in Erlestoke Woods in May 1946. In 1962 Baron de Worms stated it was 'very common most years in the woods of the county'. This species was obviously a common woodland insect until the 1950s but has declined due to lack of coppicing and general neglect of woodlands.

Status Since 1982

The national distribution of this little butterfly is similar to that of its close relative, the small pearl-bordered fritillary, except that there is one population on the west coast of Ireland. It continues to be a widespread species in the south-west of England, Wales and Scotland but has declined greatly in the last 40 years in East Anglia, the Midlands and the south of England where its survival gives great cause for concern to butterfly conservationists.

In Wiltshire during the WBMS (1982–94), the status of the pearl-bordered fritillary was found to be almost identical to that of the small pearl-bordered and the two were frequently found to occur in the same woodlands. It was reported from 22 localities and, in the mid-1980s, more than ten butterflies could be seen during a visit at eight of them.

South Wiltshire

In the south of the county, records of the pearl-bordered fritillary from Great Ridge Wood were rare, the last being of a late, very worn singleton in 1990 (Nick Wynn). It was common in Grovely Wood in the mid-80s but, by 1992, only a score was counted and only five were seen in 1993 (David Peart). There were probably two colonies in the woodlands on Porton Down in 1987 (Ian Small). One of these, Towerhill Plantation, was in Wiltshire where up to seven butterflies were regularly seen. One was seen in late May 1993 (Daphne Graiff) and another was probably seen on 6 June (Ray Anscombe). In addition to the colonies in Bentley Wood and Blackmoor Copse in the south-east, Whiteparish Common and adjacent woodlands continue to support this butterfly in very small numbers. One was seen at Dean Hill on 20 May 1992 where singletons had been seen in preceding years. The last record was of a singleton here on 13 June 1992 (Ches Carpenter). These sightings probably represent remnant colonies rather than being vagrants from

Map 51. Distribution of pearl-bordered fritillary

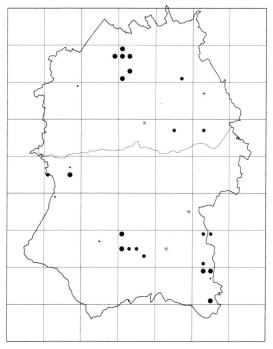

nearby Bentley Wood. The butterfly was plentiful in Hound Wood in 1987 and a small colony was reported there between 1988 and 1990 (Peter Whitehead). At Chickengrove Bottom, on the northern edge of Vernditch Chase, a singleton was seen in 1992 (Piers Mobsby) which suggests that there is a small colony in the Chase. Singletons recorded on SPTA(E) in 1987 (Ted Gange) and at Little Durnford Down in 1991 (Mobsby) were considered to be vagrants.

West Wiltshire
Recent records from the woods in West Wiltshire were of one seen in Black Dog Woods in 1984 by the author, where none has been seen since, and one in Biss Wood in 1987. Small numbers were recorded on the edge of Pomeroy Wood on the Vagg's Hill transect, the last being a singleton in June 1992 (Audrey Brown). The last record from this area was of a singleton in Biss Wood in 1993 (Brown) where the species is probably now extinct.

North Wiltshire
A small colony was known in Savernake Forest in 1984 (Keith Andrews). This appears to be the last record from the area where it used to be very common. A single worn female was seen in Stanton Park Wood by the author on 16 June 1985 and two were observed in West Woods near Marlborough on 4 June 1985 (Keith Payne). Subsequent visits to both localities suggest that these colonies are now extinct. A scattered colony was found in Braydon Wood in 1986 (Jeremy Fraser) but the wood has not been visited since. Two were recorded on 15 June 1988 by the author in Great Wood where it may still occur although it seemed to be much scarcer than the small pearl-

bordered, perhaps because this wood is too damp. Three individuals were seen on 26 May 1990 at Burderop Park (Andrew Sloan). Further visits are required to establish the status of this isolated colony. The pearl-bordered fritillary continues to be widespread at Somerford Common although in very low numbers compared with those of the mid-80s (John Grearson *et al.*). None was seen on the transect in 1994 although it is hoped that, as a result of recent management, numbers will increase in the future. This may now be the only remaining colony in the north of the county.

Singletons, assumed to be vagrants, were seen near Aldbourne in 1987 (Joy Newton) and near Avebury in 1993 (Andrew Sloan).

Future Prospects
Many of the comments concerning the demise and future prospects of the small pearl-bordered fritillary apply to this species.

Extinctions at several of the sites referred to above have probably occurred since 1986 and urgent conservation measures are needed in the remaining woodlands that support this butterfly. Its present position is very vulnerable. During the WBMS it was recorded from 32 tetrads (3.5%) and it is unlikely to be reported from any more in the future. In 1991, Humphrey Kay had permission to take 41 adults from the colonies that were thriving in Bentley Wood and Blackmoor Copse and release them in Savernake Forest in an attempt to re-establish the pearl-bordered fritillary there. Two were seen in 1992, a singleton in 1993 but none in 1994 which indicated that the re-introduction had failed. It would appear that, by 1994, the pearl-bordered fritillary was restricted to only three areas of woodland in the county.

HIGH BROWN FRITILLARY
Argynnis adippe ([Denis and Schiffermüller])

The generic name *Argynnis*, given to all the large fritillaries by Fabricius in 1807, may have been a reference to Argynnus, a lady beloved by Agamemnon, or a pun on a similar word meaning 'silver', a reference to the markings on the underside of the butterfly's hindwings. The specific name *adippe*, given by Denis and Schiffermüller in 1775, appears to be an invented name designed to be reminiscent of *cydippe*, a Nereid or sea-nymph, the name formerly given to this butterfly by Linnaeus and which had been in use for many years. This species was first recorded by James Petiver in 1699 who called it 'The greater silver-spotted Fritillary'. In about 1742 Benjamin Wilkes gave it the present name, high brown fritillary, the word 'high' meaning 'in a high degree' or 'rich'.

The similarity in appearance between the three large fritillaries has inevitably led to misidentification of these butterflies in the past. Today, when the high brown is perilously near to extinction as a British species, accurate identification is very important. It can no longer be assumed that a large fritillary seen flying in a woodland is a high brown. Detailed examination of the shape and patterning are necessary for which binoculars can be a useful aid. In unworn specimens the curvature of the outer edge of the forewings should be judged. It is slightly concave in the high brown, as shown in Nick Wynn's photograph. The undersides of the hindwings of these two species are similarly patterned but an extra row of small silver spots, encircled with brown, shown in Jim Asher's photograph on page 145, distinguishes the high brown.

The yellowish conical eggs are laid close to the ground in the vicinity of violets (*Viola* spp.). The caterpillar develops within a few weeks but does not hatch until the following spring. It feeds on violet leaves for two months before pupating within a tent formed by spinning leaves together.

The Flight Period
This rare woodland fritillary does not occur at any of Wiltshire's monitored sites in sufficient

This underside of a high brown fritillary shows the distinctive row of small silver dots ringed with reddish brown on the hindwings. These are lacking on the other two large fritillaries.

numbers to provide data on its flight period. Although several authors give the second half of June as the time of emergence, all the positive records received during the WBMS (1982–94) were in July. The earliest was 4 July 1993 when two males were seen (BC Hampshire Branch) on marsh thistles (*Cirsium palustre*) and the latest was 3 August 1983 when two were seen, also on marsh thistles (Paul Waring). All sightings were in Bentley Wood.

The earliest date given in one of the Marlborough College Lists, which span the 98 years 1865–1962, was 7 June 1893 and the latest was 11 August 1874. The entry for 10 August 1876 is the only other mention of sightings in that month.

Measures of Abundance 1980–94 (Figure 30)
Results of monitoring at three sites outside Wiltshire, Gait Barrow and Leighton Moss in Lancashire and the Wyre Forest on the Worcestershire/Shropshire border, are referred

to, illustrating the fluctuations in abundance at sites where both large and small populations occur. Correlation of the figures was close until after 1984, a year when numbers peaked at all three sites and which was obviously a good year for the high brown fritillary. It coincided with four of the singleton sightings in Wiltshire some distance from known woodland populations. A large increase in abundance at Gait Barrow from 1985 was associated with long-term coppice management which began at that time.

Another year of high abundance in 1987 coincided with a singleton seen at Picket Wood which may have been a coincidence or it may be that, in such years, the high brown fritillary wanders from its woodland home to 'pastures new'. However, it must be admitted that at least three of the other singleton sightings may have been misidentifications for the much more common, and very similar, dark green fritillary. There is also the possibility that bred specimens had been released.

Status Before 1982

The first published Wiltshire record appeared in the 1865 Marlborough College List. It was of a butterfly taken on 21 June 1865 'near the railway station' by Johnson. In all subsequent Lists until 1956 it was stated to be 'common in woods' and recorded from Savernake Forest, Rabley Copse and West Woods. In 1869, Edward Newman listed Savernake Forest and West Woods, T A Preston being his source. He considered the high brown to be seen less frequently than either the dark green or the silver-washed fritillaries.

The Rev Percy Harrison found it occurring abundantly near Lydiard Millicent (probably the Braydon Forest woodlands) in 1918 and in subsequent years until 1934. Roy Pitman did not record the species in his 1928 diary but in his 1936 report he said, 'appears to be more common than the last [dark green fritillary] and reports show an increase in recent years'. The only records from the Dauntsey School List (1931–48) were 'from the cricket field' on 8 June 1930 and at the Manor in July 1938.

Bowmont Weddell saw five near Sutton Veny on 30 June 1934 and two in woods near Trowbridge on 3 July 1934. Although his butterfly diaries continue until 1978, the last entry for the species was of three seen in Whiteparish Woods on 26 July 1947. John Kempe from Milton Lilbourne found it 'as abundant as ever' in Savernake Forest on 14 July 1951, Pitman noted a general decrease in 1957 and Ian Heslop reported it as very common in Blackmoor Copse in 1958. He added 'flies most commonly in the marsh area of the wood, greatly favouring the Marsh Thistle'. In 1962 Baron de Worms listed most of these earlier records and included others. He stated that the butterfly was very well distributed in Wiltshire although Pitman commented that it was generally scarce in the Salisbury area. Further records published during the 1970s in the WANHS reports were from Marlborough College in 1970, Biss Wood in 1971 (Frank Mead), Red Lodge Plantation in 1979 and from the woods in Cranborne Chase in 1980 (Tony Copley). There have been no further records from these localities. On 4 July 1973 Dr John Eagles

from Corsham remarked that, at Great Ridge Wood, there were 'more than before, two caught, 1 bright small male, 1 typical female'.

Pitman's references to the species in the SDNHS bulletins throughout the 1970s were from Whiteparish Woods in 1973, Whaddon in 1975 and Vernditch Chase in 1975 and 1981. He hinted that the species was generally declining but, in 1982, he stated 'General increase, a species that seemed to be on the decline during the past few years'. However, elsewhere in the county the species had probably been in decline throughout the 1970s because, in the early 1980s, at the start of the WBMS, it was a very rare butterfly.

From the above records it is apparent that this fine woodland butterfly was common and widespread throughout the county until the late 1960s. It then declined in nearly all areas until, by 1983, it was only known from Great Ridge and Bentley Woods.

The sad story at Wyre Forest, where none has been seen on the transect route since 1987, is probably typical of what happened to many populations in Wiltshire's woodlands in the 1960s and 70s.

Records Since 1982

Nationally, this butterfly has declined alarmingly over the last 40 years largely due to the cessation of coppicing, general neglect of many woodlands and the destruction of adjacent scrubby grassland. One interesting theory put forward as an additional factor is that the high brown fritillary is less aggressive than the dark green and silver-washed. This may have caused it to have been driven out gradually from marginal habitats once the population reached low numbers.

It no longer breeds anywhere in Britain east of Wiltshire and is now probably restricted to fewer than 40 colonies throughout the country. These are concentrated in the south-west, Wales, the West Midlands and the extreme southern end of the Lake District. It has never been reliably recorded from Scotland or Ireland and was always more locally distributed in northern England. Early Wiltshire records indicate that it was once common in at least 30 localities but this was probably an under-estimate since recording was less well-documented then than it is today.

During the WBMS, the high brown fritillary was observed in three woodlands but in only two since 1983. In 1982 it was seen in Vernditch Chase (L Sartin) and two were observed on the southern edge of Norridge Wood (Michael Hale). The species has not been recorded from either locality since. Singletons were reported from Great Ridge Wood every year except 1988, 1992 and 1994 and probably two individuals were seen in each of the years 1984, 1991 and 1993. A female was seen in 1991 near Stockton Wood, an extension of Great Ridge (Gordon Trebilcock). He commented 'most unexpected. I have not visited here for about 20 years as it never looked very promising'. He estimated that one in 15 fritillaries seen along the Roman road through the woods in about 1970 were high browns but by 1983 the ratio was only one in 60.

During his intensive survey in Bentley Wood in 1983, Paul Waring stated that the high brown fritillary was very rare. He only positively identified one during the whole season. Bill Newton recorded five, although only two at any one time, at the eastern end of the wood. Three were seen in Barnridge clearing in 1984 (Mike Read), none in 1985 and two in 1986 (Jonathan Stokes). It was not recorded after 1986 until 1993 when two were seen in the eastern clearing by several observers. These were considered likely to have been released bred specimens. 'The two males both had the forewing tips missing – a fate which befalls freshly emerged, soft-winged butterflies confined in small boxes' (Matthew Oates). Singletons were photographed on 19 and 20 July 1994 but no other sightings were made in spite of diligent searches by several recorders.

Singletons were seen in Picket Wood in 1980 and 1981 (Rob Turner) and during a bird-ringing session on 22 July 1984 (Turner and Ian Grier). One, seen by the author the following day and the first since monitoring began in 1978, was probably the same individual. He saw another on the transect on 6 July 1987 feeding on a marsh thistle but none has been reported since. This was the last record

from a wood in West Wiltshire. One was seen in Grovely Wood in 1985 (Roy Stockley) and a vagrant was found in a garden at Whaddon on 23 July 1985 (Pitman). In 1984 there were three unconfirmed reports of singletons from areas far from known woodland colonies.

Future Prospects

The future for the high brown fritillary in the county, as in most other parts of England and Wales, has been grim for the last decade and local extinction has been anticipated each year. However, it would appear that during this time it has managed to maintain a precarious foothold in two of the county's larger woodlands, Bentley and Great Ridge. It is hoped that, with the continuation of appropriate woodland management for butterflies in these woods and with the ecology of this species becoming better understood, it will survive and gradually increase in abundance and range.

During the WBMS it was recorded from 12 tetrads (1.5%). Two vagrants have also been included on the map.

Map 52. Distribution of high brown fritillary

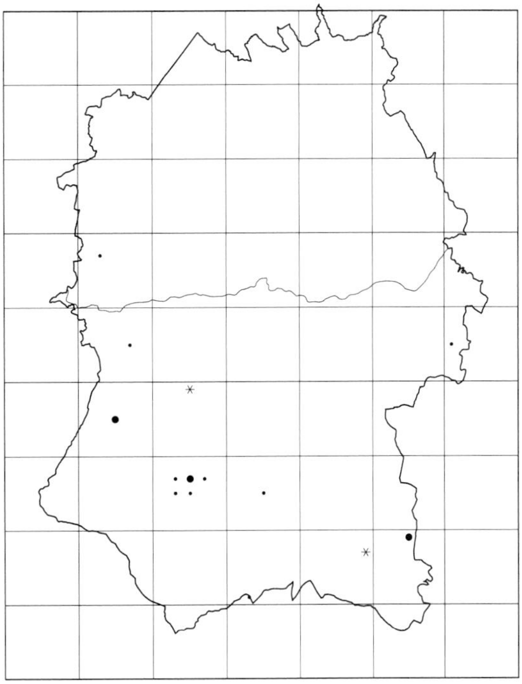

DARK GREEN FRITILLARY
Argynnis aglaja (Linnaeus)

The generic name *Argynnis* was given to all the large fritillaries by Fabricius in 1807 (see page 144). The specific name *aglaja*, given by Linnaeus in 1758, refers to Aglaia, the name of one of the three Graces who personified elegance and beauty.

The butterfly was illustrated by Thomas Mouffet in 1634 and described, but not named, by James Petiver in 1717. Benjamin Wilkes in about 1741 called it the 'Darkened Green Fritillary' which Moses Harris modified to the present name in 1766.

The dark green is the commonest of the three large fritillaries and the least likely to be seen in woodland. A large, predominantly orange coloured butterfly flying low over open grassland, with alternating bursts of fast wing-beats and periods of gliding, will probably be this species. Richard Tambling's photograph (above) is of a very fresh basking male. In woodland rides, it can only be separated from the very similar, but extremely rare, high brown with experience but it should not be confused with the larger silver-washed which has more angular wings. The underside of the lower wings is suffused with soft green and has a pattern of silver spots which are shown in Peter Durnell's beautiful photograph of a mating pair on page 149.

On warm days, males constantly search for virgin females hiding among tall grass. Nectaring by both sexes takes place early and late in the day at the tall purple flowers of thistles (*Cirsium* and *Carduus* spp.) and scabiouses (*Centaurea* spp. and *Knautia arvensis*).

The yellow conical eggs are laid singly close to violets (*Viola* spp.) the larval foodplant. On hatching three weeks later the caterpillar eats its eggshell and immediately enters into hibernation. It begins feeding on young leaves in the following spring, scurrying from one suitable plant to another in its haste to grow to its full size before pupating.

The Flight Period
The dark green fritillary is usually on the wing from early July to mid-August. The diagram shows

Dark green fritillaries and high brown fritillaries are almost indistinguishable in flight. When at rest, the differences in the markings on the underside of the hindwings can be seen.

the flight period in Roundway Hill Covert in 1987. This is typical for the species, numbers peaking towards the middle of July. At this monitored site from 1982–92 the longest flight period was seven weeks in four of the 11 years and the shortest was one week in three. The maximum number of individuals seen on a weekly transect was 20 in July 1987 and in four of the years the maximum was only one. The earliest sighting was 20 June 1988 and the latest 13 August 1991. The earliest date from the Marlborough College Lists was 17 June in 1917 and 1918 and the latest was 21 August 1867. During the years of the WBMS (1982–94), the earliest dates were 24 May 1987 at Norton Down on SPTA(W) (Godfrey Smith) and at Figsbury Ring on 8 June 1986 (Dee Stephens).

Latest dates were of one seen on Great Fore Down SPTA(W) on 28 August 1986 (Roy Fussell) and four on SPTA(C) on 28 August 1993 (Stephen Palmer).

Measures of Abundance 1980–94 (Figure 31)
This fine butterfly had mixed fortunes on the monitored sites during the 15 years. It peaked at most of them in the mid-1980s but since 1988 the index values have not exceeded single figures.

There were large increases in 1985 at Picket Wood and Roundway Hill Covert, both occurring a year after the maximum peak at other sites monitored for the Butterfly Monitoring Scheme nationwide. In 1986 numbers crashed at Picket Wood and dark green fritillaries are now rarely seen, no doubt due to the lack of large, sunny clearings in the wood. In 1987 at Roundway Hill Covert, numbers increased dramatically to a maximum value which coincided with the peak at Fontmell Down in Dorset but, since then, numbers have dropped to very low levels at both sites. The

Flight period at Roundway Hill Covert in 1987

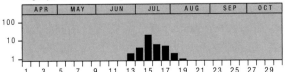

149

value at Bratton Castle Earthworks has only once exceeded single figures and fritillaries seen here are probably wanderers from the adjacent grassland on Salisbury Plain where the species is common in most years. The population at Picket Wood may also have originated from this area when wanderers colonised the wood after the clear-felling operations in the late 1960s and early 1970s had created suitable habitat.

Probably the best site for this butterfly is Porton Down where a transect was established in 1994 in a small area straddling the Wiltshire/Hampshire border. The maximum number seen was 112, mainly in Hampshire. If fears that the national decline of this species is an indication that it is heading for rarity status are realised, then Wiltshire, and in particular Porton Down and the SPTA grasslands, could be of national importance for its survival in the south of England. On 12 July 1994 the estimated number of dark green fritillaries at Porton Down was 500 (Dick Ryan) and in various areas of SPTA there were in excess of 100 throughout July.

Status Before 1982

The earliest published Wiltshire record was that of the Rev Francis Morris in 1853 who included 'Great Bedwyn and Sarum, Wiltshire' amongst several localities. In 1857 Henry Stainton stated that it 'has occurred at Corsham'. It was included in the 1865 Marlborough College List as occurring in Savernake Forest, near Great Bedwyn and 'near the railway station' on 19 June 1865 by J W Whitaker. In all subsequent Lists it was described as common and in the 1956 List as 'common in large open spaces in woods'. Roy Pitman saw it at Swanage in Dorset in July 1928 but did not record it from Wiltshire in that year. In his 1936 report he stated it was 'fairly common on flowery slopes and downs, well distributed in Wilts'..

Bowmont Weddell saw four on 1 July 1933, but did not give the locality and, on the following day, he saw one in Great Ridge Wood. He counted ten at Ford near Castle Combe on 6 July 1935, one at Erlestoke on 27 July 1940 and one on 'the

downs' above the Deverills on 10 July 1954. It would appear that he never saw this butterfly at Bratton or in the woods in West Wiltshire. The only record in the Dauntsey School List (1931–48) is from Erlestoke on 2 July 1944. In 1962 Baron de Worms stated that it was to be 'found in nearly every part of the County in woods and on downland'.

Status Since 1982

This is the most widespread of the three large fritillaries in Great Britain and Ireland. It is particularly associated with grassland and moorland and, in recent years, has become mainly restricted to suitable coastal areas. It has declined in the south-east of England, East Anglia and the Midlands but, in Wiltshire, it is still a widespread species especially on Salisbury Plain, on downland and in some of the county's woodlands. Although colonial in many areas, the butterflies are strong fliers and, in favourable seasons, cover large areas as they roam across the countryside. Therefore it has not been possible to determine the number of colonies in the county with any degree of accuracy although there appear to be at least 32 discrete populations.

The species' stronghold is in the southern half of the county, the greatest concentrations being on MOD land. However, in July, individuals are likely to be encountered throughout an area stretching from the county boundary with Somerset in the west to the Tidworth and Ludgershall area near the eastern border with Hampshire. There are some strong populations in and around Grovely and Great Ridge Woods and smaller ones in the dry river valleys of Cranborne Chase and near Verndtich Chase. The species may have been overlooked in downland areas north and south of the River Ebble.

In the south-eastern corner of the county there are small populations in the woodlands east of Salisbury and in the Redlynch area. There have been no reports from downland north of Mere and only one from the Cold Kitchen Hill area (Fuller). Until the late 1980s it was reported from the West Wiltshire woods in reasonable numbers but, since then, only an occasional singleton has been seen. This is probably because areas that had been cleared for replanting in the 1970s had become overgrown and shady.

In the mid-1980s the dark green fritillary could be seen in double figures on the downs south of Shalbourne (Jack Coates) since when only singletons have been reported. The last sighting was of a female at Ham Hill on 8 August 1993 (Piers Mobsby). The last sightings in Savernake Forest were at Hens Wood on 7 July 1985 (Geoffrey Webber) and in the main forest on 4 August 1986 (Martin Warren). Small numbers occur on Pewsey Downs NNR although, since 1984, a maximum of only four was noted on any one occasion. The downland to the north of Devizes consisting of Oliver's Castle, Beacon Hill, King's Play Hill, Morgan's Hill and Calstone and Cherhill Downs support what is probably one widespread population, part of which is monitored at Roundway Hill Covert.

Butterflies seen north of this area are rare and localised and most are probably vagrants from these downland populations. Small colonies manage to survive on some relatively small areas of the remaining unimproved grassland. There are two small colonies near Aldbourne. At one, three adults were seen in July 1990 (Susan Bailey) and another in July 1992 (Humphrey Kay). The other site is near Baydon where dark green fritillaries were reported in 1988 but had become scarce by 1990 (George Osmond). Very small numbers have been seen at Somerford Common since 1985, the last were two singletons in 1992 (John Grearson). The small population in Great Wood was last observed in July 1986 when only one was seen in a 70 minute visit (Fuller). Both these woodland colonies may now be extinct. The six sightings to the west of these woods may have been vagrants from them.

Records were received from West Yatton Down nearly every year during the 1980s. The maximum number seen was three in August 1988 (Malvyn Potter) but none has been seen since. One was recorded in Colerne Park Wood in August 1986 (Steve Chamberlain), a fresh male was observed at

Hazelbury Common in July 1991 (Wilfred Dowdeswell) and the author saw one in a valley south of Colerne in August 1993. These observations suggest that a small, thinly distributed population survives in this lovely area of the Cotswolds.

Future Prospects
The future for the dark green fritillary as a county butterfly is probably not in doubt thanks to the large areas of grassland owned by the MOD from where, in years of abundance, butterflies wander into surrounding areas. For example, individuals have been seen in gardens at Chirton, Bratton and Edington, villages lying to the north of SPTA. Its future in the north of the county is less assured and populations will probably fluctuate depending on climatic factors and the condition of the remaining suitable habitat. During the WBMS (1982–94) it was recorded from 175 tetrads (18%) and from a further 20 which were assumed to be of vagrants.

Figure 53. Distribution of dark green fritillary

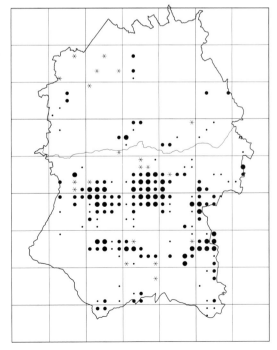

SILVER-WASHED FRITILLARY
Argynnis paphia (Linnaeus)

The generic name *Argynnis* was given to the three large fritillaries by Fabricius in 1807 (see page 144). The specific name *paphia* meaning 'of Paphos', given by Linnaeus in 1758, refers to the town in Cyprus where Aphrodite, who is often referred to as Paphia, came ashore. In 1699 James Petiver recorded this butterfly from Chelsea and named it 'The great silver-streakt Fritillary'. Moses Harris called it the silver-washed fritillary in 1766 and, although other names were proposed, this name has prevailed.

The wing-span of this butterfly is 10 mm greater than that of the dark green fritillary. Even in flight the more acutely angled forewings are evident. This is emphasised by the indentation on the outer margin of the wings. The four black sex-brands on the forewings of the male and the patterns of the dark markings of the female are shown in Steve Day's photograph (above) of a mating pair. The underside of the lower wings are washed with silver and pale green as illustrated in his photograph on page 153.

Single, pale yellow eggs are laid on tree trunks close to where violets (*Viola* spp.) grow. The author has occasionally watched females in Picket Wood enter shady areas and oviposit on the mossy, north-facing side of oaks. One or two eggs were deposited as high as two metres from the ground, a long distance for a tiny caterpillar to crawl to the violet leaves below unless it 'free-falls'! The caterpillar emerges two weeks later, eats its eggshell and hibernates within a silken pad which it spins on the bark. In the spring it descends from the tree to feed intermittently on violet leaves and bask in the sun. Pupation takes place low down among the vegetation and lasts for nearly three weeks.

The Flight Period
The first males are usually seen at the beginning of July but in early seasons they may be on the wing in mid-June. Numbers peak during the second half of July. Butterflies can be seen throughout August and occasionally, as in 1985 at Picket

*This mating pair of silver-washed fritillaries in Blackmoor Copse
illustrates the silver-washed appearance of the underwings from which
the butterfly's vernacular name was derived.*

Wood, a few linger on into September. By this time the wings are almost reduced to skeletons, the damage presumably having been done during their visits to bramble (*Rubus fruticosus* agg.) and thistles (*Cirsium* and *Carduus* spp.), their favourite nectar sources.

The delightful courtship flight can often be observed in woodland rides. The male continually loops around the female as she flies in a straight line often descending perilously close to the ground. The pair then spiral vertically upwards and over the tree canopy where mating probably takes place although mated pairs are sometimes seen at shrub level.

During the 15 years of monitoring at Picket Wood (1980–94), the longest flight period was 12

weeks in 1982 and the shortest was six weeks in 1981 and 1983. The maximum number of individuals counted on a weekly transect varied from 24 in 1993 to five in 1983. The earliest date was 11 June 1982 and the latest 11 September 1985. These were also the earliest and latest dates for the county during the WBMS. The earliest date from the Marlborough College Lists was 14 June 1917.

Measures of Abundance 1980–94 (Figure 32)
Figure 32 shows that during the period 1980–94 this fritillary maintained, or even improved, its status at most of the monitored sites. This was a reversal of the situation of the two smaller species, the pearl-bordered and small pearl-bordered fritillaries. There is very little correlation between the figures at these sites. Numbers fluctuated considerably at most, from being at low levels in the late 1980s to high in 1991 and 1992 and declining at most in 1993. In 1994 the butterfly's fortunes were mixed. There was a large decline at

Flight period at Picket Wood in 1985

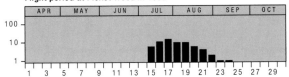

153

Picket Wood but on the Bentley Wood north transect the index value was the highest since monitoring began in 1986. By 1994 numbers on the Biss Wood and Blackmoor Copse transects were much lower than when monitoring began in the mid-1980s. This may be as a result of coppicing and clearance work but, at Picket Wood, in spite of considerable clearance work, the 1994 index value remained marginally below the 17-year average.

Status Before 1982

The first published Wiltshire record, that of the Rev Francis Morris in 1853 who included Wiltshire among 21 localities, stated 'rather uncommonly near Great Bedwyn and Sarum, as J W Lukis Esq tells me'. This record, to which the locality of Savernake was added, was included in the 1865 Marlborough College List. In the 1873 List it was stated to be 'common in woods'. In 1904 Neville Manders noticed that 'the three large fritillaries are still to be found abundantly in the Forest'. In subsequent Lists, until 1956, the silver-washed fritillary was described as 'common'. By the early 1960s it appeared to be decreasing, none being seen in 1961 and in 1963 the comment made concerning the large fritillaries was 'it is to be hoped that they are still to be found in Savernake'.

In 1921 near Damerham, which was then in Wiltshire, it was 'fairly common everywhere' but had not previously been seen on the downs (Steven Corbet). Bowmont Weddell reported it from the woods of West Wiltshire in 1932, from Great Ridge Wood in 1933 and from near Sutton Veny in 1934. In his 1936 report Roy Pitman stated that it was locally common and listed six localities. The Dauntsey School Fauna List (1931–48) only recorded it from the local woods near West Lavington in 1934 and 1946. In 1958 Ian Heslop stated that it was common in Blackmoor Copse and in 1962 Baron de Worms described it as being 'very prevalent in all the big woodland areas in the County'.

In the drought year of 1976 there was a population explosion of silver-washed fritillaries in the local woods around Warminster (Maj Gen Kit Lipscomb). By the end of July, when numbers

were phenomenal and hundreds were settling on bramble blossoms, he commented 'it became evident later that this great upsurge of numbers and variation had probably taken place in most woods. The sight of such a host of butterflies was an experience that is unlikely to occur more than once in the lifetime of most entomologists and while it lasts one finds it difficult to believe it is true'.

Status Since 1982

The silver-washed fritillary, unlike most of the other members of this family, continues to be fairly common and widespread in the woodlands of the south and west of England and in Wales and Ireland. In East Anglia and most of the Midlands it has become rare during the last 40 years and is now extinct in many areas. In Wiltshire it is widespread and often common in the larger woodlands especially in the south and west of the county. It continues to be a species that one would expect, rather than hope, to see during July and early August. Populations in the north are

Map 54. Distribution of silver-washed fritillary

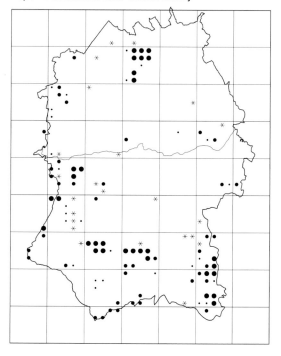

154

concentrated in the Braydon Forest area. It occurs in Savernake Forest in the east but only in small numbers. It is thinly distributed in the wooded valleys around Castle Combe in the north-west. It has not been reported from the wooded areas at Bowood or Spye Park near Calne but in most areas its distribution correlates well with that of woodlands. It is absent from Salisbury Plain and open downland areas where its place is taken by the dark green fritillary. The maps for the two species show the difference in their distribution.

Vagrants, which are usually males, may be found at a distance from their woodland breeding areas in hot summers although they seldom stray far from the cover of hedgerows or small copses. During the WBMS (1982–94) the silver-washed fritillary was recorded from 100 tetrads (10.5%) which represented approximately 50 discrete woodland populations. Vagrants were reported from a further 23 tetrads.

Future Prospects
In 1985 this species was absent from several of the county's smaller woodlands where the white admiral was invariably present, but was much more abundant than the white admiral in the larger woodlands. It was particularly common in Great Ridge Wood where it 'swarms' in good seasons. The status of this butterfly has probably changed very little during the twentieth century and it seems unlikely that it will alter greatly in the future. A few populations may be lost in small, remote woodlands if they become too dense and shady but in the larger woods there will probably always be enough open areas for the species to survive.

Aberrations
The subject of aberrations and varieties is beyond the scope of this book but a brief mention of the subject may encourage observers to look a little more closely at individual butterflies.

Most species of butterfly produce aberrant forms from time to time usually as the result of climatic or genetic factors. Some of the blue butterflies are especially subject to variation in

their wing markings. These species have been intensively collected and studied and many aberrant forms have been given names. The extent of variation can be very extreme and, in a large species such as the silver-washed fritillary, can be very striking. A good example is of a male ab. *ocellata* Frings illustrated in Rob Turner's photograph on page 156. It can be an uncanny experience to come across something so unusual in the wild.

In the drought year of 1976, many extreme aberrations of the silver-washed fritillary were seen in the woods of West Wiltshire. Six of the eight specimens illustrated in *Aberrations of British Butterflies* by A D A Russwurm had been collected in these woods by Howard Phelps, Michael Hale, Roy Stockley and Lipscomb. A summary of Lipscomb's report of these events in 1976 included the following comments. Most of the aberrations appeared towards the end of the emergence and females predominated, at any rate in the 'major' aberrations. A total of 35 was recorded including two of the form *valesina*. In 1977 during a dismal

Map 55. Distribution of silver-washed fritillary form *valesina*

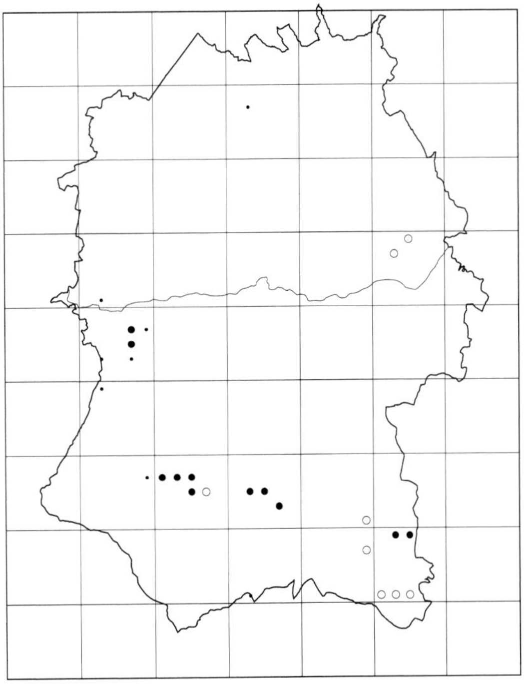

This striking aberrant form of the silver-washed fritillary, ocellata, *was photographed in Picket Wood on 22 July 1984, since when very few aberrant forms have been recorded in the county.*

summer, very few *paphia* were seen in July but in August four aberrations were taken in a population of about 200 butterflies. He concluded 'So ended our high hopes of another bumper year'. In 1994 a single ab. *ocellata* was recorded in the county (Steve Button).

Form *valesina* – Status Before 1982

Valesina is an unusual and distinctive form which occurs only in the female butterfly. The upperwings have a greenish-grey, dusky appearance as shown in Nick Wynn's photograph on page 157. It is considered rare outside the New Forest although it is regularly seen in populations in Dorset and the west of Surrey and in most of those in south Wiltshire woodlands.

Pitman reported *valesina* from the New Forest, outside Wiltshire, in August 1928 and saw it in Clarendon Wood near Salisbury in 1932. In his 1936 report he stated that it was 'met within the same localities as the normal form and fairly commonly'.

Weddell's only entries in his diaries (1932–78) were of one at Great Ridge Wood in 1933 and one in a wood near Trowbridge in 1934. This form was not mentioned in the Marlborough College Lists until 1917 when C B Lowe took one in West Woods on 25 June. Another was taken in Savernake Forest in 1933, when *paphia* was abundant there, and two in 1934 in Henswood. One was seen in Savernake Forest in 1935 and two in 1940. De Worms referred to records for 1949 and 1952, the last from the Marlborough area, and listed several woods in the south of the county where *valesina* had sometimes been numerous.

Form *valesina* – Status Since 1982

During the WBMS (1982–94) *valesina* was seen in most years in Bentley Wood and Blackmoor Copse in the south-east and in Grovely and Great Ridge Woods. In 1984, a year when the species was common, this form was most frequent in Great Ridge where the author counted nine among 35

Valesina, *the 'mysterious' form of the female silver-washed fritillary, photographed resting in Picket Wood in July 1992. This form is now regularly seen in the woods of West Wiltshire.*

silver-washed fritillaries. One seen in Picket Wood (Rob Turner) in 1984 was the first record from a West Wiltshire wood since that of Weddell in 1934. Since 1984 there have been regular reports from most woodlands in the area. The first report from Vernditch Chase was in 1984 (Ken Orpe) where it was also seen in 1993 (Wynn). In 1993 a vagrant was observed for half an hour in warm, hazy sunshine in a Bradford-on-Avon garden (Doreen Ellis).

The first record from the north of the county was in 1994 when a singleton was seen at Somerford Common (Lesley Wallington *et al.*). Annual sightings of *valesina* could be expected there if its occurrence follows a similar pattern to that in West Wiltshire in the late 1980s and 1990s.

MARSH FRITILLARY
Eurodryas aurinia (Rottemburg)

The generic name *Eurodryas*, given to the marsh fritillary by Higgins in 1978, is derived from two words meaning 'of Europe' and 'a dryad' or 'wood nymph'. The specific name *aurinia* given by Rottemburg in 1775 was the name of a prophetess revered by the ancient Germans.

The butterfly was described, but not named, by John Ray in 1710 and, in 1717, James Petiver gave it two names, 'Dandridge's midling Black Fritillary' and the 'Small Black Fritillary', in the belief that, due to the variability of the wing markings, there were two species. In 1766 Moses Harris called it the 'Greasey Fritillaria', a name which found favour for several years on account of the greasy appearance of some individuals. William Lewin first named it the marsh fritillary in 1795. This name eventually prevailed and was probably very appropriate at the time.

The upper surface of the butterfly's wings has an intricate pattern of orange, deep cream and dark brown in which each colour is outlined with dark brown to give an overall chequered effect. This is illustrated in Christine Tracey's photograph (above). The lower wings have a row of small dark spots. The pattern on the underwings is similar but all the colours are paler and there is less dark brown.

Males fly low over the sward in search of emerging females laden with hundreds of bright yellow eggs that are laid in large batches, two or three layers deep, on the underside of large leaves of the foodplant. The only foodplant in wetland meadows is devil's-bit scabious (*Succisa pratensis*) but on chalk grassland small scabious (*Scabiosa columbaria*) is also used and, in 1984 when butterflies were abundant, teasel leaves (*Dipsacus fullonum*) in a Tilshead garden were stripped. In captivity, honeysuckle (*Lonicera periclymenum*) is readily eaten.

The caterpillars hatch in four to six weeks and feed together in the protection of leaves which they have spun together. They defoliate one plant before moving to another, leaving behind brown skeletons of the leaves enclosing a mass of droppings. In early September they spin themselves a ball among the vegetation from which they

A view across the Larkhill/West Down impact area, SPTA(C), which supports large colonies of many of the county's rarer butterflies including the marsh fritillary. INSET *A 'nest' of young larvae in spring sunshine.*

sometimes emerge as early as February on sunny days but they do not resume feeding until March (see Barry Fox's inset photograph above). During the last three weeks before pupating they disperse and feed alone. The pupal stage is short, the length determined by the temperature. In some years large numbers of caterpillars are killed by parasitic wasps. At least eight species have been identified, the commonest being *Cotesia bignellii* (formerly *Apanteles bignellii*), the marsh fritillary being its only host. It synchronises its life cycle with that of its victim but may actually benefit the species by regulating the number of caterpillars and thus preventing mass starvation (Martin Warren).

The Flight Period

Flight period at Bratton Castle Earthworks in 1984

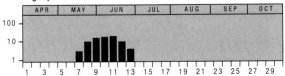

The butterflies are on the wing from late May and throughout June. The egg-laden females are sluggish and reluctant to fly unless the weather is warm. The males are very active, have a fast, but not sustained flight and generally remain within the colony's breeding area. The bases of some colonies change depending on the supply of larval foodplants and individuals can be found considerable distances from known colonies. The diagram shows the flight period and number of butterflies counted at Bratton Castle Earthworks in 1984.

The earliest Marlborough College record was 6 May 1893, a year when many species appeared exceptionally early. The earliest recorded date in the twentieth century was 5 May 1990 from SPTA(C) (David Brotheridge). The latest was 4 July 1983 at Bentley Wood (Paul Waring).

Measures of Abundance 1980–94 (Figure 33)

The dramatic fluctuations in the abundance of the marsh fritillary have been observed by lepidopterists for many decades. There are frequent references in the literature to swarms of larvae in good years and the disappearance of local colonies in times of scarcity. The present-day fragmentation and isolation of many suitable habitats means that once an area has lost its marsh fritillaries it is unlikely to become re-colonised even in years when butterflies are abundant.

Figure 33 shows the fluctuations in abundance over a 15 year period at five of Wiltshire's monitored sites. In the first half of the 1980s the species was common at three and was seen each year in Picket Wood in small numbers until 1984. From 1986 until 1993 numbers were very low on the transects at all these sites except Bentley Wood where they remained relatively high. Numbers increased dramatically at Somerford Common in 1994 and remained high in 1995 when the species had the opportunity to consolidate its status and spread into more of the habitat (John Grearson). These violent fluctuations are closely linked to the activities of the parasitic wasps. Studies have shown that warm sunny conditions during April result in an increase in most wasp populations (Warren). No studies have been carried out on Wiltshire colonies as to the effects of these predations, but the wasp was considered to have caused the failure of a colony re-established at the WWT Vera Jeans Nature Reserve (Jones's Mill) in 1991 (Humphrey Kay).

Status Before 1982

The first published Wiltshire record was that of the Rev Francis Morris in 1853 who included 'Great Bedwyn and Sarum, Wiltshire' among a long list of localities. Presumably his source was J W Lukis. The 1865 Marlborough College List included these areas and stated that the marsh fritillary was 'abundant on a bank at Clatford Bottom'. In the 1873 List it was said to be 'much scarcer than before' and in the 1883 List it was 'thought to be extinct but in 1881 had appeared singly or in small numbers all over the Marlborough district'. It was swarming at Bincknoll in 1885, occurred in plenty in 1890 at Chisbury Camp, was unusually plentiful at Froxfield in 1892 and was seen near Baydon in

1895, the recorder commenting 'hardly expected so high on the hills'. In most later Lists it was described as locally common although by the early 1960s it appeared to be restricted to Silbury Hill in the Marlborough area. The last record was of two seen there in 1965.

Weddell recorded three from Bratton Castle in 1934, one from King's Play Hill near Devizes in 1935 and from woods in West Wiltshire in 1944. In 1970 it was 'flying well' on Cotley Hill near Heytesbury. In the Dauntsey School Fauna List (1931–48) it was said to be common at the Manor and at Cheverell Hill. In 1949 Reginald Jackson found the 'males well out on May 10th, and widely distributed up and down the valley [Wylye], on both sides of the river'.

In his 1936 report Pitman stated 'locally common but erratic in appearance, some years literally swarming in certain areas and in others completely absent'. In 1958 Ian Heslop made the following comments concerning the species. 'It occurred in the Bentley Wood area in the 1920s but totally disappeared in the 1930s. It reappeared in the mid-1940s and became established in Blackmoor Copse in 1955 together with a huge revival of the principal foodplant. The ecological requirements of the species are very difficult to analyse. There is also a definite tendency for colonies to migrate. There are great fluctuations in the numbers of even comparatively fixed colonies. It is by no means confined to marshy ground. Some colonies inhabit high downland and there are woodland colonies'.

In 1962 Baron de Worms considered it to be 'well distributed and locally plentiful in woods and on downs'. He referred to most of the localities already mentioned and added some of Pitman's from near Salisbury. In 1966 Pitman saw a singleton near Clarendon and commented 'missing from the area for many years'. In 1979 he described it as very scarce and only found in restricted localities.

The marsh fritillary was included in the WANHS reports in most years from 1965 onwards but locations were rarely given. In the drought year of 1976 it was exceptionally abundant in some localities, even in gardens.

Status Since 1982

The marsh fritillary is often bred by lepidopterists in large numbers and many releases into the wild have been made. Only a few of these are well-documented and it is possible that some colonies in Wiltshire have resulted from such an activity. Roy Stockley is believed to have released many caterpillars at Bratton Castle and elsewhere on the Salisbury Plain escarpment in the early 1980s. Some of the existing colonies were reinforced but the true picture of the species' abundance was clouded. Bowmont Weddell and Roy Pitman bred and released this fritillary and in Hampshire 'there have been so many releases of this species that its current status and distribution largely result from them' (Matthew Oates).

The marsh fritillary is considered to be one of the most threatened of European butterflies. It has disappeared from most of north, east and central England. The colonies in the west of England, in Wales, western Scotland and Ireland are therefore of international significance.

In Wiltshire, the species was considered to be locally common and widespread until the mid-1980s but in 1985 numbers began to decline. By 1994 its status was probably best described as rare with a few, but scattered, strong colonies. Several reports during the years when numbers were high were probably of vagrant singletons or small satellite colonies that had been established for a few years but were unable to survive in adverse conditions. Those at Kingsdown near Box and Hankerton near Malmesbury were examples of local extinctions. There were approximately 100 colonies in Wiltshire at that time but when Warren carried out an analysis of the national data in 1990 he concluded that there were only 56. He considered the sightings of 30 singletons were all of vagrants. His results are summarised in Table 15. The figures in the table show the national importance of the Wiltshire colonies. In 1993, several of the colonies in Somerset were considered to be on the verge of extinction and in 1994 only two sites were known in Hampshire. In most counties, including Wiltshire, colonies continue to be lost. It is not easy to manage grassland in such a way that the

Table 15. Marsh fritillary colonies in Great Britain and Ireland 1990

	Number of definite colonies	% of total in English counties
Devon	85	38
Wiltshire	56	25
Cornwall	21	9
Dorset	21	9
Somerset	19	8
Hampshire	14	6
Eight other counties	12	5
Wales	111	
Scotland	35	
Ireland	58	
Total	432	

larval foodplant is neither 'grazed out' nor, conversely, 'shaded out'.

Woodland Colonies

There have been several records of marsh fritillaries from woodland rides and clearings but some were of singletons and only in the years of high abundance. In 1985 the colony in Picket Wood became extinct, although a vagrant has occasionally been seen since. In the same year the species was last recorded in Great Bradley Wood (Dick Hornby).

The small colony in Great Wood near Wootton Bassett which was last recorded in 1987 (Warren) is probably extinct having been shaded out as the planted conifers matured. A singleton in West Woods near Marlborough in 1990 (Sylvia Young) was probably a vagrant from nearby downland.

The population at Somerford Common may now be the only one remaining in the north of the county where, in 1994 and 1995, more than 100 adults were counted. With an appropriate management plan in place its future here should be secure (Grearson).

Grassy clearings within, and adjacent to, Great Ridge Wood and especially in Longdean Bottom, have supported populations of marsh fritillaries for many years (Gordon Trebilcock) and they were thriving in 1994 (Nick Wynn). Small numbers used to occur in Grovely Wood where the last sighting was in 1985 (Stephen Palmer). There are two colonies in Bentley Wood one of which appears to have a reasonably stable population (Barry Fox).

Vagrants occasionally stray into nearby Blackmoor Copse but breeding has not been confirmed.

In 1994 only the three woodland populations, at Somerford Common, Great Ridge and Bentley Woods, were known to exist in the county.

Grassland Colonies

Entomologists believe that it was not until the 1920s that the marsh fritillary began to colonise dry chalk grassland where devil's-bit scabious had always been abundant. It was at about this time that wet meadows were being reclaimed for agriculture by being drained and reseeded. Today, at the end of the twentieth century, most of the colonies remaining in Wiltshire occur in upland areas. It has been estimated that 32 colonies occur on unfarmed grassland on the Salisbury Plain Training Area (SPTA), especially on the Imber and Larkhill/West Down Ranges (see Stephen Palmer's photograph on page 159), and on grazed downland on the peripheral slopes of Salisbury Plain at Cotley and Great Cheverell Hills. This species was first recorded from two discrete areas on MOD land at Porton Down in 1984 where 25–50 could be counted in an hour (Ian Small) but, in 1994, numbers were much reduced and were only found in one area. In the same year a few were counted on the Boscombe Down transect (Gerald Nicholls).

In the early 1980s there were at least three colonies on the Limestone in the north-west of the county but the last record from the area was in 1987 at West Yatton Down (Len Ingram).

On the downs to the north of Devizes and the Vale of Pewsey the species was seen regularly in the early 1990s at Morgan's Hill (Piers Mobsby), Calstone and Cherhill Downs (John Tyler) and Pewsey Downs NNR (Dominic Ash) and there may have been ten colonies here.

There are scattered colonies on grassland south of Salisbury Plain, mainly on the steep-sloping downland valley sides north and south of the Ebble valley. In 1984 and 1985 there were sightings at Throope Down (Rob Wild), Sutton and Fovant Downs (Palmer), Knighton Hill (Peter Shallcross) and in 1988 three were seen in Ashcombe Bottom in Cranborne Chase (Palmer). Ninety-eight were

Map 56. Distribution of devil's-bit scabious

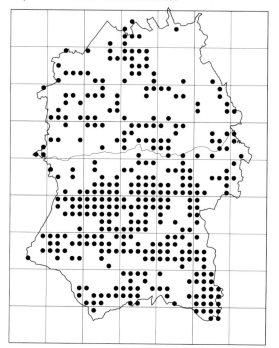

Map 57. Distribution of marsh fritillary

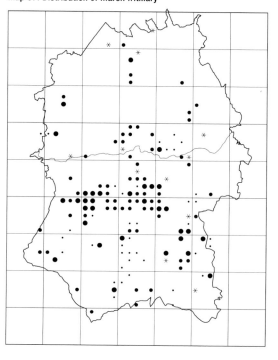

counted at Prescombe Down in 1990 (David Peart) and a few were seen at Chickengrove Bottom in 1992 (Mobsby).

In the south-west of the county there have been occasional sightings on downland near the Deverills, the last being in 1990 (Beatrice Gillam). Small numbers were seen on White Sheet Hill in 1992 (Keith Brown) and there were strong populations on the downs near Mere in 1993 (Michael Powell).

Wetland Colonies

In a fenland habitat at the WWT Vera Jeans Nature Reserve (Jones's Mill) in the Vale of Pewsey, 30 marsh fritillary caterpillars were counted in April 1983 (Gillam). One adult was seen later that year and the last sighting was of a singleton in 1985. In 1991 Kay had permission to try to re-establish a colony. From the release of 150 caterpillars in March, two adults were seen in June and one larval web was found in September. In 1992 about 15 adults were on the wing, nectaring and mating (Audrey Summers *et al.*) but in 1993 only one adult was seen (Kay) and the re-establishment is believed to have failed. A few caterpillars and three adults were found in 1983 at the western end of the Vale in a small strip of undisturbed grassland in a recently drained meadow (Roy Fussell and Gillam).

A colony was discovered in a damp, cattle-grazed pasture in Wincombe Park in the extreme south-west in 1985 (Warren). In 1994 a thriving colony was discovered in a field at Dilton Marsh (Lesley Balfe) when large numbers of caterpillars and adults were seen and 44 larval webs were subsequently counted. Ponies grazed the meadow heavily in spring 1995 and it is feared that the colony has been exterminated in spite of approaches from conservationists to try to save it.

During the WBMS (1982–94) the marsh fritillary was recorded from 130 tetrads (15%). The ten records of singletons from habitats where colonies were not thought to be established are shown as 'vagrants' on the distribution map. From a total of 104 sites, 25 had populations where more than ten individuals were seen on a single visit. Although these sites are spread across the county, 13 were on SPTA(W and C) and the Salisbury Plain escarpments. There were sightings of singletons, some of which may have been vagrants, from 43 tetrads.

Future Prospects

Although lepidopterists now know the habitat requirements of the marsh fritillary, the difficulty of implementing the desired management, and the damage that may be caused to the caterpillars by parasitic wasps, make the future prospects of this species unpredictable.

In Wiltshire, some of the strongest colonies survive on SPTA without any direct grassland management. Some of these are able to use small scabious and field scabious (*Knautia arvensis*) in addition to devil's-bit scabious as foodplants. In 1993 Palmer counted webs containing larvae and their associated foodplants. Of 20 webs in an area of 150 square metres, 19 were on small scabious, one on field scabious and none on devil's-bit scabious. A further random search on the downland produced 21 webs on small scabious, one on field scabious and six on devil's-bit scabious.

Small, isolated colonies, especially in lowland meadows and woodland, are the most vulnerable. Population fluctuations will no doubt continue to occur and it is when numbers are low that the balance swings towards extinction. Wiltshire's colonies are of great importance nationally and we have a responsibility to maintain them for future generations to admire and enjoy.

SPECKLED WOOD
Pararge aegeria (Linnaeus)

The generic name *Pararge*, given to the speckled wood by Hübner in 1819, is derived from two words meaning 'close to' and 'white' – indicating affinity with the marbled white. The specific name *aegeria*, given by Linnaeus in 1758, refers to a prophetic nymph from ancient Italy.

There is some doubt as to whether Thomas Mouffet illustrated this species in 1634 and Christopher Merrett described it only briefly in 1666. James Petiver named it The Enfield Eye in 1704 and Benjamin Wilkes used the name Wood Argus in 1747, the name that was subsequently favoured by several writers. Moses Harris gave it its present name in 1766.

The basking male in Steve Day's photograph clearly shows the wing markings, the cream spots being variable in size and intensity.

Honeydew is the main source of food until late summer when the butterflies turn to nectar on common fleabane (*Pulicaria dysenterica*), ragwort (*Senecio* spp.), hemp-agrimony (*Eupatorium*

cannabinum*) and over-ripe brambles (*Rubus fruticosus* agg.).

The yellowish-white eggs are laid singly on the underside of leaves of the broad-bladed grasses. On hatching, the caterpillar usually eats its eggshell before feeding on the leaves. Over-wintering occurs in both the larval and pupal stages of the life cycle. This behaviour is unique for a British butterfly.

The Flight Period
The speckled wood can be seen from mid-April until mid-October. There are normally two distinct peaks in the complicated flight period in which numbers rise to a maximum in the autumn. Some individuals linger on into early November.

In Picket Wood from 1980 to 1994, the longest flight period was 27 weeks in 1993 and the shortest was 18 weeks in 1994. The maximum number of individuals counted on a weekly visit varied from 44 in September 1981 to eight in

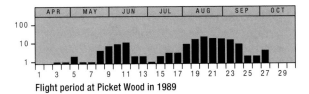

Flight period at Picket Wood in 1989

July 1986. The earliest sighting was 9 April 1981 and the latest 16 October 1986.

Measures of Abundance 1980–94 (Figure 34)

There were some large annual fluctuations on the monitored sites. The overall picture was one of decline during a period of hot, dry summers in the early 1980s reaching a low point in the mid-1980s. There followed a substantial recovery to high numbers by the end of the decade and the speckled wood was so abundant in 1987 that it was selected as Wiltshire's 'Butterfly of the Year'. During the drought of 1990 numbers slumped at all sites but had partially recovered by 1992. It is probable that the wave cycle of peaks and troughs will continue.

Status Before 1982

The earliest published Wiltshire record occurs in the 1865 Marlborough College List where it was stated to be rather 'uncommon in this neighbourhood'. The butterfly was taken by J H Johnson on 8 June 1866 and was subsequently recorded in most years until 1885. In 1893, Charles G Barrett quoted Edward Meyrick: 'Twenty years ago (c.1873) it was common in most woods round Ramsbury and Marlborough; anyone entering a wood at the proper seasons would see half a dozen flitting about the drives. It became gradually scarcer and now seems extinct'. It was absent from Dr R V Solly's 1898–1901 list of records from the Wylye area, the Rev T B Eddrupp did not include it in his 1899 list from near Calne and it was absent from E Cook's 1902 list from the Devizes area.

Roy Pitman commented in his 1936 report that it was 'only thinly distributed and not seen in some likely places in the south'. He noticed 'a few on the wing' at Fonthill Gifford on 27 August 1939 but did not record it from the Salisbury area until 8 April 1945 in Clarendon Wood. In 1946 he commented

'this insect is increasing'. In the Dauntsey School Fauna Lists (1931–1948), the first report was for 1940 and 'since then has been very common'. Bowmont Weddell recorded two at Farleigh on 6 September 1936 and another on 2 April 1938.

In 1962 Baron de Worms stated that it was to be observed 'in most parts of the county but has only recently penetrated the most northern areas'.

Status Since 1982

The speckled wood is now a common butterfly in southern Britain and Ireland but very local and much scarcer in the north of England and only locally common in some parts of Scotland.

In Wiltshire it has been a common butterfly of woodlands, hedgerows, byways and quiet country lanes, often spreading into gardens, and is one of the few butterflies seen in the shady rides of coniferous woodlands. It is widely, but thinly, distributed throughout the county and could be expected from most of the county's tetrads.

During the years of the WBMS (1982–94) this species was recorded from 674 tetrads (71%).

Map 58. Distribution of speckled wood

WALL
Lasiommata megera (Linnaeus)

The generic name *Lasiommata*, given to the wall by Humphreys and Westwood in 1841, means hairy eyes. The speckled wood and the wall butterflies are alone amongst the browns in having this feature. The specific name *megera*, given by Linnaeus in 1767, was one of the Furies, referring to the butterfly's restless movement.

The wall was illustrated by Thomas Mouffet in 1634 and James Petiver described it in 1699 as 'The golden marbled Butterfly, with black eyes'. Moses Harris gave it the name wall in 1766 in reference to its habit of 'settling against the side of a wall'.

The wall could be mistaken for a fritillary when in flight but its habit of alighting with wings spread enables the eyespots on the wings to be clearly seen, as on the male in Barry Fox's photograph.

The greenish-white eggs are laid singly on the leaves of several grass species. The caterpillar eats its eggshell before feeding on the grass leaves. The spring generation pupates within a month and the second generation larvae overwinter and begin feeding again the following spring.

The Flight Period

The first generation appears from mid-May until mid-June and the autumn generation, which is usually larger, from early August until mid-September. A small third generation sometimes occurs in late September to early October following a long, hot summer. This happened at Bratton Castle and at some other localities in 1989 and 1990. In years of scarcity, numbers can be so small that none is seen on a transect walk.

The longest flight period at Bratton Castle was 14 weeks in 1982. None was seen in 1986. The maximum weekly count on the transect was six in June 1994 for the first generation and 14 in August 1989 for the second.

The earliest county sighting on 29 April 1961 was from a Marlborough College List and the latest, an exceptionally late third generation

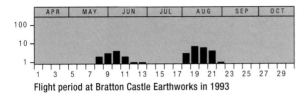

Flight period at Bratton Castle Earthworks in 1993

individual, was on 4 November 1990 at Sopworth (Harold Bennett).

Measures of Abundance 1980–94 (Figure 35)

Figure 35 shows a close correlation between the annual fluctuations in abundance at four sites. During the hot summers of the early 1980s the wall was widespread and occurred in good numbers but, during the cool wet seasons 1985–88, it became very scarce in Wiltshire. Concern was expressed that perhaps we had seen the demise of yet another butterfly, but this proved not to be the case and, in the hot summers of 1989 and 1990, the wall almost regained its former status. After slumping again in 1991 numbers have generally stabilised and, at Bratton Castle, the value in 1994 was the highest since monitoring began in 1980. These periods of high abundance, followed by scarcity or periods of absence, have often been commented upon in the literature.

Status Before 1982

The first published reference to the wall in Wiltshire appeared in the 1865 Marlborough College List. This species was subsequently recorded in most College Lists until 1906 but was not recorded from the Marlborough area between 1906 and 1912, reappearing by 1935 and common in the 1950s. It did not appear in Dr R V Solly's 1898–1901 list of records from the Wylye area or in E Cook's 1902 list from the Devizes area but the Rev T B Eddrupp included it in his 1899 list from near Calne.

In the south of the county Roy Pitman reported it on only two occasions in his 1928 diary and, in his 1936 report, described it as being 'locally common in some years but spasmodic in occurrence'. Bowmont Weddell recorded the species from near Westbury in June 1932. In 1962 Baron de Worms described it as being 'generally distributed and often common all over the county'.

Status Since 1982

The wall is widespread but thinly distributed over much of England, Wales and Ireland. It occurs more locally in the north, particularly in coastal areas, and penetrates into south-western Scotland. In hot, dry summers it can be abundant in the late summer especially on southern coastal and downland sites. It favours warm, dry, sunny situations such as sheltered open areas in woodland, hillsides having sparse vegetation, stony tracks and wasteland. Occasionally individuals are seen in gardens basking on walls and paths.

During the period of the WBMS (1982–94) records were received from many areas and the map is probably a true representation of the patchy distribution of the wall, the concentrations being on Salisbury Plain and the Marlborough Downs. It was recorded from 284 tetrads (30%) but in years of abundance it might be expected to occur, often singly, in many more.

Map 59. Distribution of wall

MARBLED WHITE
Melanargia galathea (Linnaeus)

The generic name *Melanargia*, given to the marbled white by Meigen in 1828, is derived from two words meaning black and white, an obvious reference to the wing coloration. The specific name *galathea*, given by Linnaeus in 1758, refers to a nymph beloved by Polyphemus.

The butterfly was first described by Christopher Merrett in 1666 and was named 'Our half-Mourner' by James Petiver in 1695. Moses Harris gave the names 'Marmoress' or marbled white. The latter has survived other suggested names to the present time.

In mid-summer, marbled whites seek nectar mainly from thistles (*Cirsium* and *Carduus* spp.), knapweeds (*Centaurea* spp.) and scabiouses (*Knautia arvensis* and *Scabiosa columbaria*). Graham Wall's photograph is of a butterfly resting on field bindweed (*Convolvulus arvensis*) flowers.

The female, rather than laying her whitish eggs on grass leaves, drops them randomly into the vegetation. The caterpillar emerges within three weeks, eats its eggshell and immediately begins its long period of hibernation. It starts feeding on the young leaves of red fescue (*Festuca rubra*) in early spring and pupates on the ground in June.

The Flight Period
The butterflies emerge in early July and their numbers quickly build up to a peak in mid-July with a few individuals on the wing until mid-August. At Bratton Castle from 1980 to 1994 the longest flight period was 11 weeks in 1993 and the shortest six weeks in 1983 and 1987. The maximum number of individuals counted on the transect in a week varied from 54 in July 1984 to six in August 1988. The earliest sighting was on 17 June 1982 and the latest on 5 September 1985. The earliest record in a Marlborough College List was for 16 June 1893.

Flight period at Picket Wood in 1984

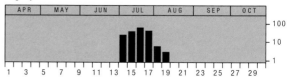

Measures of Abundance 1980–94 (Figure 36)

Butterfly numbers fluctuated fairly randomly from 1980 towards a peak in 1984 and then declined sharply to very low levels of abundance in 1988. They increased from 1989 to reach another peak in 1992 and then declined again to about average values. Figure 36 shows the decline in Picket Wood as the conifers matured and shaded out many of the grassy clearings and ride edges. The ride management and removal of conifers in the late 1980s resulted in a gradual recovery but numbers in 1994 were only 4% of the 1982 maximum value. At Upton Cow Down there was an 18-fold increase in abundance from 1988 to 1992 and a subsequent 7-fold decline by 1994.

Status Before 1982

The earliest Wiltshire reference to the marbled white is that of James Rennie in 1832 who listed Wiltshire amongst other counties. In 1853 the Rev Francis Morris named many more localities and stated 'near Great Bedwyn and Sarum, in isolated spots near woods, as J W Lukis Esq informs me'. The 1865 Marlborough College List has records from Savernake Forest and near West Woods on 21 June 1865. In later Lists it was described as 'common in many localities'. It is absent from Dr R V Solly's 1898–1901 list of records for the Wylye area, the Rev T B Eddrupp's 1899 list from near Calne and from E Cook's 1902 list from the Devizes area.

The species is absent from Roy Pitman's 1928 diary for the Salisbury area although, in his 1936 report he described it as 'locally abundant, often seen in swarms ... well distributed throughout the county'. Bowmont Weddell did not record it from the Trowbridge area until 1962 when Baron de Worms reported it as 'often abundant'.

Although colonial to some degree, in years when the marbled white is abundant they wander in search of nectar-producing plants and can be seen along country lanes and verges in many areas.

Status Since 1982

The marbled white is chiefly associated with the chalk and limestone grasslands of central-southern England and the West Country. It is very rare and local in the north of England and is absent from Scotland and Ireland. It occurs in many situations where the grass is tall but not too dense. These include lightly grazed downland, unimproved grassland, woodland rides and clearings, embankments and roadside verges.

The status of this butterfly in Wiltshire does not appear to have changed during the last 100 years although several colonies have probably been destroyed since the 1940s due to habitat destruction. Its apparent absence from some areas may well be due to under-recording. This is almost certainly true for many of the southern areas. During the years of the WBMS (1982–94) this species was recorded from 564 tetrads (59%).

Future Prospects

The marbled white's future status in the county is not likely to change a great deal so long as areas of tall grasses remain and are not regularly cut or mown in the cause of tidiness.

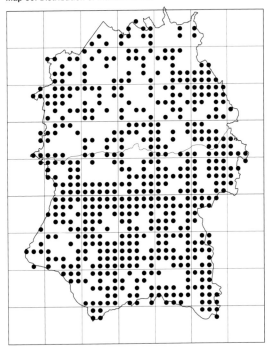

Map 60. Distribution of marbled white

GRAYLING
Hipparchia semele (Linnaeus)

The generic name *Hipparchia*, given to the grayling by Fabricius in 1807, is derived from that of the Greek astronomer Hipparchus. The specific name *semele*, given by Linnaeus in 1758, refers to a beautiful mortal who was beloved by Zeus.

It was first described by James Petiver in 1699 as 'The black-ey'd marble Butterfly' and in 1703 as 'The Tunbridge Grayling'. In 1766 Moses Harris probably meant to use the name grayling but misspelt it as 'Grailing' and it was Adrian Haworth in 1803 who first used the present name.

The grayling is the largest of the brown butterflies. Its rapid, erratic flight, generally low down, is distinctive. When disturbed it flies a short distance, alights suddenly, usually on bare ground and seems to vanish. It always settles with closed wings and adopts an angle to the sun according to its requirement for warmth at the time. Ken Lloyd's photograph on page 171 of a butterfly at Enford Down shows the camouflage when at rest.

The female lays her white eggs singly on blades of grass, probably sheep's fescue (*Festuca ovina*) or red fescue (*F. rubra*) on chalk sites, and bristle bent (*Agrostis curtisii*), early hair-grass (*Aira praecox*) or tufted hair-grass (*Deschampsia cespitosa*) on heathland. The caterpillar feeds at night on young grass shoots and hibernates in the shelter of a grass tussock. It resumes feeding the following spring and, in June, burrows into the ground to pupate.

The Flight Period
The butterflies are on the wing during July and August and occasionally into September. They are rarely seen in flight unless they are disturbed, which means that small colonies are very easily overlooked. None of the monitored sites in the county support graylings and therefore no details of the flight period or abundance are available. Grayling are only occasionally seen visiting flowers and Graham Wall's photograph (above) shows one on heather in the New Forest. The earliest sighting this century was that of a vagrant at Corsham on 10 July 1984 (Tom Burnard). The latest was on 27 September 1950 near Marlborough (de Worms).

A well-camouflaged grayling at rest amongst sparse vegetation and bare chalk at Enford Down, SPTA(C). It is unusual to find grayling colonies on chalk this far inland.

Records Before 1899

The first mention of this species in Wiltshire was by James Rennie in 1832 who listed nine localities including Salisbury Plain. In 1853, the Rev Francis Morris, who called it the Rock-eyed Underwing, included Salisbury Plain amongst several localities and stated that 'it occurs sparingly near Great Bedwyn and Sarum, Wiltshire, as J W Lukis Esq has informed me'. William Coleman also listed Salisbury Plain in *British Butterflies* (1860). It was included in the 1865 Marlborough College List and the first dated record is for 25 July 1868 at Alton Barnes (the present day Pewsey Downs NNR) by C A Sladen. He also recorded it on 23 June 1870, an exceptionally early date.

Records and Status Since 1899

North Wiltshire

The grayling was included in the Rev T B Eddrupp's list from near Calne, probably on Cherhill Down, in 1899 and in the Devizes district in the 1902 list of E Cook, possibly on Roundway Hill. It was reported from Morgan's Hill in about 1963 (BRC) and from Cherhill Down in August 1979 (BRC) but it has not been found in these localities since.

There have been 25 records from the Marlborough area since Sladen's capture, Barbury Camp, Martinsell, Forest Hill, Poulton Gorse, Clatford (Fyfield Down) and near Aldbourne (Upper Upham) being listed. In 1904, Major Manders, an old Marlburian, stated that it was widely distributed on the downs beyond Rabley and that it swarmed on Salisbury Plain. He was stationed at Netheravon at the time. The last sighting from the area was of a vagrant seen at Bedwyn Common in 1976 (David Dunbar). There were no grayling records from this area during the WBMS (1982–94) and it is most unlikely that a colony has survived due to lack of suitable habitat.

A record of a singleton at Calne sand pits on 2 August 1994 (John Tyler) suggests that there may still be a small colony in this area. If so, it will be very significant as being the only one in a sandy habitat and in the north of the county. It has been shown as a colony on the distribution map and its confirmation is most desirable.

The only records from the north-west of the county are of vagrants at West Yatton Down in 1982 (Maurice Avent), Corsham as previously mentioned and in a Bradford-on-Avon garden on 22 August 1990 (Joan Ward).

Salisbury Plain

Before 1920, the grayling was apparently common and widespread on Salisbury Plain although most of the localities were not sufficiently detailed to be mapped. In 1942 a colony was known at Yarnbury Castle (Jim Buchanan) and in 1965 was reported as 'being common near Shrewton' and as 'still increasing' in 1970 (John Kirkaldy). This was probably also at Yarnbury.

SPTA(C)

During the WBMS, a colony was discovered in August 1986 at Enford Down (Nigel Pleass) when about a dozen were seen. It was confined to one hectare of chalk from which the soil was scraped to use for the construction of a bank for military purposes and which remains almost bare of vegetation. A maximum of only four butterflies were seen in 1994, the colony would appear to be small with numbers recorded in any year rarely exceeding single figures.

Before 1982 there were records of singletons, possibly vagrants from the Enford Down colony, from other parts of SPTA(C), at Urchfont Hill (BRC) and Church Hill (Rob Turner).

SPTA(W)

The status of the grayling here is not clear. One was seen near Dirtley Wood in 1979 (Godfrey Smith) but no more were reported until 1990 when five, assumed to be vagrants, were seen. Singletons were noted on Scratchbury Hill and Bratton Castle (Nick Wynn), Tenantry Down (Jack Pile) and Stoke Hill (Harold Crossley). Crossley also recorded eight at Tenantry Down on 11 August 1990 and one on 16 August 1991. None has been recorded since but it has been assumed that there is probably a small colony on

Tenantry Down although its exact status requires investigation.

SPTA(E)

The grayling was last reported from Sidbury Hill in July 1971 (BRC) but has not been seen since a report from Beacon Hill in 1976 (Henry Edmunds).

South-west Wiltshire

In the south-west of the county the status of the species is uncertain. It was recorded in the Broad Chalke area before 1960 (Norman Moody), from Great Ridge Wood in 1967 (Philip Horton), Verndich Chase in July 1975 (SDNHS), in Grovely Wood in 1976 (Roy Stockley pers. comm.) and from Cranborne Chase before 1980 (Tony Copley). During the WBMS there were six records of singletons from this area. Those at Buxbury Hill in September 1989 (John Rowe) and Dinton in August 1990 (Stephen Palmer) were considered to be vagrants. The other four are assumed to represent three remnant colonies. One was seen near Kingston Deverill in 1985 (Tom Williams), another on Compton Down in August 1990 (Charlie Patrick) and one in the same area in August 1991 (Barbara Last) and a fourth near Berwick St John in August 1994 (Piers Mobsby). These records are considered to be too remote from known colonies for the butterflies to have been vagrants. Diligent searching of these areas will probably reveal small additional colonies to be surviving on the grazed chalk downlands.

South-east Wiltshire

In 1928, Roy Pitman reported graylings from several localities near Salisbury: at Old Sarum in July, Old Castle in August and on the Downton Road in September. In his 1936 report he described it as 'a local insect but never rare, found in suitable areas in most parts of the county'. It was subsequently recorded from Camp Hill, Pepperbox Hill, Standlynch Down, Alderbury Common, near Redlynch and Whiteparish Common. It was often common at these sites until the mid-1950s (Gerald Nicholls). By the 1960s, it was apparently very rare in the area and in 1962 Pitman commented 'fewer in the New Forest, none elsewhere'.

A strong colony was discovered on the disused railway line near Boscombe Down on 16 August 1985 when 20 were seen (Anthony Bedford-Russell). Sadly this now appears to be extinct, the last sighting being of a single butterfly on 19 July 1989 (Crossley). It maybe that this was a small satellite colony from Porton Down only 4 km to the south-east that became established for a few years. Porton Down is the only site in the county where numbers have regularly reached double figures. In 1985 and 1986 it was common and widespread (Ian Small) but, in 1994, only three individuals were seen on just three occasions (Dick Ryan).

The only records from the south-east of Salisbury during the WBMS were of singletons, presumably vagrants from the populations on the New Forest heathlands. They were seen in Downton gardens in 1986, 1989, 1990 and 1991 (Hazel Lewis and Carol McInerney) and in Blackmoor Copse and Bentley Wood in 1983, 1986, 1989 and 1993 by several recorders. At least two localities are known to support the grayling in the extreme south-eastern corner of the county bordering the New Forest where the species is relatively common on the heathland. In July 1985, two were seen by the author near Pound Bottom and seven were counted near Landford Common. In August 1986 five were seen here (Humphrey Kay). The last record from Pound Bottom was of ten seen in August 1992 (Rob Turner).

During the WBMS it was recorded from 16 tetrads (1.8%). Vagrants have been omitted and, if records of singletons are also excluded, there were only four colonies remaining by 1994.

Its distribution in Wiltshire before 1982 is shown on the map by open circles. Although they indicate the grayling's former widespread status, they probably reflect only a small fraction of its former distribution, especially from SPTA and grassland in the south. The post-1982 records from calcareous sites are indicated by graded dots and those from the New Forest heaths and Calne

sand pits by triangles. Records of butterflies assumed to be vagrants are indicated by stars.

Future Prospects
Although the grayling is widely distributed in Great Britain and Ireland, in much of its range it is a coastal species, frequenting inland heaths and, more rarely, downland in the south of England. Colonies of graylings in Wiltshire are now restricted to the south of the county, unless there proves to be one at Calne sand pits. It is now a very local and rare insect.

The future for this species in the county is poor since it is sedentary and appears reluctant to establish new colonies. The habitat of the small colony at Enford Down on SPTA(C) is likely to be maintained, by management if necessary, but the colony at Landford Common will disappear if the area becomes too shady due to invasive birch scrub. The colonies at Porton Down and Pound Bottom are probably strong enough, and the habitat is large enough, for them to survive.

Map 61. Distribution of grayling

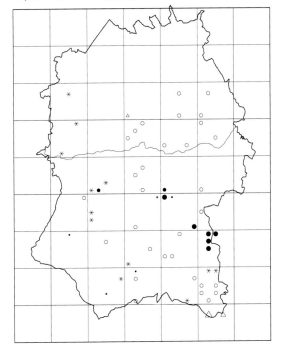

GATEKEEPER or HEDGE BROWN
Pyronia tithonus (Linnaeus)

The generic name *Pyronia*, given to the gatekeeper by Hübner in 1819, means the purchase of wheat, surely an error for another word, perhaps *pyropus*, meaning gold-bronze a reference to the wing coloration. The specific name *tithonus*, given by Linnaeus in 1771, was a Trojan youth granted immortality but not eternal youth by the gods.

This species was first described by Christopher Merrett in 1666 and called 'The lesser double-eyed Butterfly' by James Petiver in 1699. Moses Harris was the first to name it the gatekeeper in 1766 and it was subsequently given many other names. Hedge brown, given by Frederick Frohawk in 1924, is still in use although gatekeeper appears to be favoured by most Wiltshire recorders.

The gatekeeper is often seen nectaring in warm sunshine particularly on bramble (*Rubus fruticosus* agg.) flowers. The proboscis of the gatekeeper is short and its length restricts it to feeding on plants with relatively short corollas. These include yarrow (*Achillea millefolium*), common fleabane (*Pulicaria dysenterica*) and creeping thistle (*Cirsium arvense*).

The male in Steve Day's photograph is nectaring on common ragwort (*Senecio jacobaea*).

The pale-yellow eggs are laid singly on narrow-bladed grasses and other plants or deposited freely while the female is flying. The caterpillar partially eats its eggshell and then feeds on grass leaves until autumn when it hibernates among dead leaves. It resumes feeding in the following spring and the chrysalis is formed in June suspended on the underside of vegetation.

The Flight Period
This butterfly is on the wing from mid-July until mid-September. Numbers peak from early to mid-August.

From 1980 to 1994 the longest flight period in Picket Wood was 11 weeks in 1986 and the shortest was seven weeks in 1983, 1989 and 1990. The maximum number of individuals counted on the transect in a week varied from 186 in August 1984 to 26 in August 1987. The earliest sighting was on 6 July 1992 and the latest on 21 September 1986

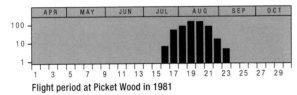

Flight period at Picket Wood in 1981

but the earliest Wiltshire date, 18 June 1925, was reported in a Marlborough College List.

Measures of Abundance 1980–94 (Figure 37)

The gatekeeper was usually abundant along the rides in Picket Wood during August and, in some years, accounted for between a quarter and a half of the total butterflies seen. At the Kennet and Avon Canal towpath site the low index value for 1984 was almost certainly due to habitat disturbance during 1983. In that year, as is apparent in Figure 37, numbers at all the other monitored sites reached their highest values but steadily declined to low levels until 1989. Numbers increased again during the hot, late summer periods of 1990–92 when the gatekeeper became abundant in many areas. However, in the season of poor weather in 1993 numbers fell sharply at all sites recovering at several in the good season of 1994 but with values still below their site averages. The further large decline in 1994 along the towpath was against the trend at most other sites and was probably due to habitat disturbance when the towpath was rebuilt and considerable damage was caused to the adjacent vegetation. The gatekeeper would be expected to remain a common species but regular disturbances of this kind may account for the loss of local populations.

Status Before 1982

The first published record of this species in Wiltshire appears to have been in the 1865 Marlborough College List. In the 1873 College List the gatekeeper was described as being abundant and in subsequent lists as being usually common in the Marlborough area. It was included in the 1899 list of the Rev T B Eddrupp from near Calne.

In the Salisbury area Roy Pitman recorded it from Old Sarum in July 1928 and in his 1936

report described it as being 'very common along hedgerows'. Bowmont Weddell reported it from the Trowbridge area in July 1932 and in 1962 Baron de Worms stated that it was 'usually abundant along hedgerows and in woods throughout the county'.

Status Since 1982

The gatekeeper is a common butterfly occurring over all southern Britain and the Midlands but is scarce and localised in the north. It is absent from Scotland and restricted to the south and east of Ireland. It occurs most frequently in woodland rides and clearings, in scrub and along roadside verges with hedgerows, especially where the favoured nectar sources occur. The gatekeeper is rarely seen on open, closely-grazed downland.

It has been a common species in Wiltshire for many years, often recorded as being abundant in hot dry summers. During the period of the WBMS (1982–94) it was recorded from 719 tetrads (75%) but, considering its usual abundance in August, there are surprisingly few records from some areas.

Map 62. Distribution of gatekeeper

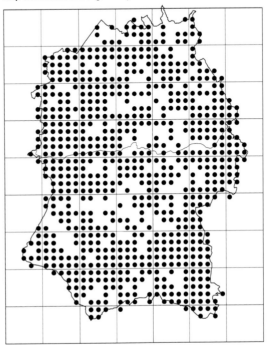

MEADOW BROWN
Maniola jurtina (Linnaeus)

The generic name *Maniola*, given to the meadow brown by Schrank in 1801, is a diminutive of Mania or Manes, the souls of the departed, a reference to the gloomy appearance of some members of this sub-family. The specific name *jurtina*, given by Linnaeus in 1758, has no meaning and is probably an error for Jurturna, the nymph of a fountain near Rome.

This species may have been described by Christopher Merrett in 1666. In 1699 James Petiver named the male 'The brown Meadow, ey'd Butterfly' and the female 'The golden Meadow, ey'd Butterfly'. In 1720 Eleazar Albin adapted Petiver's name to meadow brown.

Typically, the male has little or no orange on the upperwings while the amount on the upperwings of the female varies. The pattern on the underside of the hindwings of both sexes is similar, the dark and pale brown areas being demarcated by a sharp wavy line. This is illustrated in Christine Tracey's photograph of a female on bramble blossom. The butterflies rarely fly more than two metres above the ground. The flight tends to be of a lazy, floppy nature although, when disturbed, the females in particular rise and quickly travel a short distance before alighting again in a similar fashion to the grayling.

Bramble (*Rubus fruticosus* agg.) flowers are favoured for nectar. Thistles (*Cirsium* and *Carduus* spp.), ragworts (*Senecio* spp.) and hogweed (*Heracleum sphondylium*) are also visited.

The cream-coloured eggs are laid singly on grass or other vegetation. The caterpillar eats its eggshell and then feeds on the grass blades. After over-wintering, most caterpillars begin to pupate in early June.

The Flight Period
In Picket Wood butterflies emerge towards the end of June with peak numbers occurring about mid-July. After mid-August only an occasional female may be seen but, at Bratton Castle and other grassland sites, a greater number of adults can frequently be seen until later in the year. In the

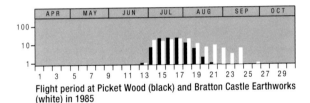

Flight period at Picket Wood (black) and Bratton Castle Earthworks (white) in 1985

diagram the difference in the typical annual flight patterns at the above-named sites is illustrated.

At Bratton Castle from 1980 to 1994 the longest flight period was 17 weeks in 1992 and the shortest ten in 1987. The maximum number of individuals counted on the transect in a week varied from 90 in July 1984 to 12 in July 1987. The earliest sighting was on 4 June 1992 and the latest on 25 September 1985.

An exceptionally early sighting on 11 May 1878 is recorded in a Marlborough College List. Another early, and more likely, date of 23 May 1866 is also listed.

Measures of Abundance 1980–94 (Figure 38)
The fluctuations in abundance of the meadow brown at monitored sites were very similar to those for several other species including the common blue and marbled white. Numbers peaked in 1982 and 1984 then dropped to very low levels over the next three years to reach their lowest in 1986 and 1987. During the generally hot summers of 1990 to 1992 there was a remarkable increase and numbers were at their highest since monitoring began at the majority of sites. At Upton Cow Down they rose from 105 in 1987 to 1,406 in 1992, a 13-fold increase. However, during the next two years they returned to near 'normal' levels except at Pewsey Downs where they slumped to less than a quarter of the 15 year average, the lowest since monitoring began.

Status Before 1982
It was included in the 1865 Marlborough College List and was seen by H W Hockin on 23 May 1866. In all subsequent College Lists it was described as very common. It was included in the Rev T B Eddrupp's 1899 list from near Calne and in E Cook's 1902 list from the Devizes district.

Roy Pitman reported it from several localities around Salisbury in 1928 and in his 1936 report described it as being 'abundant in every field, down, wood or hedgerow'. Bowmont Weddell recorded it from the Trowbridge area in June 1933 and in 1962, Baron de Worms described it as being abundant in every part of Wiltshire.

Status Since 1982
This is one of the most widespread species throughout Great Britain and Ireland and is often very abundant. In almost any type of grassland habitat, especially where the grass is tall but not too dense and even where flowers are scarce and no other species of butterfly is present, the meadow brown will almost invariably be found.

During the years of the WBMS (1982–94) it was recorded from 838 tetrads (88%) and was the second most comprehensively mapped species after the small white. It will surely remain a common species in the future.

Map 63. Distribution of meadow brown

RINGLET
Aphantopus hyperantus (Linnaeus)

The generic name *Aphantopus*, given to the ringlet by Wallengren in 1853, is derived from two words meaning made invisible and the foot, a reference to the degenerate forelegs of this species and others of its family. The specific name *hyperantus*, given by Linnaeus in 1758, was one of the 50 sons of Aegyptus.

This butterfly was first described in 1666 by Christopher Merrett and in 1699 James Petiver named it 'The brown ey'd Butterfly with yellow circles'. In 1766 Moses Harris called it the ringlet.

The wings of the ringlet are uniformly dark brown edged with a distinctive white fringe. The ringed eye-spots are variable but those in Anthony Tyers' photograph are typical. In Picket Wood, the author has observed ab. *arete*, individuals with the ringlets replaced by small white dots, apparently a fairly common form at other sites in the county. The other extreme form ab. *lanceolata*, in which the ringlets are greatly enlarged, has rarely been reported in Wiltshire. The ringlet may be mistaken for a dark meadow brown. Its weaker, bobbing

flight compared with the meadow brown's floppy gait, often low down among long grass, helps with identification.

Flowers of bramble (*Rubus fruticosus* agg.) and privet (*Ligustrum* spp.) are the preferred nectar sources but knapweeds (*Centaurea* spp.), thistles (*Cirsium* and *Carduus* spp.) and field scabious (*Knautia arvensis*) are also visited.

The buff-white eggs appear to be laid at random among the coarse grasses on which the larva will feed. It may feed on warm days during the winter, but recommences regular feeding in March. The chrysalis is formed close to the ground within a grass tussock in June.

The Flight Period

The males emerge at the very end of June, a few days before the females. Numbers build up quickly to reach a peak in mid-July and then decline equally quickly although a few females usually linger on until mid-August. The longest flight period over the 17 years of monitoring in Picket

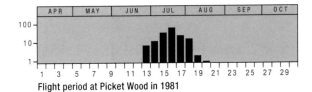

Flight period at Picket Wood in 1981

Wood was nine weeks in 1987 and the shortest was four weeks in 1979. The maximum count on the transect in a week varied from 99 individuals in July 1982 to 33 in July 1990. The earliest sighting was on 13 June 1992 and the latest 21 August 1987. The exceptionally early date of 7 May 1868 in a Marlborough College List must surely have been an error. The next earliest date mentioned was 17 June 1893.

Measures of Abundance 1980–94 (Figure 39)
Figure 39 shows the ringlet's mixed fortunes. Numbers, although fluctuating, remained at high levels until 1988, then declined but recovered again in 1992 and have continued to increase at most of the monitored sites to above their average values. The exception was at Vagg's Hill where numbers during 1993 and 1994 slumped to their lowest, less than half the average.

Status Before 1982
The ringlet was included in the 1865 Marlborough College List as present at Great Bedwyn and plentiful on White Horse Down. It was said to be common in the Marlborough area in the mid-1930s and it maintained this status into the 1950s. It was included in the Rev T B Eddrupp's 1899 list from near Calne and in E Cook's 1902 list from the Devizes district.

In his 1936 report Roy Pitman stated it to be 'locally common in woodlands and damp lanes'. Bowmont Weddell's diary records the ringlet in July 1932 in the Trowbridge area and in 1962 he was quoted by Baron de Worms as saying that it was 'fairly abundant in woods but often seen in open country on the downs'.

Status Since 1982
The ringlet is widely distributed in most of England and Ireland, but scarcer and more localised in the north of England and Scotland. In Wiltshire it is often abundant in July, especially in damp, grassy areas of woodland rides and clearings. It occurs on downland and other areas where the grass is tall but not too dense and on roadside verges and embankments.

During the WBMS (1982–94) the species occurred widely and was particularly abundant in some years. It was recorded from 657 tetrads (69%). From 1985 to 1987 it was more commonly noted than the meadow brown when numbers built up on areas of open downland as shown in the graphs for Pewsey Downs and Bratton Castle Earthworks. Godfrey Smith reported a huge population explosion on SPTA(W) in 1986 from where there had previously been very few records. That year the ringlet was chosen as the Wiltshire 'Butterfly of the Year'. This butterfly may become less common in some areas as urbanisation continues and the tidying-up of the countryside destroys more of its breeding areas.

Map 64. Distribution of ringlet

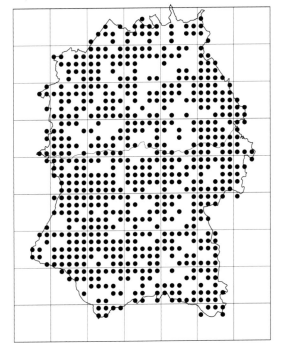

SMALL HEATH
Coenonympha pamphilus (Linnaeus)

The generic name *Coenonympha*, given to the small heath by Hübner in 1819, is derived from the two words meaning 'shared in common' and 'a nymph'. The specific name *pamphilus*, given by Linnaeus in 1758, was one of the 50 sons of Aegyptus.

This little butterfly was first described by Christopher Merrett in 1666 and named by James Petiver in 1699 as 'The Small Heath Butterfly'. Other names have subsequently been proposed, including two more by Petiver, but small heath is the one that has survived.

The small heath is the smallest of the British 'brown' butterflies and always closes its wings on alighting. It may rest with the eye-spots on the underside of the upper wing-tips visible for a short while, as in Steve Day's photograph, before hiding them behind the dappled grey-brown lower wings.

Small heaths are most likely to be seen nectaring on low-growing plants, wild thyme (*Thymus* spp.) being a favourite on short downland. Larger plants, knapweed (*Centaurea* spp.) and common fleabane (*Pulicaria dysenterica*) are also acceptable.

The pale-green eggs are laid singly on the leaves of fine-leaved grasses, most frequently on sheep's fescue (*Festuca ovina*) (Wickman). Development of some caterpillars is rapid and is followed by the formation of pupae from which adults emerge as a second generation in August and September. Those that develop slowly hibernate in the grass and recommence feeding the following spring and pupate in late April.

The Flight Period
The butterflies are usually on the wing from late May until late September. At Bratton Castle, 1980–94, the longest flight period was 20 weeks in 1990 and the shortest eight weeks in 1992 when no second emergence occurred. The maximum weekly counts on the transect for first and second emergences varied from 25 in July 1993 and 34 in August 1989 to five in July 1993 and nil in 1985 and 1992. Except for 1989, the numbers in the

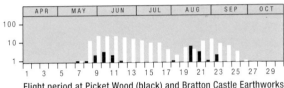

Flight period at Picket Wood (black) and Bratton Castle Earthworks (white) in 1990

first emergence were much higher than in the second. The earliest sighting was on 16 May 1990 and the latest 26 September 1990. The earliest dates given in Marlborough College Lists are 3 May 1893 and, more recently, 4 May 1945.

Measures of Abundance 1980–94 (Figure 40)

Numbers fluctuated erratically and dramatically at most monitored sites. Large declines in 1981 were followed by a recovery lasting until 1986 when numbers dropped again. The small heath's rapid decline at Picket Wood, from being fairly common in the late 1970s to its apparent absence from 1986 to 1988, was not unexpected. It reappeared in 1989 but has declined again in spite of the continued removal of conifers. It has been suggested that this species is very intolerant of shade and declines rapidly when open woodland becomes more shaded. At the other sites, very large increases in abundance in the late 1980s reached new peaks in 1990 but were followed by equally rapid declines to very low numbers at all sites in 1994. The fluctuations at Upton Cow Down were amazing. Numbers declined by over 100-fold between 1990 and 1994.

Status Before 1982

The small heath was included in the 1865 Marlborough College List and one was taken by J H Johnson on 19 May 1866. In all subsequent Lists it was described as being very common. It was included in the Rev T B Eddrupp's 1899 list from near Calne, from near Wylye between 1898 and 1901 by Dr R V Solly and E Cook listed it in 1902 from the Devizes district.

Roy Pitman reported it near Salisbury in May 1928. His 1936 report stated that it was 'very common in every meadow, field, or down'. Bowmont Weddell recorded the small heath in

June 1932 near Westbury. In 1962, Baron de Worms stated that it was 'generally common'.

Status Since 1982

This butterfly occurs widely throughout Great Britain and Ireland in many grassy habitats and often in abundance in favoured localities. In Wiltshire it is particularly common on some of the grasslands of Salisbury Plain, on the downlands in the south of the county, on many of the chalk grassland areas around Devizes, Pewsey, Aldbourne and Shalbourne and on the limestone grassland around Castle Combe. However, it appears to be less frequent than in former times in woodland. It can still be found in small numbers along grassy byways and a few roadside verges.

During the period of the WBMS (1982–94) the small heath was recorded from 478 tetrads (50%). Its small size and inconspicuousness when at rest may have resulted in it being overlooked by recorders, especially in the south of the county. Elsewhere it could be that the patchiness of the distribution reflects its true status.

Map 65. Distribution of small heath

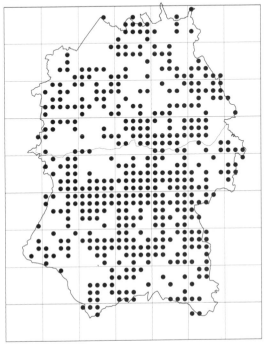

INDICES OF ABUNDANCE

The graphs (Figures 4–40) have been plotted using the annual IoA values (see page 16) and are referred to in the text. These figures show a mixture of short-term fluctuations, such as those for the large skipper, where numbers vary significantly from year to year but indicate little overall change. For other species there are longer-term trends, such as that of the grizzled skipper which showed a steady decline and that of the green hairstreak for which there were dramatic periodic fluctuations. There are similarities between the figures for the white admiral, marbled white and meadow brown.

Comments and observations made in the text concerning the IoA are of a very general nature to indicate major factors, changes, or significant events. A detailed statistical analysis of the data could form a substantial document on its own and is beyond the scope of this book.

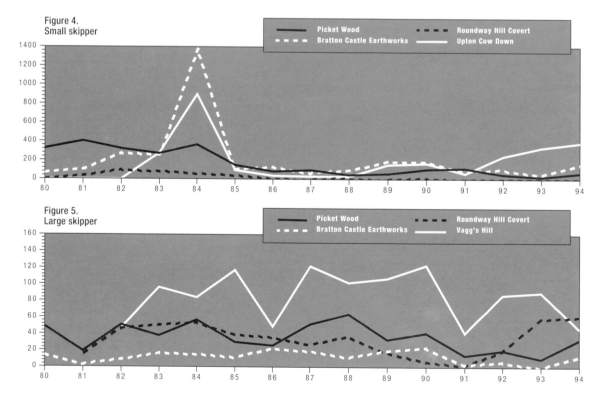

Figure 4.
Small skipper

Figure 5.
Large skipper

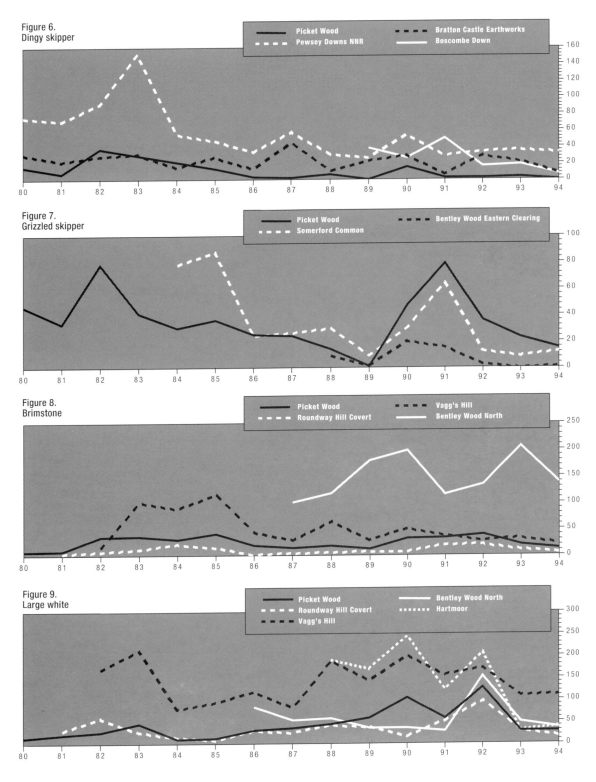

Figure 6.
Dingy skipper

Picket Wood
Pewsey Downs NNR
Bratton Castle Earthworks
Boscombe Down

Figure 7.
Grizzled skipper

Picket Wood
Somerford Common
Bentley Wood Eastern Clearing

Figure 8.
Brimstone

Picket Wood
Roundway Hill Covert
Vagg's Hill
Bentley Wood North

Figure 9.
Large white

Picket Wood
Roundway Hill Covert
Vagg's Hill
Bentley Wood North
Hartmoor

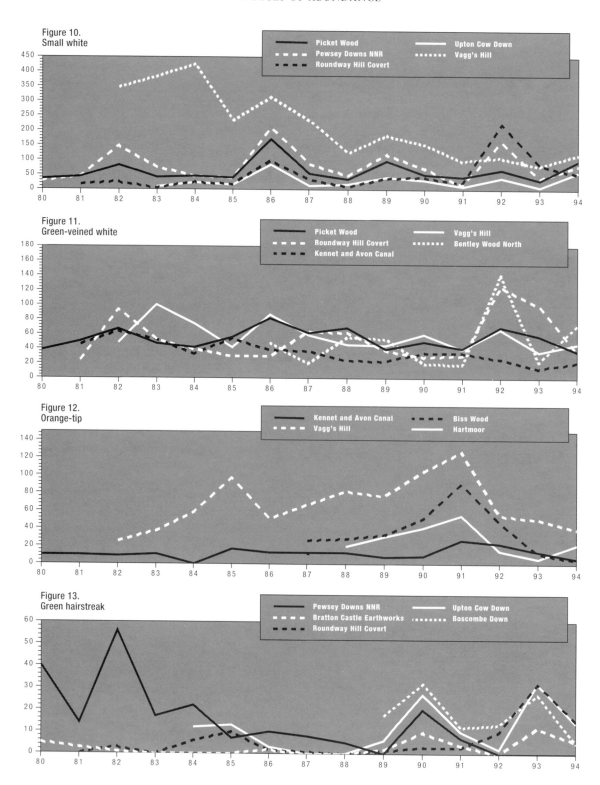

Figure 10.
Small white

Picket Wood
Pewsey Downs NNR
Roundway Hill Covert
Upton Cow Down
Vagg's Hill

Figure 11.
Green-veined white

Picket Wood
Roundway Hill Covert
Kennet and Avon Canal
Vagg's Hill
Bentley Wood North

Figure 12.
Orange-tip

Kennet and Avon Canal
Vagg's Hill
Biss Wood
Hartmoor

Figure 13.
Green hairstreak

Pewsey Downs NNR
Bratton Castle Earthworks
Roundway Hill Covert
Upton Cow Down
Boscombe Down

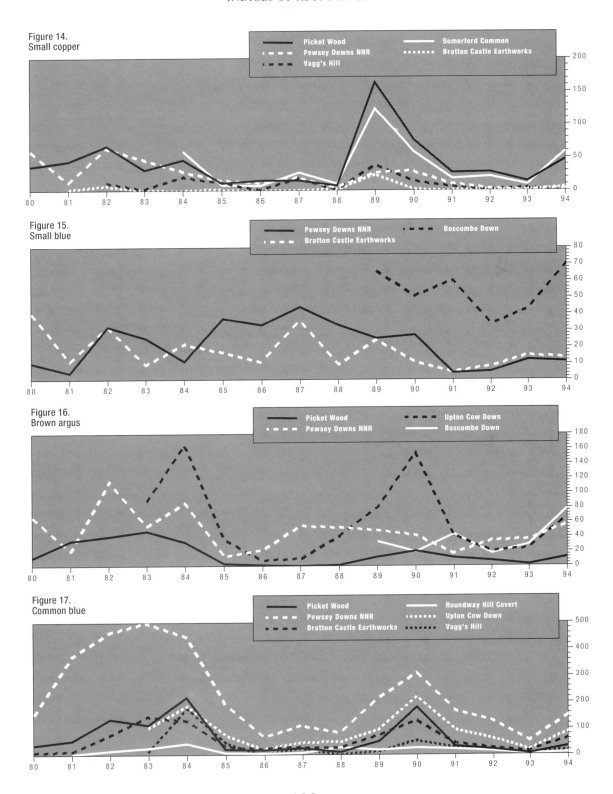

Figure 14.
Small copper

Picket Wood
Pewsey Downs NNR
Vagg's Hill
Somerford Common
Bratton Castle Earthworks

Figure 15.
Small blue

Pewsey Downs NNR
Bratton Castle Earthworks
Boscombe Down

Figure 16.
Brown argus

Picket Wood
Pewsey Downs NNR
Upton Cow Down
Boscombe Down

Figure 17.
Common blue

Picket Wood
Pewsey Downs NNR
Bratton Castle Earthworks
Roundway Hill Covert
Upton Cow Down
Vagg's Hill

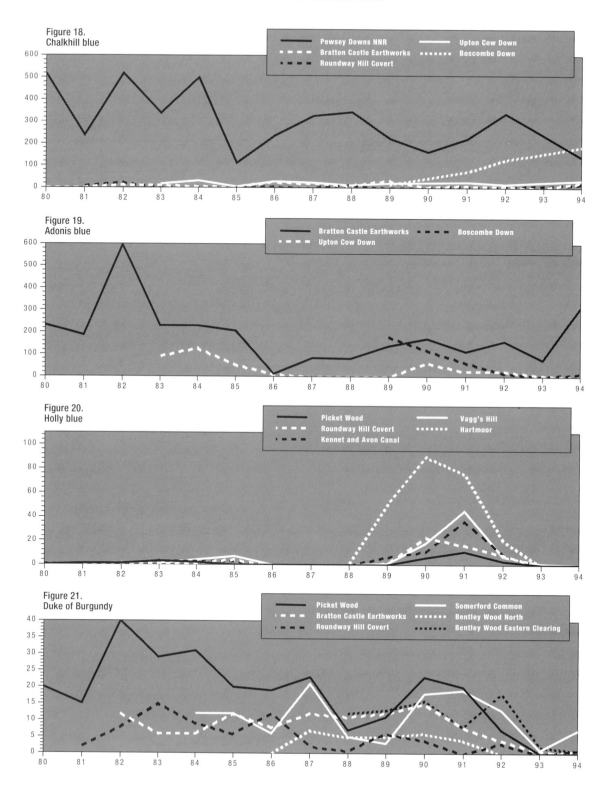

Figure 18.
Chalkhill blue

Pewsey Downs NNR
Bratton Castle Earthworks
Roundway Hill Covert
Upton Cow Down
Boscombe Down

Figure 19.
Adonis blue

Bratton Castle Earthworks
Upton Cow Down
Boscombe Down

Figure 20.
Holly blue

Picket Wood
Roundway Hill Covert
Kennet and Avon Canal
Vagg's Hill
Hartmoor

Figure 21.
Duke of Burgundy

Picket Wood
Bratton Castle Earthworks
Roundway Hill Covert
Somerford Common
Bentley Wood North
Bentley Wood Eastern Clearing

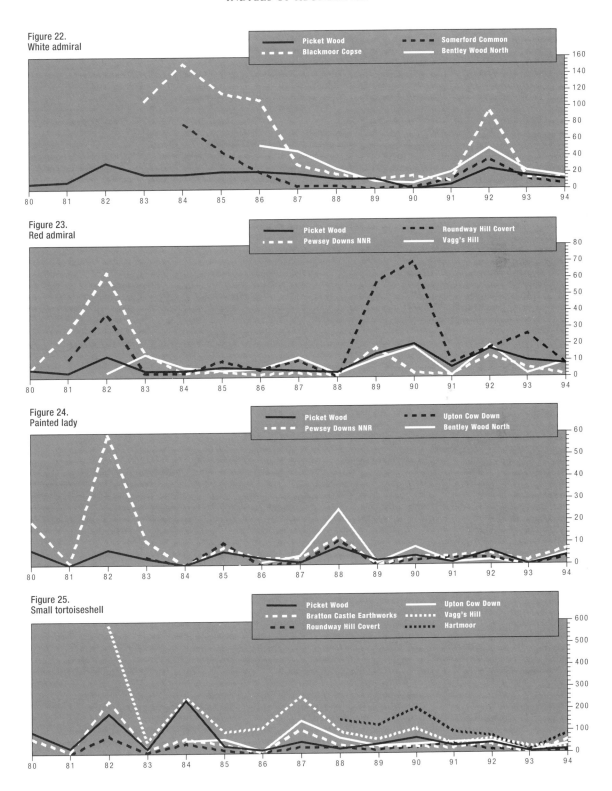

Figure 22.
White admiral

Picket Wood
Blackmoor Copse
Somerford Common
Bentley Wood North

Figure 23.
Red admiral

Picket Wood
Pewsey Downs NNR
Roundway Hill Covert
Vagg's Hill

Figure 24.
Painted lady

Picket Wood
Pewsey Downs NNR
Upton Cow Down
Bentley Wood North

Figure 25.
Small tortoiseshell

Picket Wood
Bratton Castle Earthworks
Roundway Hill Covert
Upton Cow Down
Vagg's Hill
Hartmoor

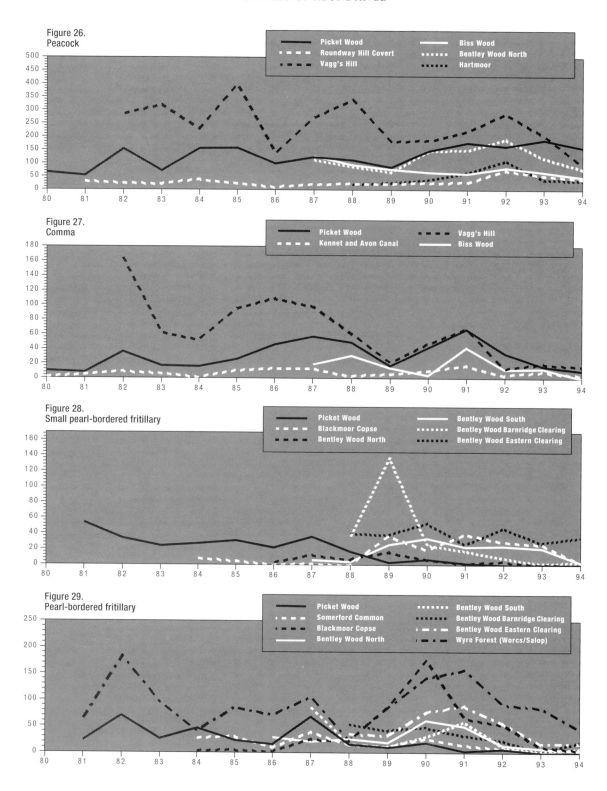

Figure 26.
Peacock

Picket Wood
Roundway Hill Covert
Vagg's Hill
Biss Wood
Bentley Wood North
Hartmoor

Figure 27.
Comma

Picket Wood
Kennet and Avon Canal
Vagg's Hill
Biss Wood

Figure 28.
Small pearl-bordered fritillary

Picket Wood
Blackmoor Copse
Bentley Wood North
Bentley Wood South
Bentley Wood Barnridge Clearing
Bentley Wood Eastern Clearing

Figure 29.
Pearl-bordered fritillary

Picket Wood
Somerford Common
Blackmoor Copse
Bentley Wood North
Bentley Wood South
Bentley Wood Barnridge Clearing
Bentley Wood Eastern Clearing
Wyre Forest (Worcs/Salop)

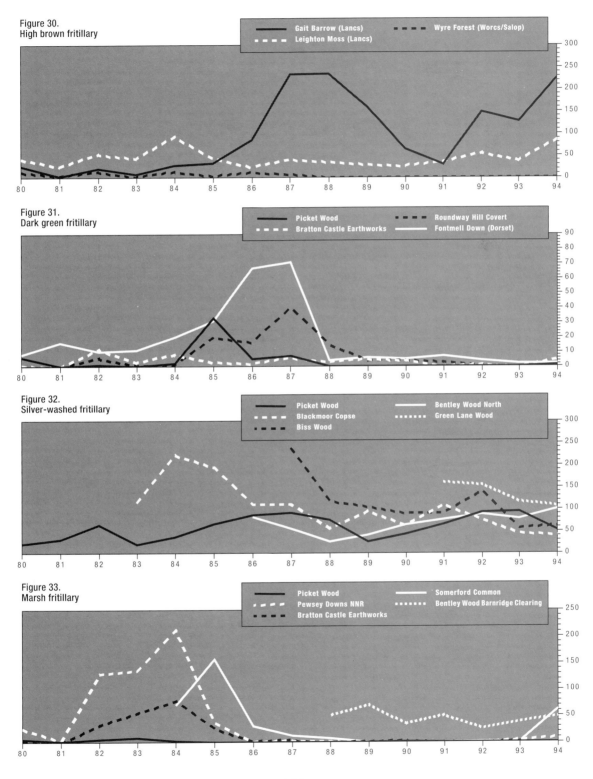

Figure 30.
High brown fritillary

Gait Barrow (Lancs)   Wyre Forest (Worcs/Salop)
Leighton Moss (Lancs)

Figure 31.
Dark green fritillary

Picket Wood   Roundway Hill Covert
Bratton Castle Earthworks Fontmell Down (Dorset)

Figure 32.
Silver-washed fritillary

Picket Wood   Bentley Wood North
Blackmoor Copse   Green Lane Wood
Biss Wood

Figure 33.
Marsh fritillary

Picket Wood   Somerford Common
Pewsey Downs NNR   Bentley Wood Barnridge Clearing
Bratton Castle Earthworks

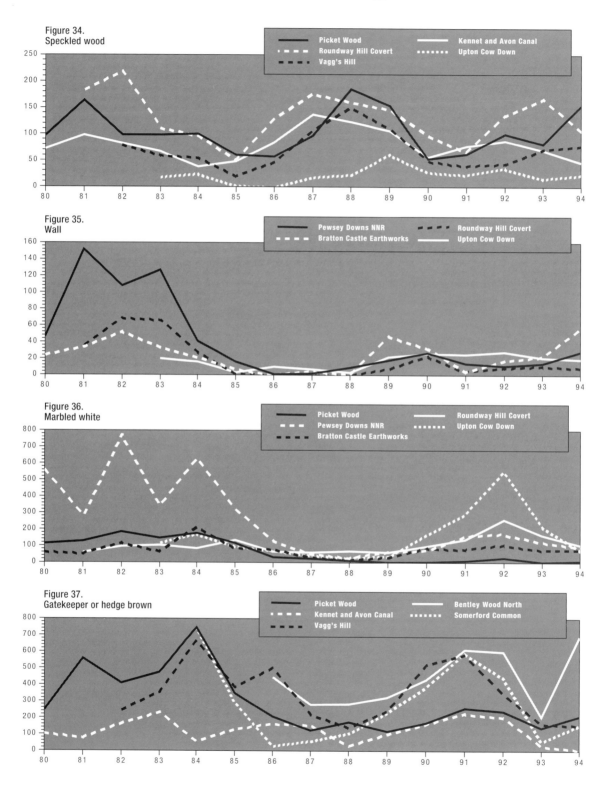

Figure 34.
Speckled wood

Picket Wood
Roundway Hill Covert
Vagg's Hill
Kennet and Avon Canal
Upton Cow Down

Figure 35.
Wall

Pewsey Downs NNR
Bratton Castle Earthworks
Roundway Hill Covert
Upton Cow Down

Figure 36.
Marbled white

Picket Wood
Pewsey Downs NNR
Bratton Castle Earthworks
Roundway Hill Covert
Upton Cow Down

Figure 37.
Gatekeeper or hedge brown

Picket Wood
Kennet and Avon Canal
Vagg's Hill
Bentley Wood North
Somerford Common

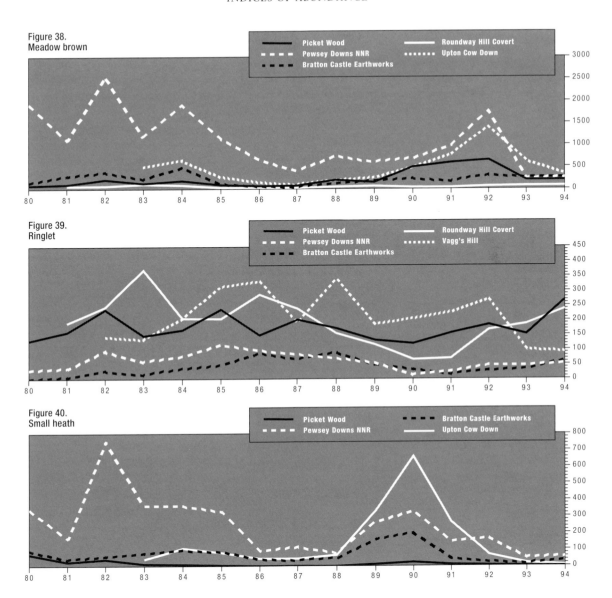

Figure 38.
Meadow brown

Figure 39.
Ringlet

Figure 40.
Small heath

RARE IMMIGRANT, EXTINCT, RARE RESIDENT AND EXOTIC SPECIES

Several of the 17 butterflies included in these categories are on 'The Wiltshire List' only because they have been recorded once or twice and not all have been confirmed. They have been accepted either on hearsay or because they have appeared in a publication. The possibilities of incorrect identification, over-enthusiastic recording when the rare rather than the common species was believed to have been seen, escaped or released bred specimens and 'fraudulent activity' have all been ignored.

RARE IMMIGRANT SPECIES

Of the eight species that have been recorded in the county, seven are fairly common and widespread on the continent. Except for the monarch, all these species utilise larval foodplants that occur commonly in this country and are not particularly colonial. Climate is the main factor in preventing them from becoming established in Great Britain and, if the so-called 'global warming' occurs, they may become residents at some time in the future.

Swallowtail
Papilio machaon Linnaeus
The English race of this beautiful butterfly has been confined to the Norfolk Broads for many years. Marlborough College lepidopterists were breeding swallowtails in Wiltshire as long ago as 1865. There are only six county records: in 1898 one was taken by H Harris near Bentley Wood (Ian Heslop); three were recorded on the Wiltshire Downs in 1945; in 1984 the author identified one taken in a vegetable garden in Holt and in 1992 eight nearly full-grown caterpillars were found feeding on garden rue (*Ruta graveolens*) at Kingsdown near Box (Mr and Mrs Brown). Two of these pupated and were seen by the author but he did not hear whether any adults emerged.

Pale Clouded Yellow
Colias hyale (Linnaeus)
and Berger's Clouded Yellow
Colias alfacariensis Berger
Until 1948 these two butterflies were not recognised as separate species and all earlier sightings were recorded as *hyale*. The adults are indistinguishable from each other unless captured and closely inspected and even then doubt remains unless both species are available for comparison. A further confusion arises in 'clouded yellow years' when the female form *helice*, which is similar to the two rarities, is fairly common.

All records have been treated as one species most being referred to as 'pale clouded yellow' by the recorders. The earliest record was of one seen at Ramsbury in 1868 and in August 1876 more than a dozen were seen near Marlborough (Neville Manders). In 1900 and 1901 'a good many specimens were captured at Wylye' (R V Solly). Occasional singletons were seen in 1904, 1922 and 1928. There was a relatively large invasion in 1934 and in 1945 it was numerous in the meadows on the fringes of Blackmoor copse (Heslop) and two were positively identified as *alfacariensis* on the downs near Salisbury. Since 1945 ten pale clouded yellows have been reported in the county. In August 1947 two were seen near Bodenham (Roy Pitman) and one at Bratton (WAM). One was recorded on Pepperbox Hill in August 1955 (Heslop), another in August 1959 (Pitman) and one in 1967 (Roy Stockley). There were no further sightings until March 1985 when 'I was amazed to see one on a dandelion in Folly Lane, Warminster' (Stockley). There were two sightings in 1992, one in the south of the county (Gordon Trebilcock) and one near Farley on 5 July (Ted and Irene Gange). A battered female was identified near Imber village on 1 September 1993 (Trebilcock).

Bath White
Pontia daplidice (Linnaeus)

This is a very rare immigrant that reaches southern England sporadically. The year 1945 was exceptional for immigrant species and about 600 Bath whites were reported (Baron de Worms). There have been only ten Wiltshire records. One butterfly was taken by a boy near Salisbury in 1928 and another near Downton in 1930 (Roy Pitman). In 1945 three were seen on Pepperbox Hill between 4 and 12 August (H H Peach), one was taken on nearby Standlynch Down at about the same time (C Peach), a male was taken near Bentley Wood on 8 September (D G Bishop) and a pair by Major Stuart Maples at Farley (Heslop). The last report was of one at Great Bedwyn on 12 June 1981 (Mary Ainsworth).

Long-tailed Blue
Lampides boeticus (Linnaeus)

Although occurring quite commonly in the Channel Islands, there were only 30 known British records before 1945 when, in that remarkable year for immigrants, 31 were taken (de Worms). The only record from Marlborough College was in the 1935 List which stated 'one caught, probably 1923'. One was taken on Heytesbury Down on 26 September 1953 by G W Cruttwell (de Worms) and one was seen by Lady Young at Stratford Tony on 13 September 1967 (WAM).

Camberwell Beauty
Nymphalis antiopa (Linnaeus)

This fine species occasionally arrives in Great Britain mainly from Scandinavia, and is most likely to be seen in the east of the country. There are a few Wiltshire records, the earliest being that of Henry Stainton in 1857 who stated that his correspondent in Corsham reported it occasionally but it had 'hardly been seen since 1847'. In the 1865 Marlborough College List a specimen was reported as having been taken in Savernake Forest in 1860 by W J Baverstock. On 30 August 1880 a perfect specimen was taken 'beyond the railway bank' by Mr Coleman and in 1883 one was taken at Hilmarton near Calne by Canon E H Goddard

and on 3 July 1884 one was seen 'along the Bath road' by E Robertson. One was taken at East Grimstead near Salisbury in 1928 (Roy Pitman), singletons were seen in 1936 in a Woodford garden (Sir George Aston) and at Westbury railway station (Col F A Labouchere) and on 5 October 1945 one was observed at Pantawick near Marlborough (A E Mitton). One was seen in Blackmoor Copse by a shooting party in October 1957 (Ian Heslop) and one was there for two days in July 1961 (Heslop *et al.*). Sir Michael Creagh noticed one in his garden at Homington on two consecutive days in September 1961 (Pitman) and in 1976, a year when about 200 were recorded in the country, three were seen in Warminster on 25 August and on 2 and 5 September (Stockley). During the WBMS there were three records of singletons in the north of the county in 1984: one in June at Tockenham near Lyneham (Mr Richmond), one in a Corsham garden (Mr Bain) and one photographed in September at Luckington near Malmesbury (J Thomson-Glover).

Queen of Spain Fritillary
Argynnis lathonia (Linnaeus)

There have been two years when this butterfly was relatively abundant, in 1872 when 50 were recorded and 1945 when 37 were seen (de Worms). At other times it is an exceedingly rare visitor to Great Britain. In 1893 Charles Barrett included Wiltshire in a list of 13 counties in which this species had been observed but gave no further details. In 1936 Graham Borthwick-Clarke saw one in his garden at Rushall near Pewsey. These are the only known Wiltshire records.

Monarch or Milkweed
Danaus plexippus (Linnaeus)

This is a large American migrant which was first seen in Great Britain in 1876, since when about 450 have been recorded. It cannot survive in this country because milkweeds (*Asclepia* spp.), the larval foodplants, are absent. On 6 September 1965, J F Burton carried out an experiment to find out how far the butterflies could travel by releasing 50 marked adults at Cadbury Camp, Clevedon in

Somerset. A few days later there were reports of three singletons in Wiltshire: at Aldbourne on 9 September, 80 km from the release point; Corsham on 22 September, 35 km distant and Lacock on 26 September, 45 km distant. The only other county reference is of one found dead, but in good condition, behind timber in a storehouse in Chippenham in 1984 (Shirley O'Brien).

EXTINCT SPECIES
Records indicate that three species which became extinct in Great Britain occurred in the county before 1900. No proof in the form of collected specimens has been found and the evidence relies on a single statement for most of them.

Black-veined White
Aporia crataegi (Linnaeus)
This was a widely distributed species over much of central-southern England, the Midlands and South Wales in the early nineteenth century. However, by the beginning of the twentieth century it had become very localised and was mainly confined to Kent where it finally became extinct in the early 1900s. There have been many unsuccessful attempts to re-establish the black-veined white as a British species. There are only two Wiltshire records. In 1857 Henry Stainton's correspondent at Corsham reported the species 'occurring there commonly' but there appear to be no further details. In 1984 a mating pair that 'graced the sunny house wall for at least half an hour' in Bradford-on-Avon (Doreen Ellis) were presumably from locally-bred stock.

Mazarine Blue
Cynaniris semiargus (Rottemburg)
Of very local occurrence across southern England and the Midlands in the nineteenth century, this butterfly became extinct in the 1880s. The first, and probably the only, Wiltshire record was that of J F Stephens, who in circa 1828 referred to 'Amesbury, Hants'. In 1853 the Rev Francis Morris stated 'It occurs also near Sarum, Wilts'. which may have been the locality referred to by Stephens. In 1924 Frederick Frohawk commented that

formerly it had a wide distribution and he included Wiltshire in his list of 22 counties. Since 1900 the mazarine blue has been reported in Britain on about 14 occasions; all were probably immigrants and none was from Wiltshire.

Large Blue
Maculinea arion (Linnaeus)
William Lewin was the first to record this lovely blue from 'the hills near Bath and on the Downs near Marlborough' in 1795 but he did not name the localities. Later authors, including Charles Barrett in 1893 who mysteriously added 'and other localities in Wiltshire', all repeated Lewin's comment. Those referred to by Barrett were never found or referred to again. The 1865 Marlborough College List stated 'Savernake Forest not Marlborough Downs' but there was no further clarification. In 1904 in his *Notes on Marlborough Butterflies*, Neville Manders commented 'There is a tradition that this was once to be found on the Downs near Marlborough and Salisbury Plain, but I think this must be dismissed as founded on error. I have carefully explored Salisbury Plain this summer and am quite satisfied that not only does it not occur but that it is improbable that it ever did. The thyme on which the larva feeds is by no means abundant; in fact may be called a somewhat scarce plant. It might occur near Collingbourne Woods'.

In 1924 Frederick Frohawk included Wiltshire in a list of 11 counties and, in the mid-1940s, Vere Temple from Tollard Royal wrote in *Butterflies and Moths in Britain*, 'I once saw a solitary specimen in Wilts'. Pitman, like many others of his day, became very interested in the large blue and in the mid-1950s attempted an introduction on the south Wiltshire downs. He included details of his attempt in *A Naturalist at Home*. Nine females were released and in July the following year, in spite of searching for many days, only two males were seen. The record in WAM from Shawhill in 1976 was an error in identification.

RARE RESIDENT SPECIES
These four species are rare and very local in Great Britain and it is doubtful if any has ever occured

in Wiltshire. However, there are short published records which warrant inclusion here. Mis-identification and confusion with similar, less rare, species are likely.

Chequered Skipper
Carterocephalus palaemon (Pallas)

This little butterfly was always extremely rare and local in England and became extinct in the mid-1970s but populations survive near Fort William in western Scotland. There are two brief references to the chequered skipper in Wiltshire. It was included in the 1983 Invertebrate Site Register as being present in the Cranborne Chase woodlands between 1965 and 1980 but no details were given. There is a curious entry in Roy Pitman's diary for 2 June 1957 following a visit to Bentley Wood with his friend Dr Davies. It stated 'No *Palemon* [*sic*]'. This was presumably a reference to the chequered skipper, but did he really expect to see it there? Perhaps an introduction had been attempted in the previous year, although there was no mention of one in his 1956 diary. Perhaps it was simply a 'slip-of-the-pen' when he intended referring to some other species.

Black Hairstreak
Satyrium pruni (Linnaeus)

This is a rare and very local species occurring mainly in woodlands between Oxford and Peterborough. The 1923 Marlborough College Report stated that one adult was caught on a privet bush in West Woods on 10 June by J N H Justice. The record was omitted from the 1956 College List because 'we could find little information about it, its occurrence in the district in 1922 [*sic*] was very doubtful'. The only other reference to this species appears in Heslop's *Survey of the Butterflies of Blackmoor Copse Nature Reserve* of 1958 in which he stated 'I am convinced that this butterfly has a station fairly close to this wood system ... a specimen was taken a few years ago in Whiteparish Wood – only four miles from Blackmoor'. Roy Pitman did not know of this species in the area and the capture at Whiteparish remains a mystery.

Glanville Fritillary
Melitaea cinxia (Linnaeus)
and Heath Fritillary
Mellicta athalia (Rottemburg)

These two species have probably always been rare and local in southern England. Both are superficially very similar to the marsh fritillary and mistakes in identification are thought to have been made frequently in the nineteenth century. The only Wiltshire records are those published by the Rev Francis Morris who, in 1853, said of the heath fritillary, 'also not very uncommon near Great Bedwyn and Sarum, Wiltshire, as J W Lukis Esq informs me'. He said of the Glanville fritillary, 'J W Lukis Esq informs me that this extremely interesting insect is taken, though very rarely, in the neighbourhood of Great Bedwyn and Sarum, Wiltshire'. These records were repeated by several later authors, although most doubted their veracity.

EXOTIC SPECIES
Apollo
Parnassius apollo (Linnaeus)

There have been about 20 records of this spectacular alpine butterfly in Great Britain in the past 130 years (de Worms). There are only two Wiltshire references. The first, in the 1872 Marlborough College Report, stated 'A specimen is said to have been seen by Coleman, and many other persons near Great Bedwyn, towards the end of May'. On the continent the species is on the wing mainly in July and August. The second reference is of one being taken by J H Craw on Silbury Hill near Avebury in mid-August 1920 (de Worms) but the whereabouts of the specimen, if it still exists, is not known.

Slate Flash
Rapala schistacea (Moore)

The occurrence of this Indian species in Wiltshire is the most curious of all. On about 22 August 1922, Major J W Cardew was collecting in Savernake Forest in very windy conditions and took three butterflies from small holly bushes. In 1938 they were identified by staff at the Natural History Museum as female slate flashes but how they came to be in Savernake Forest remains a mystery.

BIBLIOGRAPHY

Asher, J (1994). *The Butterflies of Berkshire, Buckinghamshire and Oxfordshire*. Pisces Publications, Newbury.

Baines, C (1984). *Chris Baines' Wildlife Garden Notebook*. The Oxford Illustrated Press, Yeovil.

Barrett, C G (1893). *The Lepidoptera of the British Islands*. L Reeve and Co., London.

Brooks, M and Knight, C (1982). *A Complete Guide to British Butterflies*. Jonathan Cape, London.

Butterflies Under Threat Team (BUTT) (1986). *The Management of Chalk Grassland for Butterflies*. Nature Conservancy Council, Peterborough.

Coleman, W S (1860). *British Butterflies*. George Routledge & Sons, London.

Duncan, J (1835). *The Natural History of British Butterflies*. W H Lizars, Edinburgh.

Emmet, A M (1991). *The Scientific Names of the British Lepidoptera – Their History and Meaning*. Harley Books, Colchester.

Emmet, A M and Heath, J (eds.) (1989). *The Moths and Butterflies of Great Britain and Ireland. Volume 7 (1): The Butterflies*. Harley Books, Colchester.

Frohawk, F W (1924). *The Natural History of Butterflies*. Hutchinson & Co., London.

Frohawk, F W (1934). *The Complete Book of British Butterflies*. London.

Gillam, B (ed.) (1993). *The Wiltshire Flora*. Pisces Publications, Newbury.

Harris, M (1775). *The English Lepidoptera; or, The Aurelian's Pocket Companion*. J Robson, London.

Harris, M (1766). *The Aurelian or Natural History of English Insects; Namely, Moths and Butterflies. Together with the Plants on Which They Feed*. London.

Haworth, A H (1803–28). *Lepidoptera Britannica*. London.

Heath, J, Pollard, E and Thomas, J (1984). *Atlas of Butterflies in Britain and Ireland*. Viking, Harmondsworth.

Heslop, I R P, Hyde, G E and Stockley, R E (1964). *Notes and Views of the Purple Emperor*. The Southern Publishing Co. Ltd, Brighton.

Lewin, W (1795). *The Papilios of Great Britain*. London.

Lisney, A A (1960). *A Bibliography of British Lepidoptera 1608–1799*. The Chiswick Press, London.

Merrett, C (1666). *Pinax rerum Naturalium Britannicarum, Continens Vegetabilis, Animalia et Fossilia, in hac Insula Reperta Inchoatus*. London.

Morris, F O (1853). *A History of British Butterflies*. John C Nimmo, London.

Mouffet, T (1634). *Insectorum Sive Minimorum Animalium Theatrum*. London.

Newman, E (1871). *An Illustrated History of British Butterflies*. William Tweedie, London.

Peachey, C (1983). *Invertebrate Site Register, Provisional Review of Wiltshire*. Nature Conservancy Council, London.

Petiver, J (1695–1703). *Musei Petiveriana Centuria Prima-decima*. London.

Petiver, J (1702–06). *Gazophylacii Naturae et Artis*. London.

Petiver, J (1717). *Papilionum Britanniae Icones*. London.

Pitman, C M R (1984). *A Naturalist at Home*. Wiltshire Library and Museum Service, Trowbridge.

Pollard, E and Welch, J M (1977). *Butterfly Monitoring Scheme: Instructions for Recorders*. Institute of Terrestrial Ecology, Cambridge.

Pollard, E, Hall, M L and Bibby, T L (1986). *Monitoring the Abundance of Butterflies 1976–1985*. Nature Conservancy Council, Peterborough.

Proctor, M and Yeo, P (1973). *The Pollination of Flowers*. Collins, London.

Ray, J (1710). *Historia Insectorum*. Royal Society, London.

Rennie, J (1832). *A Conspectus of the Butterflies and Moths found in Britain*. William Orr, London.

Revels, R (1994). The Rise and Fall of the Holly Blue Butterfly. *British Wildlife 5(4)*: 236–239.

Russwurm, A D A (1978). *Aberrations of British Butterflies*. E W Classey Ltd, Faringdon.

South, R (1906). *The Butterflies of the British Isles*. Frederick Warne & Co. Ltd, London.

Stainton, H T (1857). *A Manual of British Butterflies and Moths, 1*. John Van Voorst, London.

Temple, V (1945–46). *Butterflies and Moths in Britain*. B T Batsford Ltd, London.

Thomas, J A (1986). *RSNC Guide to Butterflies of the British Isles*. Newnes Country Life Books, Twickenham.

Thomas, J and Lewington, R (1991). *The Butterflies of Britain and Ireland*. Dorling Kindersley, London.

Thomas, J and Webb, N (1984). *Butterflies of Dorset*. Dorset Natural History and Archaeological Society, Dorchester.

Tubbs, C R (1991). Grazing the Lowland Heaths. *British Wildlife 2 (5)*: 276–289.

Tutt, J W (1896). *British Butterflies*. George Gill & Sons, London.

Waring, P (1983). *A Survey of the Lepidoptera Fauna of Bentley Wood, Wiltshire*. Report for FC and NCC.

Warren, M S (1984). The Biology and Status of the Wood White Butterfly, *Leptidea sinapis* L. (Lepidoptera: Pieridae) in the British Isles. *Entomologist's Gazette 35*: 207–223.

Warren, M S (1987). *Butterfly Site Register – Wiltshire. Part 1: Summary*. Nature Conservancy Council, Newbury.

Wilkes, B (1741–42). *The British Aurelian. Twelve New Designs of English Butterflies*. London.

Willmott, K J (1987). *The Ecology and Conservation of the Purple Emperor Butterfly*. Report for World Wildlife Fund.

Worms, Baron C M G de (1962). *The Macrolepidoptera of Wiltshire*. WANHS, Devizes.

Other reference works that have been consulted fully or partly.
Dauntsey School Fauna List (1931–48).
Dr J Eagles' collecting notes (1961–76).
The Entomologist (1900–present).
Entomologist's Record and Journal of Variation (1900–present).
Marlborough College Natural History Society *Annual Lists* and *Reports* (1865–1965).
C M R Pitman's diaries (1928–86).
Salisbury and District Natural History Society *Annual Reports* and *Bulletins* (1953–present).
R Thompson's collecting notes (1947–55).
Wiltshire Archaeological and Natural History Society *Annual Entomological Reports* (1947–86).
B W Weddell's diaries (1932–78).